FIRE & ICE
The Cascade Volcanoes

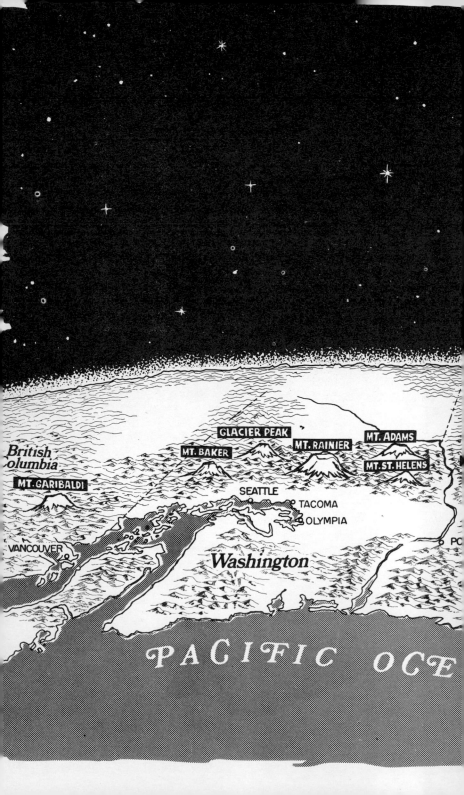

FIRE & ICE
The Cascade Volcanoes

Revised Edition

Stephen L. Harris

THE MOUNTAINEERS

PACIFIC SEARCH PRESS

The Mountaineers: Organized 1906 ". . . to explore, study, preserve and enjoy the natural beauty of the Northwest."

Revised edition: first printing, April 1980; second printing, May 1980; third printing, June 1980; fourth printing, June 1980.

Published by
The Mountaineers
719 Pike Street, Seattle, Washington 98101

Co-published by
Pacific Search Press
222 Dexter Avenue North
Seattle, Washington 98109

Published simultaneously in Canada by
Douglas & McIntyre Ltd.
1615 Venables Street
Vancouver, British Columbia V5L 2H1

Manufactured in the United States of America

Design by James Sobota
Maps and drawings by Gary Rands
Cover photo of Mount St. Helens by Jack Leffler, Sky Eye

Library of Congress Cataloging in Publication Data

Harris, Stephen L.   1937-
    Fire and ice.

    Bibliography: p.
    I. Volcanoes—Cascade Range.   II. Cascade
Range.   I. Title.
QE524.H18   1980   551.2'2'09795   80-16095
ISBN 0-89886-009-1

This book is dedicated to my grandfather, Louis E. Harris, who introduced me to the physical grandeur of the Cascade Range; and in loving memory of my grandmother, Mabel E. Harris, who encouraged my first enthusiasms about Cascade volcanology.

About the author:

Tacoma native Stephen Harris double-majored in European History and English Literature at the University of Puget Sound, where, he says, "Geology was one of my favorite classes." The almost daily sight of nearby Mt. Rainier's icy bulk provoked a fascination with the contrast between the peak's volcanic origin and its glacial mantle.

After winning a Woodrow Wilson fellowship, Harris earned his M.A. and Ph.D. at Cornell University, then taught English for a year at Washington State University, Pullman. Now a Full Professor of Humanities at California State University, Sacramento, Harris served from 1972-76 as first chairman of the interdisciplinary Humanities Department. He is the author of "The Humanist Tradition in World Literature," published in 1970, and "Understanding the Bible: A Reader's Guide and Reference," published in 1980.

In addition to courses in his field, he currently teaches a course on volcanology in the CSUS Geology Department. "This allows me to give free rein to my life-long obsession with the Cascade volcanoes," Harris admits," and to conduct field trips to Lassen, Shasta and other parts of the Cascades. Summer vacations, of course, always find me somewhere in the mountains." In 1974 he was a member of the Eastern Washington State College team which first explored and mapped the steam caves in Mt. Baker's Sherman Crater. When Mt. St. Helens began its explosive activity in March 1980, Harris was flown to the mountain by helicopter, for live coverage on network television news while hovering over the crater.

Preface and Acknowledgments

Most Americans are probably not aware that some of the world's great volcanoes are located in the Pacific Coast states of Washington, Oregon, and California. The crowning feature of the Cascade Range, these snowcapped giants are seen or visited by millions of people every year. Yet many persons who most admire their scenic magnificence do not know that these white cones—the highest free-standing landforms in the conterminous United States—are potentially the most dangerous mountains in the country.

Fire and Ice is the only full-length work which brings together in a single, non-technical volume all published—and much hitherto unpublished—information about the volcanic and glacial history of the major Cascade volcanoes. The book concentrates on the individual mountains, from Lassen Peak in California to Mt. Garibaldi in British Columbia, explaining the geologic forces which created them. It also provides full discussions on the hazards involved when the volcanoes next erupt.

Although not conceived as a field guide or reference book on the weather or plant and animal life found in the range, *Fire and Ice* includes at the end of almost every chapter specific directions on how directly to enjoy a particular mountain by car, by foot, or, in some cases, by climbing to its summit.

In acknowledging my general debt to the many scientists whose work is cited in the bibliography, I would like to give special thanks to Dr. Dwight R. Crandell, research geologist with the U.S. Geological Survey, Denver, Colorado, who patiently edited the manuscript for technical accuracy. His comments and suggestions were invaluable in giving the book its present form. What is authoritative in the text is largely due to his efforts; any remaining errors I must acknowledge as my own.

In addition, I would like to thank several other geologists for their contribution to this volume: Professors W. S. Wise of the University of California, Santa Barbara, and Kenneth Hopkins of the University of

Northern Colorado for their reviews, respectively of the Mt. Hood and Mt. Adams chapters; the late LeRoy Maynard, formerly of the University of Oregon, for his extraordinarily generous help in preparing the material on Oregon's hitherto most neglected volcano, Mt. Mc Loughlin; Mr. Kenneth Sutton, presently at the University of Hawaii, for permission to use his unpublished research and field studies on Mt. Jefferson.

Dr. Eugene P. Kiver, Eastern Washington State College, provided helpful comments for sections dealing with Cascade glaciers, as did Austin Post of the U.S. Geological Survey, Tacoma. Both Messrs. Kiver and Post, as well as David Frank of the University of Washington, supplied much welcome information on Mt. Baker, including unpublished reports and photographs of its current thermal activity.

I am also grateful to Drs. C. Dan Miller and Robert Christiansen, of the U.S. Geological Survey, for generously sharing the results of their field work on Mt. Shasta. Their discoveries about the development of California's largest volcano appear here in print for the first time.

Others also helped in various stages of preparation: I thank Miss Mary Hill, a geologist formerly with the California Bureau of Mines and Geology, for obtaining photographs of the Lassen Peak eruptions; Dr. Howel Williams, professor emeritus at the University of California, Berkeley, for his kind permission to use some of his diagrams; my conscientious typists, Mrs. Jane Matsueda and Frederick Mayer; Mr. David Branstetter, for producing the original drawings on which many of the illustrations are based; Gary Rands, whose art work considerably enhances the value of this volume; and Tom Boucher of The Mountaineers, who so patiently and cheerfully saw the book through production.

Table of Contents

List of Illustrations

1
An Introduction

From northern California to southwestern Canada stretches a chain of towering volcanoes. These fire-born, ice-carved giants dominate the Cascade mountains, a heavily forested range famed for the myriad waterfalls and cataracts which tumble from its alpine snowfields. Nowhere else in the 48 adjacent states has nature so dramatically linked these two great forces — volcanic fire and glacial ice.

The power latent in the Cascade volcanoes was dramatically illustrated on March 27, 1980, when Mt. St. Helens abruptly ended a 123-year-long dormant interval by blasting a new vent through the summit glacier and hurling ash high into the air. In the days that followed, the volcano exploded intermittently, spewing out blocks of ice reportedly 60 feet in diameter and sending columns of steam and ash over 10,000 feet above the mountain's crest. Increasingly heavy ashfalls soon blanketed all sides of the cone. Shifting winds carried ashclouds in almost every direction, drifting as far as Spokane, Washington, 300 miles distant.

The Pacific Ring of Fire

Mt. St. Helens is one of a procession of active, dormant, and recently extinct volcanoes which encircles the Pacific Ocean. Known as the "Ring of Fire," this volcanic zone marks the point of contact between great slabs of the earth's crust as they grind past or override each other. According to the currently accepted theory of plate tectonics, the Pacific Ocean floor, a complex of interlocking basaltic slabs or "plates," is slowly expanding as new lava rises through crustal fractures to the surface, pushing oceanic plates toward the bordering continents. Because they are formed chiefly of lighter granitic material, the continents ride higher on the underlying plastic rock of the mantle than does the denser ocean floor. As a result, it is believed that the expanding oceanic crust is being thrust beneath the continental margins, where it is at least partly remelted at depth, creating pockets of molten rock known as magma. Such underground accumulations of magma become the feeding chambers of volcanoes. This process, known as subduction, explains why chains of volcanoes border almost all sides of the Pacific basin.

Historic Eruptions in the Cascades

Two Cascade volcanoes — St. Helens and Lassen Peak—have erupted thus far in the 20th century, but several others have also been active during the past 150 years. In Washington, Mt. Baker and Mt. Rainier ejected steam and tephra (air-borne rock fragments) several times during the mid-1800s and still emit varying quantities of heat, steam, and other volcanic gases. Recent avalanches of rock and mud at Baker and Rainier are thought to have been triggered by continuing thermal activity. Before its current explosive cycle began in 1980, St. Helens was already noted for its historic eruptions. Between 1831 and 1857 missionaries and other early settlers observed more than a dozen different outbursts. Because it is by far the youngest mountain in the United States, geologists familiar with its history were not surprised when St. Helens again broke into eruption.

Oregon's Mt. Hood also has a record of 19th-century activity, which may have marked the end of an eruptive cycle that began about the year 1760. A recent U.S. Geological Survey report indicates that Crater Rock, a craggy andesite dome at about the 10,000-foot level on Hood's south side, was emplaced only about 220 years ago, creating part of the avalanche and mudflow debris which underlie the volcano's smooth south slope. This activity apparently destroyed an earlier plug dome that grew at the same site about 1700 years ago. Although Mt. Hood's last reported eruption occurred in 1865, fumaroles near Crater Rock occasionally produce enough steam and other sulphurous fumes to create clouds visible from Portland, 50 miles away.

California has at least three historically active Cascade volcanoes. During 1850-51, night flares of Cinder Cone, a small peak in Lassen Volcanic National Park, were bright enough to be seen many miles away. Mt. Shasta was probably the erupting volcano sighted by a Spanish explorer in 1786; it may have been mildly active again in the 1850s and still produces a hot sulphur spring near the summit.

Until upstaged by Mt. St. Helens, Lassen Peak was celebrated as the most recently active volcano (south of Alaska) in the continental United States. Beginning in May, 1914, and continuing sporadically until 1921, Lassen ejected steam, tephra, and lava; the climax occurred a year after the activity began, when it blew an enormous mushroom cloud an estimated seven miles into the stratosphere.

Since the first pioneers began to settle the Far West these, among other Cascade vents, have revealed their fiery nature. Yet today, except for escaping gases and sporadic steam explosions, they remain strangely quiet. This inactivity was once believed to represent a general diminution of volcanic energy in this part of the Pacific rim; but recent geologic studies indicate that there have been as many Cascade eruptions during the past few thousand years as during any comparable period in the past. Since the end of the Ice Age, the Cascades have produced, on the average, *at least* one major outburst per century.

The Cascade Landscape

When Lewis and Clark made their overland expedition to the Pacific in 1805, they followed the Columbia River through the mountains. The explorers were greatly hindered in the last stages of their trek by a series of whitewater rapids where the Columbia narrowed to run at dizzying speeds through a steep rocky gorge. Amid the overhanging lava cliffs and roaring cataracts, Lewis and Clark encountered the last serious obstacle to the success of their mission.

Because the route Lewis and Clark chose was the only practicable one and was consequently followed by traders and settlers, the mountains that loomed above the Columbia River rapids became known as *the mountains by the cascades*. Although that part of the range which gave it its name is highly atypical, the designation proved ultimately appropriate, for few spots in the Cascades are far removed from the music of running water.

The Cascades offer today's visitors a spectacularly scenic recreational area. The range is unsurpassed for the variety of its topography, its extensive glaciers, and its dense evergreen forests, which provide an emerald background for the countless lakes, streams, and waterfalls. About 30 to 50 miles wide and 4500 to 5000 feet high at its southern extremity, the range expands in northern Washington to a glaciated wilderness at least 80 miles across, where scores of peaks exceed 8000 feet. Built on top of this mountainous foundation, the individual volcanic cones tower above the range itself.

The highest points in the Rockies or Sierras tend to be only slightly higher than other elevations around them. The mightiest Cascade summits, however, completely dominate the surrounding landscape for 50 to 100 miles in every direction. Mt. Rainier, for example, rises abruptly above the Puget Sound lowland and has a visual height nearly equal to its actual vertical height of 14,410 feet. Spreading over 100 square miles of lesser mountains which themselves rise more than a mile above sea level, Rainier soars high above its nearest competitors.

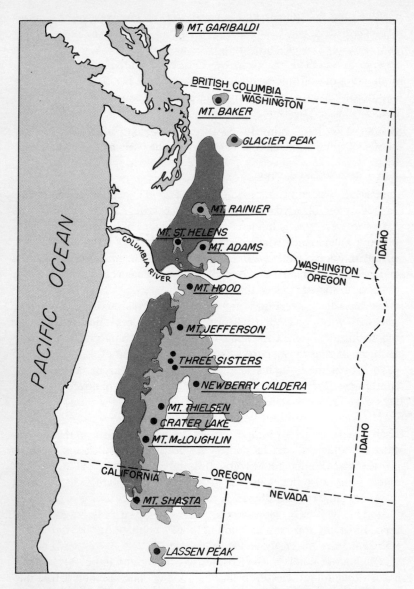

Figure 1–1. Map of the Cascade Range, showing areas covered by the older "Western Cascade" lavas and the High Cascade basalts and andesites of the Pleistocene–Holocene Epochs. Note that the three northern volcanos are not surrounded by older volcanic material.

Baker, Adams, Shasta, Jefferson, and Hood likewise visually
overwhelm encircling peaks, many of which, if placed elsewhere in the
nation, would be regarded as major landmarks.

Because of their altitude, the Cascades form a formidable climatic
barrier. Running roughly parallel to the Pacific Coast on a generally
north-south axis, the range intercepts moisture-laden winds moving
eastward from the Pacific. Rapid cooling causes the marine air to
condense and fall as rain or snow. Although precipitation is less in the
southern Cascades, it can reach over 150 inches annually on the wettest
slopes; winter snowcover in the Pacific Northwest is often heavy at
elevations as low as 2000 feet. As much as 90 feet of snow has fallen in
a single season at Mt. Rainier. As a result, the western slope of the
range is abundantly watered and thickly forested.

East of the Cascade crest, the scenery and vegetation change
abruptly. The eastside forest is drier, free of the lush ferns, briars, and
brush that entangle the western timberlands. Instead of the moisture-
loving Douglas fir, pine becomes the dominant species. Because the
annual rainfall dwindles to as little as eight inches east of the divide, the
inland foothills are typically brown in summer, spotted only with dry
grass, sagebrush, and occasional scrub growth. Almost nowhere else in
the nation do a few miles mark so dramatic a transformation of the
landscape.

To people living in western Washington and Oregon, the country
"East of the Mountains," as it is popularly called, is a different world.
Instead of the verdancy that characterizes the western region, the
eastward-moving traveler encounters an arid plateau. This is the great
basalt desert created during an extended period of volcanism that began
about 15,000,000 years ago—long before the present Cascades were
uplifted. In Miocene and Pliocene time enormous floods of liquid rock
poured from cracks in the earth's surface to bury almost 250,000 square
miles of eastern Washington, Oregon, and parts of Idaho and
California. This lava formation is second in size only to the great
Deccan plateau in India.

Draining the lava highlands and moving irresistibly westward to the
Pacific, the Columbia River cuts the only breach through the Cascades
in almost their entire 700-mile length. The Columbia existed before the
Cascades began their uplift during the Pliocene Epoch 7,000,000 years
ago. Its eroding power kept pace with the rising mountain front, which
eventually reached about 4500 feet above sea level at the highest point
above the river.

The Columbia River Gorge provides a geologic window into the
interior of the range. As the river sliced through the layered basalts on

its way to the ocean, it exposed folds and arches of these ancient strata, showing how pressures within the earth caused a warping of the crust. These upwarped rocks, eroded into peaks and ridges, became the Cascades of southern Washington and northern Oregon.

Near the westward-flowing Columbia grew three of the largest Cascade volcanoes, Mt. Adams and Mt. St. Helens in Washington and Mt. Hood in Oregon. Because they stand like white sentinels above the river, they are locally known as the Guardians of the Columbia. A favorite subject of Indian lore, the guardian peaks compensate for the otherwise undistinguished topography of the Cascades in this area.

History and Exploration

Although earlier explorers had noted their existence, it was not until the British navigator George Vancouver sailed into Puget Sound in the spring of 1792 that the Cascade peaks began to receive their present names. Mt. Baker, northernmost of the U. S. volcanoes, was named for Vancouver's third lieutenant. Mt. Rainier honored Admiral Peter Rainier, while Mt. St. Helens commemorated a then-famous diplomat. While exploring the Columbia River, Vancouver's first lieutenant, Broughton, sighted a gleaming white spire which he mistakenly took to be at least 25,000 feet high, and named it after Samuel Hood, another highranking naval officer. Although he correctly guessed that all these individual peaks were probably joined by a continuous mountain chain, Vancouver made no attempt to christen the range itself.

On their return trip, Lewis and Clark observed still another high snowy pinnacle, standing about 40 miles south of Mt. Hood. This Matterhorn-like peak they named after Thomas Jefferson, the sponsor of their expedition.

The remaining high peaks received their names almost casually from early explorers or settlers during the 19th century. Oregon's Three Sisters were first called Faith, Hope, and Charity by wagon train members who used them as landmarks. Shasta, the exact source of which name is unknown, was first sighted by Russian and/or Spanish scouting parties in northern California. Adams was named purely by accident (see Chapter 13); and Crater Lake was not even discovered until 1853.

The National Parks

Congress has recognized the unique qualities of the Cascade Range by establishing four major national parks within its boundaries. Lassen Volcanic National Park was created in 1916 while the volcano was still in the midst of its latest series of eruptions. The Park encompasses not only 10,457-foot Lassen Peak, but also dozens of associated volcanoes, such as Cinder Cone and Chaos Crags. Lassen Park includes extensive thermal areas, marked by sizzling steam jets, boiling sulphur pits, and miniature mud volcanoes with craters full of bubbling, spattering, hot mud. These thermal displays are the largest and most varied in the country outside of Yellowstone National Park.

One hundred seventy miles north of Lassen Peak, in southern Oregon, lie the indigo waters of Crater Lake, cradled in the six-mile-wide basin of a collapsed volcanic giant. This ruined volcano, posthumously named Mt. Mazama, contains what is probably the most magnificently situated body of water on earth. Crater Lake National Park also preserves evidence of a volcanic explosion that may have been greater than any other which occurred in post-glacial time. Even that of famous Krakatoa, the volcanic island near Java which, in 1883, produced the most tremendous outburst of historic times, was perhaps less violent. The titanic blasts which led to the destruction of ancient Mt. Mazama ejected over 42 cubic miles of material. That cataclysm occurred about 6600 years ago, but even today geologists watch warily lest old Mazama reawaken.

In size, height, and grandeur the climax of the Cascade Range is reached in Mt. Rainier, principal feature of Mt. Rainier National Park. The mountain's enormous bulk is visible from Canada to Oregon to the Pacific. It is unique in being the only landform in a national park to combine volcanism with active glaciers. With 45 square miles of unmelting snow and ice covering its lava cone, Mt. Rainier supports the largest glacier system in the United States south of Alaska, yet the summit cone is indented by two geologically youthful craters, still hot enough to keep the crater rims free of snow and generate scores of steam vents and fumaroles. One of these craters contains a lake which the steam has melted out *beneath* the summit icecap, 14,000 feet above sea level.

The North Cascades

North of Mt. Rainier the Cascades change radically in character. Composed chiefly of extremely old metamorphic and sedimentary rock, the North Cascades have been uplifted and eroded into a maze of sharp peaks and twisting narrow valleys. Seemingly locked in a contemporary ice age, this remote and stormy terrain is one of the last true wilderness areas in the United States. Its austere and primitive qualities have been safeguarded by the establishment in 1968 of a fourth national park, the North Cascades.

Although this part of the range is essentially nonvolcanic, its highest elevations are the two northernmost volcanoes in the American Cascades, Mt. Baker and Glacier Peak. Both, unfortunately, lie outside the boundaries of North Cascades National Park. While Glacier Peak is isolated in the center of the range, Mt. Baker is readily accessible. Baker's crater, the source of several historic eruptions, still seethes with escaping steam, which sometimes rises in billowing, fleecy clouds (Figure 17-4).

About 50 miles beyond the Canadian boundary stands the Mt. Garibaldi group of volcanoes. Although most maps place Garibaldi in the "Coast Mountains" of southern British Columbia, it actually represents a northern spur of the Cascade Range. The Fraser River valley which separates the two mountain areas is only an erosional feature, not a structural division.

Cascade Prototypes and Personalities

Of all the high volcanoes that crown the Cascades, no two are precisely alike, either in appearance or geologic history. The Pacific Northwest Indians recognized this individuality and spun some of their most attractive legends about the white giants who overshadowed their daily lives. Several of the peaks figure conspicuously in native stories of the Great Flood during which the mountains played the role of Noah's ark; Baker, Jefferson, and Shasta offered their summits as places of refuge when the Deluge swept away all life below.

In myth, the mountains were also warrior gods, given to catapulting red-hot boulders at each other. Sometimes their aim was accurate enough to decapitate a mountain rival. Mt. Adams' flat top is accounted for in this picturesque fashion. The Indians also invested the peaks with romantic interests. They said that Mt. Hood and Mt. Adams feuded over the love of the youngest and fairest of all mountain deities, Mt. St. Helens. The story of the ensuing battle and its consequences is told in Chapter 14.

Volcanoes as Benefactors

As farmers and ranchers of the Pacific Northwest are aware, the volcanoes' activity has not been wholly destructive. Volcanic rocks are typically rich in minerals and are quickly weathered into unusually fertile soil. Near Mt. Rainier formerly uneven terrain has been leveled and filled by huge mudflow deposits, which make excellent grazing and farmland. Widespread ash blankets from St. Helens, Mazama, and Glacier Peak have further enriched the ground with potassium and other nutrients. In addition, the volcanoes' covering of snow and glacial ice supplies meltwater to fill reservoirs and provide both electric power and water to irrigate parched ranchlands east of the mountains.

Volcanoes may provide a partial solution to the present energy crisis. Enormous amounts of heat energy are available in the Cascades, if scientists can find a way to harness it. The benefits of tapping geothermal power include its cheapness and its freedom from environmental pollution. Unlike atomic power plants or utilities burning coal or oil, natural steam power is clean and relatively safe. Already the southern Oregon town of Klamath Falls uses volcanic steam to heat public buildings; and geologists are now exploring ways to draw upon the hot magma underlying Mt. Hood and other Cascade peaks.

Vulcanism is also the means by which water from the earth's interior reaches the surface. Over hundreds of millions of years of geologic time, all our water and all the atmosphere have been liberated from the bowels of the earth by volcanic action. Not only is the land we live on either built or enriched by volcanoes, the water we drink and the very air we breathe we owe to them.

Because there are literally thousands of volcanoes in the Cascade Range, it is impossible for one book to describe them all. This volume concentrates on the 17 most distinctive volcanic land forms, in most cases devoting a chapter to each.

Before starting our survey of the range, it may be helpful to review briefly what a volcano is, theories about how it works, and what kinds of volcanoes are found among the Cascade mountains.

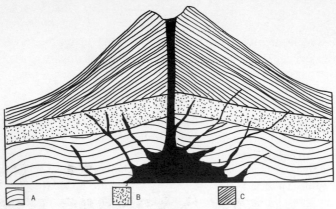

Figure 2–1. Simplified cross-section of a typical cinder cone. Legend—A. Basement rock; B. Pre-cinder cone deposits; C. Pyroclastic material. Solid black denot magma chamber and feeder pipes.

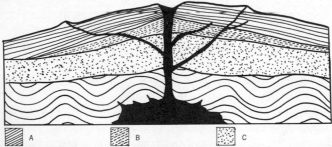

Figure 2-2. Simplified cross-section of a typical shield volcano. Built of extremely fluid lava, shield volcanoes typically have broad bases and gentle slopes. Legend—A. Lava; B. Ancestral deposits; C. Non-volcanic rock. Solid black denotes magma chamber and feeder pipes.

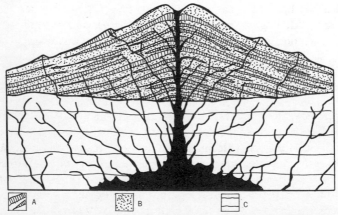

Figure 2–3. Simplified cross-section of a typical stratovolcano. Legend—A. Lava flows; B. Pyroclastic and mud flow deposits; C. Basement rock. Solid black denotes magma chamber and feeder pipes.

2
The Fire:
How A Volcano Works

To primitive man, the volcanoes which sometimes blazed along the Cascade Range were a source of terror and superstition. The Oregon Indians who survived the outbursts which destroyed the summit of ancient Mt. Mazama later created fascinating legends about the event. To them, volcanoes like Mazama and Shasta were divine and therefore unknowable—supernatural personalities who thundered in wrath and often devastated the land.

Science has stripped the volcano of its divinity; no one any longer believes that gods inhabit its molten interior or stand hurling thunderbolts from its blazing crest. We do know that the volcano is capable of frightful destruction. In this century alone, many thousands of persons have been killed and many square miles of land laid waste by volcanic activity. In the hope that future damage can be minimized, volcanoes have been carefully studied, especially during the past half century. Although there is still much that remains mysterious about them, we now know something about how volcanoes work.

Defining a Volcano

A volcano is both an opening in the earth's crust through which hot rock is thrown out, and the hill or mountain formed by the accumulation of ejected material. Rock which volcanoes bring to the earth's surface is called *lava*, whether it is erupted in a solid or liquid state. Geologists usually divide such volcanic rock into two broad categories. When it emerges as a molten stream, it is known as a *lava flow*. Solidified, it is called *lava rock*. But when the lava is blown out in fragments and solidifies or partly solidifies before reaching the ground, the term *pyroclastic* is used (from the Greek, meaning "fire-broken").

Volcanoes built entirely of pyroclastic or fragmental rock are called *cinder cones* (Figure 2-1). So named because the volcanic fragments composing them resemble cinders, these pyroclastic cones contain rocks of many different sizes and shapes. Extremely fine material, lava pulverized to the size of sand grains or smaller, commonly is blown by the wind away from the erupting vent and settles to form a blanket of *volcanic ash*. Sometimes explosive volcanoes discharge material very rich in gas, which results in fragments full of bubbles and extremely light in weight. Lumps of this frothy material are called *pumice*, which is typically buoyant in water.

Some of the best examples of young cinder cones associated with the Cascades occur near Bend, Oregon, where the black and orange mass of Lava Butte stands at the edge of U.S. Highway 97. Named for the long streams of lava which issued from its base, this cinder cone is a study area of the University of Oregon's Center for Volcanology. Another accessible example of a geologically recent cinder cone is that forming Wizard Island, which rises above the surface of Crater Lake.

The summits of both Lava Butte and Wizard Island are indented by a circular depression called a *crater*. This bowl-shaped hollow found at the top of most volcanoes encloses the vent through which volcanic rocks are erupted. Usually funnel-shaped in cross-section (Figure 2-1), the crater occurs at the opening of the volcano's internal feeding-pipe, the channelway which connects the vent with an underground supply of molten rock. The channelway inside the volcano is called the *conduit*.

Volcanic cones which are built around a single central opening usually have a circular ground plan and a generally conical form. Other eruptive vents, however, may appear at any point along the volcano's slopes. Such *lateral* or *parasitic* eruptions can result in a mountain composed of several superimposed cones, such as Mt. Adams in Washington State (see Chapter 13).

The *shield volcano* (Figure 2-2), usually much larger than a fragmental cone, is built by a succession of extremely fluid lava flows. All of the volcanoes in the Hawaiian Islands—Mauna Loa, Mauna Kea, Kilauea—are of the shield variety. Such volcanoes are rarely explosive, although they often generate enough gas pressure to shoot up brilliant fountains of molten rock. These fiery displays are common during an eruption in Hawaii's Volcano National Park.

Because highly liquid flows often travel a considerable distance from the erupting crater, the shield volcano characteristically builds a broad gently-sloping mound that resembles a warrior's shield laid flat with the curved side upward. During the early part of the Pleistocene Epoch of geologic time, which probably began 2 to 3 million years ago, many shield volcanoes were constructed in the Cascade Range, particularly in Oregon. Although some retain their original mound-like forms, many have been eroded so extensively that the masses of solidified lava which plugged their central conduits have been exposed. These lava plugs now form the spires of Mt. Washington, Mt. Thielsen, Union Peak, and Three Fingered Jack, the "Matterhorns" of southern and central Oregon.

The largest and best-preserved shield near the Cascades is Oregon's Newberry Volcano. As is common with volcanoes of this nature, the summit of Newberry's enormous shield has subsided or collapsed to form a huge central pit called a *caldera*, which is by definition much larger than any explosion vent or crater.

The third—and most impressive—form is the *composite* or *stratovolcano*, which is built of both lava flows and fragmental material (Figure 2-3). All of the loftiest Cascade peaks—Rainier, Shasta, Hood, and Adams—are of this type. Although most of the large composite cones are formed principally of lava flows, they are higher and steeper than any of the shield volcanoes. Erected at various times during the Pleistocene Epoch, the original conical forms of most of these mountains have been severely modified by glaciation (Chapter 3). A few have built the visible parts of their cones during the 10,000 years since the Pleistocene ended. Of these, Mt. St. Helens—sometimes called the Fujiyama of America because of its symmetry—offers the most striking example of how the large stratovolcanoes may have looked in their prime.

A fourth kind of volcano in the Cascades is the lava *dome*. Unlike the cinder cone, shield, or stratovolcano, it is not constructed of layers of material added during successive eruptions. Instead, it is a single mass of lava rock that has been extruded through a vent. At the time of its formation the lava forming the dome was too stiff and pasty to flow away from the opening, and as a result, it piled up around the erupting orifice to form a steep-sided mound or dome.

When such a viscous mass fills or plugs a previously existing crater it forms a *plug dome* (Figure 4-13). Most plug domes rise no higher than about a thousand feet, although Lassen Peak, one of the world's largest domes of this type, rises perhaps twice that high above the crater it buried. The slopes of Lassen Peak, as on other similar volcanoes, are formed by the disintegration of the sides of the dome. Fragments crumbling from the dome margins eventually create aprons of material that give the otherwise almost vertical-sided plug the appearance of a smoothly sloping cone. Lassen Peak has several craters at the summit, although many plug domes, such as Black Butte, at the edge of Interstate Highway 5 near the city of Mt. Shasta, have none.

Figure 2-4

SIMPLIFIED GEOCHRONOLOGY OF THE CASCADE RANGE

Geologic Period	Approximate Age (years)	Geologic Events (Representative)
Holocene (Postglacial)	60-200	Historic eruptions: (mainly small, pyroclastic) at Shasta (?), Hood, St. Helens, Baker, Cinder Cone, Rainier, Lassen, etc.
	300	Creation of Chaos Jumbles, Lassen area.
	450	Layer W erupted by St. Helens, followed by emplacement of summit dome and other plugs.
	1,000-1,200	Growth of Chaos Crags, Lassen area.
	1,500	Latest lava flows at McKenzie Pass, Oregon.
	1,800-2,000	Eruption of plug dome at Hood; associated debris flows.
	2,000	Building of Rainier's summit cone.
	2,500	Beginning of ''modern'' St. Helens.
	3,000-4,000	Eruptions of layer Y by St. Helens.
	6,600	Eruption of Mazama ash, destruction of Mazama and formation of Crater Lake.
	c. 7,000++	Postglacial lava flows at Newberry Caldera, Bachelor Butte, South Sister, Adams, McLoughlin.
	.... 10,000	Melting of last Ice Age Glaciers (end of Fraser Glaciation).

Epoch	Years Ago	Event
Pleistocene Epoch (Ice Age)	11,000	Growth of Lassen Peak Plug Dome.
	12,000	Eruption of Glacier Peak ash.
	25,000	Beginning of Fraser Glaciation, equivalent to "latest Wisconsin"
		Birth and growth of principal Cascade stratovolcanoes, Hood, Rainier, Adams, Sisters, Shasta, Jefferson, Mazama, etc.
		At least FOUR MAJOR GLACIATIONS occur during and between episodes of volcanism.
	2,000,000 - 3,000,000	
Pliocene Epoch		Growth of large shield volcanoes and stream deposition of volcanic debris along edges of mountain front.
		Uplift and erosion of modern Cascade Range.
		Explosive volcanism in Washington in area of present Cascades.
	7,000,000	
Miocene Epoch		Late Miocene explosive volcanism at site of Washington Cascades.
	15,000,000	Eruption of Columbia Plateau basalts begins; flows cover part of present Cascade Range.
	26,000,000 (?)	

What Makes a Volcano?

The exact mechanism that causes the earth to open up and belch out enough material to build a mountain many cubic miles in volume is still a mystery. The underground forces that trigger the initial eruptions as well as maintain activity at the site for hundreds of thousands of years are hidden too deep in the earth's interior to be easily understood. All that we know for sure is that miles beneath the surface the earth is extremely hot, partly because of radioactivity. Forty miles down the temperature is probably close to 1200 degrees Centigrade, more than hot enough to melt rock. But the rock remains solid, for the tremendous pressure at that depth prevents liquefaction.

When a crack or fault in the earth's crust allows room for the superheated rock to expand and liquify, it does so immediately, moving upward along narrow fissures toward the surface. A few miles below the surface it characteristically displaces the enclosing rocks to form an underground reservoir. This subsurface molten rock is called *magma* and its reservoir a *magma chamber*. These enclosed storehouses of gas-charged liquid become the feeding chambers of volcanoes. When the crystallization of various minerals within the magma liberates enough gas, the resulting pressure forces the magma upward until it blasts an opening to the surface.

Initial eruptions are usually violent and spew forth clouds of gas (up to 95 per cent of which is steam) carrying rock fragments, blobs of molten matter called *volcanic bombs*, and quantities of brown, gray or black volcanic ash. The ash gives the volcano its familiar column of "smoke." Electrical discharges or the glow reflected from incandescent rock onto clouds of water vapor give the appearance of fire, although no actual burning occurs in the volcano during an eruption. (References to volcanic "fires" are metaphoric.) When the gas pressure is less intense the rising magma is not blown to bits but instead flows from the vent as streams of liquid lava.

Cascade Lavas

The erupted lava sometimes displays a smooth ropy surface, which hardens into billowy, wave-like undulations. This kind of lava is called *pahoehoe*, after its Hawaiian prototype. At other times, often from the same volcano and even during the same eruption, the lava presents a rough, jagged crust resembling a heap of black clinkers from a smelter. This type is called *aa* and is usually thicker and moves more sluggishly than the pahoehoe variety. On still other occasions, the lava surface is covered with large angular blocks. It then seems to advance rather like a slow avalanche as the blocks tumble over one another on their way downslope. Climbing over the surface of such a *blocky flow*, as on the upper reaches of Oregon's Mt. McLoughlin or Bachelor Butte, is a tedious and exhausting experience.

In addition to being classified by the appearance of their solidified crusts, lavas are also catalogued by their chemical and mineralogical compositions. The four most common types—all found in the Cascades—are *basalt, andesite, dacite*, and *rhyolite*. The nature of the lava is largely, but not entirely, determined by the amount of silica it contains. Basalts, relatively low in silica (45.8 to 50.8 per cent), are highly fluid and may move rapidly over great distances. The extraordinarily liquid lavas that built the plateau country of eastern Washington and Oregon were basalts. Shield volcanoes, with their broad bases and gradual slopes—such as Newberry Volcano in Oregon—are formed almost entirely of basalt.

The most commonplace Cascade lava—that of which most of the stratovolcanoes are built—is *andesite*. So named because it is plentiful in the Andes Mountains of South America, andesite has an intermediate silica content of about 54 per cent. Less fluid than basalt, it flows shorter distances and thus piles up to form a moderately steep cone around the eruptive vent. Varieties of andesite are generally named from the iron-and-magnesium-rich minerals they contain; the most common in the Cascades is *pyroxene andesite*. Some Cascade peaks, like Mt. Baker and Mt. Rainier, are constructed almost exclusively of this kind of lava. Others, like Mt. St. Helens and Mt. Mazama (Crater Lake), demonstrate a much wider variety in the chemical composition of their lavas, erupting basalts and dacites as well as andesite.

When the silica content of the lavas exceeds about 64 per cent, *dacites* or *rhyolites* are formed. If the excess silica crystallizes to quartz, dacite is the result. Dacite is very rich in silica (63+ per cent), has a low melting point (about 850 degrees Centigrade), and is pasty and viscous when molten. It tends to form bulbous, steep-sided domes, such as those of Lassen Peak and the nearby Chaos Crags. When the silica content is even higher (73+ per cent), rhyolite is produced. Probably the most interesting kinds of rhyolite in the Cascades are the glistening *obsidians* (black volcanic glass) that poured into the Newberry caldera from fissures high on the caldera wall. Another spectacular series of obsidian domes burst through the southeast base of the South Sister and can be seen rising like glittering black minarets along the Cascade Lakes Highway southwest of Bend, Oregon.

Age of the Cascade Volcanoes

While most cinder cones are born, grow and die within a decade or two, some Cascade stratovolcanoes have a life history that stretches back several hundred thousand years or more. At one time geologists estimated that several of the largest cones, like Rainier and Shasta, represented millions of years of accumulation and erosion. Recent studies, however, suggest that many of the composite volcanoes of the Cascades may be much younger than formerly supposed. Measurements of the magnetic polarity of the lavas that built Mt. Jefferson, The Three Sisters, and perhaps Mt. Mazama as well, indicate that they have been emitted since the last reversal of the earth's magnetic field.[1] Except for two short-lived periods of magnetic reversal, the earth's magnetic field has been normal for about 770,000 years.[2] The peaks thus dated have been erected since that time. The Cascade Range itself, on top of which the great volcanoes are built, is much older, but the high volcanic cones are surprisingly young.

Volcanoes as "Geologic Clocks"

The Cascade volcanoes are extraordinary geologic clocks. This discovery has been of great importance in the advance of geology. By erupting wide-spread layers of ash, distributed over hundreds of thousands of square miles, several of the more explosive vents have laid down distinctive "time markers" which enable the geologist to date the relative ages of other events. When bits of carbonized wood are found associated with a particular deposit, scientists can analyze the wood sample by the Carbon 14 method. The radiocarbon technique has succeeded in dating several extensive ash layers from Northwest volcanoes:

Source	Approximate Age (years)	Layer Designation
St. Helens	175	T
St. Helens	450	W
St. Helens	4,000-3,000	Y
Mazama		
(Crater Lake)	6,600	Mazama ash
Glacier Peak	12,000	Glacier Peak ash

(See "Cascade Geochronology," Figure 2-4).

Age limits of recent formations can also be determined by the tree ring method. Sometimes trees are damaged by an ashfall or by proximity to volcanic heat. Using a sample core from a surviving tree, and counting back the annual growth rings to the points at which the tree suffered growth constriction, one can often pinpoint the exact year of the event. Using a similar method, scientists can date the age of recent glacial moraines. When the growth rate of certain kinds of fungus is known for a particular area, it is possible to assign relative ages to lava surfaces on which the fungus is growing. Other means of determining approximate ages of volcanic deposits include the potassium-argon method, used for dating very old lava rock.

In the pages ahead we shall find that many familiar Cascade features are, geologically speaking, remarkably new. Crater Lake, the summit area of Mt. Rainier, the McKenzie lava beds, the visible cones of Mt. St. Helens, Lava Butte, Cinder Cone, Newberry Caldera, and Bachelor Butte— have all been created during the past few hundred to few thousand years. The summit configuration of Lassen Peak, in fact, was formed during the 20th century. After a look at how glaciers work, and how they have helped carve the present Cascade landscape, we shall examine that most recent of Cascade eruptions.

Chapter 2 – References

1. *McBirney, 1968, p. 101*
2. *Ibid.; Crandell, written comm., 1973.*

3
The Ice:
How A Glacier Works

Among the most striking features of the high Cascade peaks are the masses of ice which descend from their summits. These gleaming white ribbons are glaciers—flowing rivers of ice. The basic difference between an ordinary ice field and a true glacier is that the latter is *moving*. Because of this constant movement, they play an important role in sculpturing the Cascade terrain.

How does a glacier form, and how can a snowfield be transformed into a stream of moving ice? The creation of a glacier does not necessarily require snowfalls of enormous depth, although they certainly help. All that is absolutely needed is a long series of cool summers during which the previous winter's snowpack does not entirely melt. If the rate of accumulation significantly exceeds the rate of melting over many years, the fallen snow loses its light fluffy texture. Gradually the air is forced out of it and it forms dense layers of ice crystals. The tightly compacted snow slowly changes into granular ice. Impelled by gravity, it begins to slide downward over the underlying bedrock and flow between and within ice crystals. If winter storms regularly supply more snow each year than can melt in the summer months, the glacier will continue to grow and advance. Conversely, if the annual precipitation decreases or the climate turns warmer, the glacier will diminish in size and may entirely disappear.

In the Cascades of Washington, Oregon, and part of northern California, there is presently enough snow every year to maintain glaciers on the higher peaks. At Mt. Rainier more than 50 feet of snow falls annually, much of which does not melt above the 7000 to 8000-foot level.[1] Large amounts of snow accumulate in the North Cascades; Mt. Baker is almost entirely sheathed in ice. Glaciers tend to be larger in the northern section of the range because the low sun angle at northerly latitudes provides less solar energy to thaw the ice. Even as far south as Crater Lake, Oregon, the seasonal snowfall approximates 50 feet, although because of lower elevations and warmer summers most of it vanishes by mid-July. Throughout much of their length, the Cascades are whitened down to about the 3000-foot level from autumn until late spring.

The elevation above which snow persists throughout the year is called the *annual snowline*. On a glacier it is also known as the *firnline*. These elevations may vary with fluctuations in the weather from year to year. They also differ considerably in various parts of the range. On Lassen Peak, which rises 10,457 feet above sea level, only a few patches of snow on the shaded side of the mountain usually survive the hot California summers. Mt. St. Helens, nearly 800 feet lower in altitude, but about 390 miles farther north, supports five glaciers and remains snowcapped all year long.

That portion of a glacier below the firnline where melting exceeds accumulation is called the *ablation zone*. In the California Cascades this zone lies much higher than it does farther north. The glaciers of Mt. Shasta (elevation 14,161 feet) do not descend below about 9000 feet. On Mt. Rainier, only about 250 feet higher, some glaciers extend into canyon bottoms as low as 3500 feet.

How Glaciers Work

On volcanic mountains, glaciers are particularly effective eroding agents because volcanoes are not composed of very solid rock. Built of hundreds of individual lava streams and layers of fragmental material, they offer little resistance to glacial scouring.

As a glacier flows, it scoops up chunks of bedrock and transports them downslope. The underlying rock surface is also ground down by the abrasive action of the debris frozen into the glacier's base. The glacier thus sinks ever deeper into the trench it cuts for itself, polishing and smoothing some surfaces it passes over, gouging grooves and furrows into others.

The mechanics of its quarrying action are aided by the presence of numerous fractures in the rock known as joints. These fractures form prior to glaciation and are enlarged by frost action. Ice moving over such a surface is able to quarry or extract these joint blocks and incorporate them into its base. Although the quarrying action at the base of the glacier cannot be observed, it may be initiated when water enters these cracks, freezes, expands, and pries the joint block up where the moving ice can exert its tremendous force. Large boulders, as well as small stones, thus become embedded in the glacier; as it moves forward, the loosened rock is plucked from place and carried away in the moving ice stream. The rock subsequently becomes a tool of the glacier, used to scrape out still other fragments from the glacier's bed.

Although a clean, white glacier may be esthetically pleasing, a dirty ice stream is doing more work. Impregnated with sharp fragments of rock and grit, a blackened glacier is removing and transporting large quantities of material. Not only do active glaciers quarry and scour an area, they bulldoze along their margins, undermining and steepening canyon walls. Avalanches of rock fall on top of the glacier's surface, adding to its weight and cutting power. When a glacier enters a winding V-shaped valley cut by streams, it typically broadens it by digging into the valley walls, planing off projections. Widened, deepened, and straightened, the valley becomes a U-shaped canyon, with steep sides

Figure 3–1. Close-up view of a typical glacier. The giant cracks—crevasses—which split the ice stream are caused by tension as the glacier flows over an uneven bed at irregular speeds. (Winthrop Glacier, Mt. Rainier, photo by Bob and Ira Spring.)

and a rounded bottom. One of the most typical and accessible of these glacier-scoured canyons is that occupied by the Nisqually Glacier on the south side of Mt. Rainier. Along the south rim of Crater Lake, the beheaded remnants of prehistoric glacial trenches—the U-shaped notches of Munson, Sun, and Kerr valleys—scallop the caldera wall.

When a glacier descends to low elevations where melting exceeds replenishment of the ice from above, the glacier terminus dumps its load of rock. These deposits contain fragments ranging in size from large boulders to a gray flourlike substance. This unsorted aggregation of debris is called glacial *till*. The long ridge of material thus formed at the glacier's front is called a *terminal moraine*. Those laid down along the edges of the glacier are known as *lateral moraines*. Such deposits, unmistakably the work of glaciers, are often found many miles downvalley from the site of today's ice streams or in valleys throughout the Cascade Range where glaciers no longer exist.

Around Mt. Rainier, moraines occur as far as 65 miles away from the peak, yet the glaciers which deposited them clearly originated at high elevations on or near the mountain. One of the clues to the fact that a great volcanic cone once towered above Crater Lake is the presence of moraines 17 miles from the lake rim. From the regional distribution of moraines, it is apparent that in ages past the Cascade glaciers were vastly larger and longer than they are now. Several times during the past 2 to 3 million years glacier ice virtually buried much of the Cascade Range.[2] During some of these glaciations, ice flowing down valleys in the northern Cascades merged with a stupendous icesheet which blanketed the Puget Sound lowland to a point somewhat south of Olympia, Washington. During the last of these glacial advances, the Fraser Glaciation, the site of Seattle was submerged beneath 4000 feet of grinding ice. This giant ice lobe withdrew only about 13,500 years ago.[3] At the same time, a nearly unbroken ice cap smothered the high Cascades in Washington, and in Oregon from south of Mt. Hood to the base of Mt. McLoughlin.[4]

In addition, thick ice sheets mantled local areas, such as the mountainous regions bordering all of the major peaks, including those in California. The full number and extent of these repeated glaciations are not yet fully understood, but their cumulative effects on the landscape were tremendous.

Most of the Cascade stratovolcanoes were built during and between episodes of intense glaciation. Consequently, during much of their history the cones of Baker, Rainier, Adams, Hood, Jefferson, the Three Sisters, Mazama, and Shasta were probably encased in ice to a far greater extent than they are today. During intervals of mild climate between glaciations, the growing cones of Rainier and its fellows may have been nearly as smooth and symmetrical as Mt. St. Helens is now. But recurring glacial attacks deeply modified their conical forms, sculpturing trenches and bowl-shaped *cirques* into their slopes. Thus many of the older peaks are now highly asymmetrical, their original forms almost obliterated.

Figure 3–2. Although they may appear smooth from a distance, glacier surfaces are typically shattered and broken into colossal blocks—seracs—which present a towering challenge to ice climbers. (Ingraham Glacier, Mt. Rainier, photo by Bob and Ira Spring.)

The period of geologic time during which huge glaciers repeatedly developed is known to geologists as the *Pleistocene Epoch*, popularly called the Ice Age. It began with a world-wide cycle of cold, wet weather 2 to 3 million years ago and ended about 10,000 years ago. Since intervals between Pleistocene glacial advances often lasted many thousands of years, it is by no means certain that the period in which we now live is not merely an extension of the Pleistocene. Geologists, however, designate the present epoch of geologic time as the *Holocene*. Even this short time has encompassed significant climatic fluctuations, which resulted in at least two episodes of renewed glacier growth within the last 3000 to 5000 years. A third *Neoglaciation* (the "Little Ice Age") ended only a century or two ago.

In exploring the Cascade volcanoes, we encounter the work of glaciers at every hand. The present shape and appearance of the peaks is due almost as much to the power of moving ice as to the fiery volcanism which originally built them. The eons-long contest between the constructive "fires" which raised the high cones and the erosive forces of ice which work to level them is not yet over; nature's two opposing powers are still working on their Cascade masterpiece.

Chapter 3 – References

1. *Stager, 1966, p. 54.*
2. *Crandell, 1965.*
3. *McKee, 1972, pp. 299, 302.*
4. *Crandell, 1965, pp. 348-349.*

4
Lassen Peak— Center of Lassen Volcanic National Park

The summer traveler driving northward on Interstate Highway 5 is likely to be disappointed by his first glimpse of Lassen Peak. As he approaches the northcentral California town of Red Bluff, the motorist will see in the far distance on his right—usually through haze caused by agricultural burning—a barren, earth-colored dome looming above what might be either a purplish cloudbank or a mountainous ridge. That rocky dome, standing 10,000 feet above the Sacramento River, is Lassen Peak, the most recently active volcano in the conterminous United States.

Lassen is located too far south to maintain glaciers, or even a year-round snowcap. By mid-July winter's snows have vanished, thus depriving the mountain of the glistening white mantle that beautifies the more northern Cascade peaks. Moreover, the mountain does not appear to rise much higher than its equally barren volcanic neighbors. For example, Brokeoff Mountain and Mt. Diller are more than 1000 feet lower in elevation, but from the Sacramento Valley they seem to be almost as high. Other nearby peaks, such as the jagged Chaos Crags just north of Lassen, also diminish its visual impact.

If the traveler leaves the interstate freeway and drives eastward up the slope toward Lassen Volcanic National Park, he will discover that the smudgylooking "cloudbank" or "ridge" is actually a volcanic plateau which forms the eastern margin of the upper Sacramento Valley. In the lower foothills, it is a bleak, arid country whose thin stony soil supports little besides scrub pine and wild grasses. This is the Tuscan Formation, an uninviting accumulation of ancient rock debris washed down from the volcanic highlands to the east. Farther upslope, the road winds among scattered cinder cones and lava flows. Southward, reaching almost to the Feather River Valley, lies a straggling collection of shield volcanoes and steep cinder cones—the southernmost extremity of the Cascade Range.

At about a mile in elevation, just west of the Lassen National Park entrance, the landscape becomes more attractive. The forests thicken, and streams and lakes appear. Lassen Peak turns its best profile toward tree-shaded Manzanita Lake, until 1974 the site of the park visitor center. Since its mountain competitors are not visible from this point, Lassen dominates the surrounding terrain. Framed by towering firs and pines, its image reflecting in Manzanita's still waters, Lassen's slopes reveal shades of pink, gray, slate blue, and warm earthen tints. Rising 4500 feet above the former visitor center, the volcano has at least a share of the majesty and "presence" that characterize the greater peaks to the north.

The 1000-foot-long tongue of coal-black lava which clings to the western summit reminds us that Lassen has one unmistakable distinction. It is the only volcano in the adjacent United States to erupt during the 20th century. Lassen's reawakening in May, 1914, was sudden, and apparently unheralded by an earthquake or other observed warning of any sort. The first officially recorded outbreak occurred on May 30, when a local resident named Bert McKenzie happened to be looking directly at the peak. At about 4:30 or 5 p.m. Lassen suddenly belched forth a cloud of dense black "smoke" (actually steam laden with dark volcanic ash), which rose several hundred feet into the air.

Although McKenzie is usually credited with witnessing the first eruption, it may be that Lassen had sent up some preliminary puffs of steam the day before. Anna Scharsch (now Mrs. James DeBow of Scharsch Meadows, a ranch near the present Park) was then 19 years old and lived a few miles west of the peak. During the evening of May 29, she observed a "column of smoke" rising from Lassen's summit.

Figure 4–1. Close-up of new crater, June 2, 1914. Note that the fragmental material thrown out was too cool to melt the snow it fell upon. (Photo courtesy of Mary Hill.)

She and other family members concluded that the newly constructed fire lookout atop Lassen must be burning. At 10 o'clock the next morning (May 30) they saw another, larger, smoke cloud rise from the peak. If Mrs. DeBow's recollections are correct, the volcano may have resumed activity a full day before the first officially recognized eruption.[1]

The first person to investigate the phenomenon at close range was Harvey Abbey, a forest ranger who climbed through deep snow to reach the mountain's summit on Sunday, May 31. Abbey found that a new vent—measuring about 25 by 40 feet—had opened high on the northwestern wall of Lassen's old summit crater. The old crater, which filled with lava in 1915, was then an oval-shaped depression about 1000 feet in diameter. A small lake occupied part of the crater floor, which lay about 360 feet below the highest point on the rim. Hot water from the new vent poured downward into the lake, cutting a channel in the snow.

Abbey noted that the mountaintop was strewn with material blown out by the first eruptions. Stones up to 18 inches across and mud had fallen one or two feet deep over an area 200 feet in diameter.

Volcanic ash and sand covered an area about one mile wide, extending down the volcano's slopes. As Figure 4-1 shows, none of the solid material brought up was hot enough to melt the snow it fell on. Most of the rock debris ejected during the first year of eruptions was probably old lava that had plugged the volcano's conduit.

A second (or possibly fourth) explosion occurred at 8:05 on the morning after Ranger Abbey had made his ascent. This was a heavier discharge and hurled out boulders "weighing all of a ton." The active vent, from which lateral fissures extended 100 feet in an east-west direction, was enlarged to 60 by 275 feet. As the steam explosions increased their duration and intensity, the new opening continued to expand until it occupied all of the pre-1914 crater.

On June 13 ashes fell for the first time on the village of Mineral, which lies about 11 miles southwest of the peak. The first eruption to endanger human life occurred on Sunday, June 14. A party consisting of several local millworkers, including R. E. Phelps, F. A. Tipple, and Lance Graham, climbed Lassen to view the new crater, which had by then grown to 450 by 125 feet. The men were resting on the crater rim when:

> Without any warning, or explosion that could be heard, a huge column of black smoke shot upward with a roar, such as would be caused by a rushing mighty wind, and in an instant the air was filled with smoke, ashes, and flying rocks from the crater. They all ran for their lives. Mr. Phelps hid under an overhanging rock, which sheltered him from the rocks which brushed past him as they fell. Lance Graham was a few feet away when he was struck by a flying rock, which cut a great gash in his shoulder and broke his collar bone.

He was left on the mountain for dead [but was soon after revived by his companions].

[Another member of the party, Jimmy Riggins, made a run for it]: . . . coming to a snowdrift, [he] slid down the mountain like a shot. The cloud of smoke kept pace with him, and the rocks from the crater came rolling down the mountain with a hum, and when he reached the bottom of the snowdrift he found a clump of bushes, and diving into it, buried his face in the snow to keep out the blinding smoke and ashes. The smoke is described as causing the blackest darkness, black as the darkest night. If it had lasted much longer some of them would have been smothered.[2]

While Graham and his friends were being peppered with sharp rocks, a local businessman and amateur photographer recorded the June 14 eruption in a series of six remarkable exposures. (Figures 4-2 through 4-5). B. F. Loomis, hoping to record the volcano in action, had set up his tripod near Manzanita Lake, about six miles west of the peak. As Loomis' photographs demonstrate, the eruption clouds were very dark—heavily charged with ash and dust. After shooting to a height of about 2500 feet above the mountaintop, they rolled downslope to enshroud the whole dome—as well as Phelps, Graham and the others—in "inky black smoke."

Although it is famous because of Loomis' photos, the June 14 outbreak was not nearly so violent as many of those which followed during the summer of 1914. Beginning at noon on July 15, a series of detonations which lasted the entire afternoon hurled an ash cloud nearly 9000 feet above the mountaintop. The crater remained in eruption intermittently throughout the next two days, scattering ash over an ever-widening area. The climax of this cycle of explosions was reached at 5:28 in the morning of July 18, when Lassen roared furiously, sending a black column of ash 11,000 feet above the mountain. One explosion followed another almost the entire morning. People living in nearby settlements began to calculate how quickly they could hitch their horses for a retreat from Lassen's lethal reach.

But the mountain had temporarily exhausted its energy. Attention turned again to a more sinister outbreak—military violence in Europe—which daily threatened to overwhelm the civilized world. By the time Lassen revived, on August 10, the European war had become a reality. However, local interest, plus the fact that the United States had not yet entered the conflict, helped ensure that the volcano would again monopolize headlines in northern California.

The August 10 outbreak was moderate, but nine days later Lassen began a new cycle of particularly intense activity. For four and a half hours on August 19 the volcano sent up "huge clouds of ash" which rose

Figures 4–2 through 4–5. Four successive views of Lassen in eruption, June 14, 1914.

Figure 4–6. West end of the new crater, June 28, 1914. The new vent is expanding along an east-west trending fault. (Photo courtesy of Mary Hill.)

Figure 4–7. Close-up of ash cloud rising from Lassen's crater, September 29, 1914. (Photo by Jack Robertson, courtesy of Mary Hill.)

10,500 feet above the crater and were visible throughout the northern Sacramento Valley. Two days later the ash column (as measured by the Forest Service) towered 10,560 feet above Lassen's summit. On August 22 the volcano introduced a variation on its usual behavior. This time, instead of rising vertically as it had on all previous occasions, the eruption cloud "shot up obliquely" and rushed down the mountainside. It was not then known, but this kind of laterally-directed explosion was a forerunner of what was to be the most dangerous aspect of Lassen's activity.

During the latter part of August and all of September, the eruptions lasted longer and produced heavier ash falls. From September 5 on, eruptions occurred almost daily, showering ash over Mineral, Viola, Chester, and other hamlets on all sides of the mountain. Eye-witnesses spoke of "terrific rumblings," "heavy vibrations," and the sound of rocks crashing against each other. Slides of rock debris tumbling down the mountainside must have added to the din.

On September 21, in what was described as "probably the most violent eruption to date," ash darkened almost the entire sky over Mineral. A week later "luminous bodies hurled high into the air" and flashes of light from the crater led some observers to conclude that molten lava was now being erupted. It is likely, however, that electrical flares rather than hot lava fragments were responsible for the phenomenon. There is no clear evidence that molten lava was ejected until 1915.

Eruptions continued throughout the winter of 1914-1915. As soon as winter snows fell, they were often blanketed with black ash and cinders. Most of these eruptions were relatively mild, although that of October 22 lasted two hours and reportedly produced a fall of genuinely hot ashes. A Mr. Charles Yori of Drakesbad climbed the mountain the next day and found "that the ashes were so hot he could not remain long at one place and that his dog's feet were burned."[3] By that date the fire look-out atop Lassen had been demolished by falling rocks.

New Year's eve, 1914, marked Lassens' 110th observed eruption (not counting the two reported by Mrs. DeBow). Between then and May 14, 1915, another 60 outbursts were recorded. The official reports, however, are not likely to be complete. During most of the winter, storms obscured the mountain, and most observers had departed. An unknown number of eruptions undoubtedly took place unnoticed.

E. N. Hampton, who made the season's first ascent of the mountain on March 23, 1915, noted that the new crater had then expanded to a diameter of about 1000 feet. This enlargement is not surprising, since several of the observed winter eruptions had sent clouds more than 10,000 feet into the air (as on December 24, and March 20 and 21).

The snowfall of 1914–1915 was one of the heaviest on record. As warm spring weather began to melt the snowpack, quantities of water undoubtedly trickled into the open fissures and vents of the volcano. Draining into the mountain's interior, some water may have reached hot magma and been transformed into steam. The rapid melting reached its height during May. In that month, almost exactly a year after the volcano had reawakened, the climax of Lassen's latest eruptive activity occurred.

Clouds hid the peak from view from May 7th until the morning of the 13th, when brief clearings revealed almost continuous eruptions from what seemed to be a new crater. On the 14th, Miss Alice Dines, postmistress at Manton, 20 miles west of the peak, began to telephone her friends that "fire" was visible for the first time. A glow was observed all that night and again on the 15th and 17th. This time the reports of hot material were accurate.

B. F. Loomis and Miss Dines were apparently the first to detect what appeared in daylight as "a small black mass pushing up into the cleft in the rim of the western summit." Miss Dines recalled in a letter of June 8, 1916, that the "dark formation began to rise above the level of the mountain about the 16th or 18th of May, black during a clear day."[4] The "black mass" was the solidified crust of a lava column rising from the volcano's throat.

The night of May 19, 1915, brought the first of two spectacular eruptions. First, pasty lava oozed from the summit crater through V-shaped notches in the eastern and western crater walls. To observers at the town of Volta, 21 miles west of the mountain, it looked as if the volcano were literally boiling over. In a letter to J. S. Diller, G. R. Milford described the most colorful fireworks Lassen had yet produced:

About 9:15 p.m. word was sent in by telephone that Lassen Peak was in eruption and fire could be seen coming from the crater. . . . Our attention was first drawn to the deep-red glow which appeared over the crater and was of sufficient intensity to illuminate the entire outline of the mountain-top. There was no moon, the heavens were clear, yet this glow was bright enough to be reflected in the dense clouds of steam and smoke arising from the crater. From time to time the glow seemed to change in brilliancy, now brighter, now dimmer—this variation due, no doubt, to the varying density of the clouds of steam and smoke issuing from the crater.

As we continued to gaze at the wonderful spectacle, the glow commenced to increase in brilliancy, now brighter, now still brighter, until, behold, the whole rim of the crater facing us was marked by a bright-red fiery line which wavered for an instant and then, in a deep-red sheet, broke over the lowest part of the lip and was lost to sight for a moment only to reappear again in the form of countless red globules of fire about 500 feet below the crater's lip. These globules, or balls of fire, were of varying size, the largest appeared at that distance [21 miles] about 3 feet in diameter, the smallest appeared as tiny red sparks. All maintained their brilliancy as they rolled down the mountainside until lost to sight behind the intervening range of hills.

These phenomena took place at intervals of about 8 minutes for a period of some 2 hours, and to the writer it appeared as though we were looking at a titanic slag-pot being slowly filled by molten slag in some smelter. The glow over the rim gradually increased in intensity until the pot's rim was brilliantly marked by the appearance of slag itself. Finally, the slag spills over the lip in a vivid red sheet and, as it runs down upon and into the slag dump, it breaks through the crust of older slag and appears against the background as splashes of deep-red molten material.

As stated earlier in this article we watched this re-occurring boiling-over, as it were, of the crater for a period of two hours, at the end of which the activity seemed to decrease. Concluding that the display for that evening war nearly at an end, we returned to the power house and made preparations for a trip on the morrow to Manzanita Lake, which lies almost at the foot of the mountain.

Next day proved a disappointment, as the sky was overcast and the peak was shrouded in dense storm clouds. Nevertheless we started, and arrived at the lake about 10 in the morning. At brief intervals the clouds would break sufficiently to permit us to see the peak, which was steaming and smoking in great volumes, indicating that the activity had immensely increased. We also observed that there was on the western slope a dark mass of matter appearing almost black. This mass appeared about 1,000 feet across and extended down the slope for possibly a distance of 2,000 or 2,500 feet. From our location this mass appeared like volcanic mud and must have been of consistency greater than ordinary mud, as the surface still maintained its roughed, furrowed appearance.[5]

The "dark mass" which Milford's group saw was not mud, but a genuine lava flow which had spilled over the western gap in the crater wall. Three-hundred feet wide at the crater lip, it had moved about 1000 feet downslope, where it cooled in position. Composed of glassy black dacite, its surface bristles with irregular spires and pumiceous blocks.

At about the same time, another arm of the flow issued through a gap in the eastern crater wall. But the second flow did not hold together as a coherent mass. Ploughing into the snowpack on Lassen's steep northwest side, it soon broke into pieces, rapidly melting the snow with which it came in contact. The resulting melt water, mixed with the accumulated debris of more than 170 previous eruptions, was quickly transformed into a large mud-flow—a mixture of water, mud, and boulders—which rushed down the volcano's northeastern face.

Carrying blocks of hot lava weighing up to 20 tons, the mudflow poured into Lost Creek with such velocity that it easily rode over the 100-foot-high divide into Hat Creek. Streaming down the two valleys, it overwhelmed everything in its path: trees, fences, bridges, and farm buildings were destroyed and previously fertile meadows and grazing land were buried under the mud, which was said to resemble wet concrete as it flowed (Figures 4-9 and 4-10).

The effect which the volcanic flood had on the people living in these valleys is vividly described by Wid Hall, a rancher on Hat Creek:

Mr. Elmer Sorahan was a homesteader living in a tent about a mile and a half above here on Hat Creek. In the night his dog barked, raved, and stuck his paw against him in the bed to wake him up. Elmer thought it might be some kind of animal, a bear or panther, so he got up and dressed, put on his high top boots and laced them up. He put his gun by his bed, then peeped out to see what the dog was barking at.

He saw the mudflow coming like a wave about twelve feet high which looked like a white streak on top. The flood made a roar something like a gale of wind in the trees, with a crash and boom of the logs and rocks as they came tumbling along in the flood. He realized that it must be a flood coming, so without waiting for his guns, he left everything and ran down the creek to awaken those who lived below him on the creek.

It was about eleven or twelve o'clock when the flood reached our place. Elmer came with a rush, and he was perhaps five minutes ahead of the wave that struck our house. He gave a yell that startled us, and we all jumped up in a hurry. Frank Bartlett happened to be staying there that night, but he was sleeping in the barn across the creek, 150 yards distant. Elmer then ran across the creek to awaken him, and just got back across the creek when the bridge went out. Frank remained on the other side. In the meantime, Mrs. Hall telephoned to the people below on the creek that the flood was coming. The people on the lower Hat Creek were very much excited, but the flood did but very little damage below the Wilcox place, and it was near daylight when the flood reached the lower Hat Creek.

As soon as Elmer returned he took the two girls, one by each hand, and beat it for higher ground. The older girl, Marian, was fairly well dressed, but the younger one was too slow and had no shoes on, and in their haste she stubbed a toenail off. The crash and roar of the flood was so intense that you could hardly hear one yell even at a short distance.

After we went to the woods it began to rain, so we went to the high ground, and made our camp under a tree. I had just two stubs of matches in my pockets, and we managed to get a fire.

About three o'clock we tried to get back to the house, which had moved 53 feet and lodged against a tree and the yard fence, but could not reach it at that time. We had some provisions in the house that were not affected by the flood, so we could eat. On leaving the house we left the door open and the flood entered about two and a half feet deep, then on the ebb flow part of the mud and water ran out, but when the mud had dried it was about sixteen inches

Figure 4–8. Lassen's giant mushroom cloud of May 22, 1915, viewed from Anderson, 50 miles west of the volcano. (Photo courtesy of the National Park Service.)

Two views of the terrain northeast of Lassen Peak:

Figure 4–9. Before the eruptions (Jensen Meadow in foreground).

Figure 4–10. After the mudflow of May 19–20 and only hours before the great hot blast of May 22. Note the wide swath which the mudflow cut through the forest on Lassen's flank. The large boulder in the left foreground is part of the lava erupted on May 19. (Photos courtesy of National Park Service and Mary Hill.)

deep in the house. A green log also had floated in, a rough old thing, which was about all four of us could do to get it out of the house. The mud flow looked more like mortar than water, and where it ran over the ground it left it slick and smooth like a pavement.

When daylight arrived, five of the neighbors from below came to our assistance with horses, but the trails were so bad and rough, that we declined to go away. But during the day we put a temporary bridge across the creek so we could get to the barn where the horses were, so if anything serious should happen we could get away. Water had run through the barn, but not enough to take it away. On their way over, the younger girl, Evelyn, saw a small pond of muddy water and asked if she could wade through it. And when she did so, found that the water was warm, something more than 'milk' warm, and that was in the afternoon of May 20th.[6]

Other settlers along Hat and Lost Creeks had equally narrow escapes. Harvey Wilcox, who lived on Hat Creek below the Hall property, was also awakened by his dog. He had just time to run—barefoot—for high ground before the flood swept away his log house as well as two heavy iron stoves and other new furniture he had not yet placed inside. The mudflow destroyed four other ranches, including the prophetically named "Lost Camp."

The "Great Eruption"

Worse was yet to come. Damaging as were the lava-triggered mudflows (see Figures 4-9 and 4-10), Lassen had still to demonstrate its full destructive power. Although it was erupting regularly from what seemed to be new fissures and vents north and west of the main crater—now choked by the black dacite that had overflowed the night of May 19—tremendous steam pressure was building up within the mountain. It reached the bursting point at about 4:30 on Saturday, May 22. The "Great Eruption" began moderately, but rapidly increased in force and volume. Before the eyes of thousands of persons throughout northern California, an enormous cloud boiled upward from Lassen's summit. Churning and rolling into a clear blue sky, the pale-gray to deep black cloud reached an estimated height of five to seven miles above the crater. As the giant umbrella spread out over the northern Sacramento Valley, ash rained down over a wide area. The prevailing winds carried the eruption cloud far to the east, where ash fell on towns located as far as 200 miles from the volcano.

The Reno *Evening Gazette* of May 24 reported that the Nevada villages of Imlay, Elko, Winnemucca, Golconda, and Gerlach were "covered with a fine white ash." The article also noted that two Western Pacific overland trains arrived late in Oakland, California plastered with "ashes and a film of mud thrown out by Lassen Peak. . . . Members of the crew reported they first noticed the baptism of ashes near Winnemucca, nearly 200 miles east of Lassen. When 100 miles from the mountain, they said, the trains were enveloped in an ashen cloud and were forced to decrease speed because the headlights could not penetrate."

The *Humboldt Star* of Winnemucca of the same date recorded that ashes began to fall about 8 o'clock in the evening of May 22 and continued for two and a half hours. " . . . people in the street noticed that their clothing was becoming coated with a grayish substance resembling soapstone. So thickly were the floating particles in the air that the moon became almost totally obscured. The fall of ashes continued until about 10:30 o'clock, when it began to subside, quieting the fear of those who fancied that Winnemucca might meet the fate of Pompeii. . . ."

While columns of ash rose into the stratosphere, showers of fresh pumice blanketed areas northeast of the volcano and hot volcanic bombs were catapulted down the north slope. As the photograph in Figure 4-8 illustrates, Lassen's 1915 mushroom cloud bore a sinister resemblance to that of an atomic blast. Viewers on the west side of the mountain saw only an upward-moving eruption cloud, but a terrific horizontal blast was simultaneously moving *downward* across Lassen's northeast slope and into the Hat Creek and Lost Creek Valleys. This mass of steam, hot dust, and rock fragments rushed through thick stands of virgin timber, snapping off trunks as much as six feet in diameter and hurling them hundreds of feet from their stumps. Altogether, an estimated five and a half million board feet of timber were destroyed. So great was the force of the eruption that trees toppled along its margin defied gravity by falling *uphill*, away from the explosion center.

The horizontal blast melted additional snow on the eastern slope, causing another flood to travel down the valleys of Hat and Lost Creeks. Following this second inundation in three days, even the tenacious Wid Hall family moved away to safer quarters. Since most of the loose material had been swept from the mountain by the mudflow of May 19, that of May 22 was smaller and considerably more fluid. In any case, little remained to be affected by this second flow. What the first had not buried the hot blast had scoured clean.

Heat from the May 22 explosion sent four additional mudflows streaming down the west and northwest sides of the peak. According to B. F. Loomis, all four reached Manzanita Lake, thus passing through or near the former site of the National Park Visitor Center and campground. Porous snowbanks of Lassen's lower flanks absorbed most of the meltwater so that only small amounts of mud and pumice actually washed into the lake.[7]

Figure 4–11. The devastated area in 1939. Twenty-four years after the horizontal blast of May 22, 1915, the land had not yet begun to recover. Today, reforestation is well underway. (Photo courtesy of the National Park Service.)

Today a paved road runs through the heart of this four and a half mile-long region lying northeast of Lassen Peak, which has been aptly named the "Devastated Area." Natural reforestation is beginning to cover the old scars, but enough evidence of the 1915 eruption remains to give visitors an idea of Lassen's destructive potential (Figure 4-11).

Lassen's Declining Activity: 1915-1921

Lassen had expended enormous energy during the blowoff of May 22, but it was not yet ready to settle into retirement. The activity which followed during the next five and a half years did not in any single instance equal the force of the "Great Eruption," but it was sometimes of major proportions. The explosions of May 22 had opened—or considerably enlarged—a new crater northwest of that plugged by the May 19 lava. It, as well as two other new craters which were blasted out by subsequent eruptions, continued to send up impressive columns of ash and pumice. These eruption clouds typically soared more than 10,000 feet into the air.

J. S. Diller, the pioneer geologist who had mapped the Lassen region and written a geologic history of the volcano during the late 19th century, returned to the area shortly after the hot blast to study its effects. He noted that on the night of July 13, 1915, "ashes fell at Drakesbad so that we could write our names on the porch railing in the morning."[8] Other "heavy" eruptions lasting from one to two hours occurred on August 25 and 27, while billowing clouds of ash were visible for miles down the Sacramento Valley. Additional outbursts, accompanied by "rumblings" and sulphurous fumes, occurred spasmodically throughout the summer of fall of 1915.

On the evening of October 25, 1915, "flashes and bombs were seen shooting from the crater."[9] Five days later the Forest Service reported a "heavy" eruption which produced a "glow over the crater and luminous bodies." One experienced observer, George W. Olsen, who lived at Chester, 20 miles east of the peak, also reported "large flashes of light and bombs" soaring "high over the top of the mountain."[10]

An explosion the forenoon of November 13 produced a cloud 11,000 feet high. But this was the last significant eruption for nearly a year; between December 29, 1915, and September 24, 1916, the crater was silent.

During the fall and winter of 1916–1917, Lassen began another cycle of activity. White steam alternating with "black smoke" issued frequently during the first months of 1917. On April 5, George Olsen reported "the heaviest eruption" he had seen "since the big one of May 22, 1915."[11] This was soon exceeded by a six-hour disturbance on May 18, 1917, during which clouds rose 10,000 to 12,000 feet above the peak and were "accompanied by loud rumblings."[12] Activity was nearly continuous during May 19th and 20th.

Twenty-one eruptions were reported during June when the renewed activity reached its height. During this period, according to Day and Allen, who made a careful study of the disturbances, explosions were "of such violence as to displace large masses of material at the top of the mountain, and materially to change the appearance of the crater."[13] Probably the major change was the blasting out of a new vent on the extreme northwest corner of the summit.

After June 29, 1917, no further action was reported until January 9 and 10, 1919, when Miss Dines observed "small smoke" issuing from the peak. If these were genuine eruptions, they were extremely mild and lasted for no longer than an hour each. Two more spurts of mild activity reputedly occurred on April 8 and 9 of that year. Except for two days in October, 1920, when the volcano was seen to "smoke" for 10 to 12 hours at a time, the last eruptive incident occurred on February 7, 1921, when Miss Dines sighted "great clouds of white steam issuing from eastern fissures."[14]

Even today, when humidity and temperatures are favorable, enough vapor escapes from tiny fissures in the summit to produce an occasionally visible puff of steam. According to Paul Schulz, a former Lassen Park naturalist, about 30 of these steam vents were still active in the early 1950s.[15] At present, the fumaroles seem to be fewer in number. Although the steam currently being emitted gives more evidence of Lassen's volcanic nature than existed before the 1914 eruptions began, the volcano now must be regarded as entirely dormant.

The Geologic History of Lassen Peak

It was implied earlier that Lassen Peak is, in appearance, perhaps the least impressive of the principal Cascade volcanoes. Certainly no other Cascade summit with an elevation of more than 10,000 feet so fails to inspire the viewer with a sense of grandeur. This lack of majesty does not derive merely from the fact that Lassen rises only 2500 to 3700 feet above the immediate terrain. It is primarily because Lassen is a particular *kind* of volcano.

Lassen Peak is the only mountain higher than 10,000 feet in the Cascade Range which is not a stratovolcano. That is, Lassen is not composed of alternate layers of lava and fragmental material deposited during long ages of geologic time. Instead, Lassen's dome is fundamentally all of a piece, a single solid mass of dacite lava that was thrust into place during a brief period of time, perhaps only a few months or years. Born in a single eruptive episode near the close of the Pleistocene Epoch, Lassen is one of the youngest of the Cascade fire-mountains.

To understand Lassen's story, we must go further back in time, perhaps a million years or more into the past when glaciers covered most of what is now Lassen Volcanic National Park. At that time a large stratovolcano was slowly building its cone near where Lassen now stands. This ancient

Figure 4–12. Diagrammatic cross-section of Lassen Peak, showing its relation to the prehistoric Brokeoff Volcano. The dotted line indicates the height of Brokeoff Volcano before erosion.

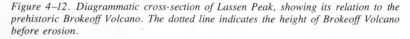

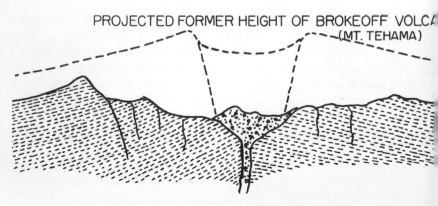

PROJECTED FORMER HEIGHT OF BROKEOFF VOLCA
(MT. TEHAMA)

volcano, known as the "Brokeoff Volcano" (or, Mt. Tehama), was in effect the parent of Lassen Peak.

As the drawing in Figure 4-12 illustrates, the old Brokeoff Volcano once towered above the present Brokeoff Mountain and Mt. Diller, which are now the highest remnants of its vanished cone. When the Brokeoff cone reached its full growth, perhaps mid-way in the Pleistocene, it was probably 11,000 feet high and its lavas covered 100 square miles.[16]

Familiar landmarks in the Park did not then exist, including Cinder Cone, Chaos Crags, and Lassen Peak itself. But during an interval between glaciations, a vent opened on the northeast flank of Brokeoff Volcano, perhaps at the present site of Lassen. From this new crater an unusually fluid dacite lava spread to the north, northeast, and west. Some of these black glassy flows traveled three or four miles from their sources and filled pre-existing depressions to a depth of 1000 feet.[17] Professor Howel Williams of the University of California, Berkeley, who made a thorough study of the Park's geology in the late 1920s, has called these flows the "pre-Lassen dacites."

These pre-Lassen lavas originally covered an area of perhaps 20 square miles,[18] but at least half of them have since been covered by later eruptive material or buried by glacial deposits. For between the time these pre-liminary flows were erupted and the appearance of Lassen itself, a period of severe glacial erosion occurred. By then Brokeoff Volcano had apparently ceased to erupt, although it continued to emit steam and acidic, corrosive gases. These gases gradually decayed the summit rocks through which they issued and hastened the disintegration of Brokeoff's upper cone. As returning Ice Age glaciers dug into the volcano's surface, the escaping gases dissolved whole layers of rock and converted them into clay, opal, and other vulnerable substances. After glaciers had breached the hard outer shell of the mountain, the soft, altered core was attacked

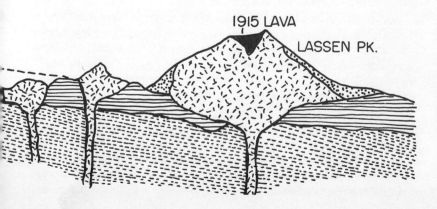

1915 LAVA

LASSEN PK.

and easily carried away by the moving ice. Even today considerable steam and other gases issue from Brokeoff's hollowed-out basin, where the thermal displays of Bumpass' Hell and the Sulphur Works continue to transform solid rock into soft clay. The headwaters of Mill Creek also continue their work of cutting into Brokeoff's decayed interior.

About 11,000 years ago, long after Brokeoff Volcano had been reduced to ruins, Lassen Peak came into being.[19] Although clouds of steam probably accompanied the emergence of the new mountain, Lassen did not rise in a burst of pyrotechnic glory. Rather, dacite lava oozed and pushed its way through the old vent which had produced the pre-Lassen lava flows. At the time of its extrusion, the new dacite was too stiff and viscous to flow outward as the more liquid dacites had done thousands of years before. Instead the lava piled up around the vent to form a cylindrical plug. As the dacite mass was pushed up by gas pressure from below, the sides of the plug were polished and abraded by the sharp edges of the conduit. While rising, the growing dome probably bristled with spires and spines of hardened dacite. Some of these protrusions are still visible on the southeast flank of the mountain.

Relatively little of Lassen's solid core is open to view. As the semi-solid mass emerged, like toothpaste being squeezed from a tube, the surface rocks cooled and hardened rapidly when exposed to the air. As more lava was thrust up from below, the brittle outer shell shattered and crumbled to form the banks of debris that now blanket most of the peak. These rocky avalanches which slid down all sides of the dome now form the visible outer slopes of the mountain. Williams estimated that Lassen's solid core, together with the talus that surrounds it, represents about one cubic mile of material. Lassen Peak is thus one of the largest plug domes in the world, certainly the largest of its kind in the Cascade Range. But it is minuscule in size when compared to the great stratovolcanoes like Hood, Rainier, or Shasta.

Recent studies by Dwight R. Crandell, a research geologist with the U.S. Geological Survey, indicate that Lassen appeared during a brief interval near the close of the Pleistocene Epoch, after an extensive ice-cap glacier which formerly mantled the area had mostly melted away.[20] Had glaciers covered the site when Lassen first appeared, they would soon have carried off the loose debris which comprise its slopes.

Glaciers did, however, briefly re-form shortly after Lassen had come into being. Linear deposits of glacial debris, called moraines, now mark the limits of these recent glaciers, at least one of which extended three miles beyond the peak. Further evidence of their presence are the shallow cirques which indent Lassen's east and northeast slopes above 8000 feet.

In addition to its unusual size, Lassen's dome is distinguished by the presence of four summit craters. Most volcanic domes are formed during a single eruptive episode and do not ordinarily have an explosion vent or crater at their summits. Chaos Crags, on the northwest flank of Lassen Peak, and the conical Black Butte at the foot of Mt. Shasta, are typical large domes without craters. In most cases, explosions accompanying the rise of such domes burst from underneath their lower edges, as they did at Hood, Shasta, and St. Helens. The fact that a fairly large crater existed prior to 1914 suggests that Lassen may have had several cycles of activity similar to those of ordinary stratovolcanoes. Some explosive outbursts apparently occurred early in Lassen Peak's history, for pumice flow deposits are found interbedded with late glacial sediments.[21] Precisely how long the volcano had been quiet prior to 1914 is not now known.

Chaos Crags and Chaos Jumbles

After Lassen Peak itself, and the steam-and-sulphur displays at Devil's Kitchen, Bumpass' Hell, and Boiling Springs Lake, one of the most remarkable sights in the Park are Chaos Crags and Chaos Jumbles. These are huge piles of sharp, angular boulders, formed so recently that nature has had little time to clothe them with greenery. The Crags, which stand 1800 feet above their surroundings on Lassen's northwest flank, are, like Lassen itself, massive dacite plugs heaved into place through previously existing craters. As explained by Williams, explosive violence preceded their appearance.[22] Not only were pumice and ash blown high into the air, but incandescent avalanches of pumice fragments rushed westward along Manzanita Creek and northward along Lost Creek. The cinder cones built during this activity were later mostly destroyed by the rise of viscous dacite lava, which, like that forming Lassen Peak, was too stiff and pasty to flow away from the eruptive vent. As it emerged it broke into confused heaps of large boulders. The resultant masses are now known as Chaos Crags, whose magmatic kinship with Lassen is suggested by their similar—but fresher—pink and gray surface colors.

Recent studies indicate that the Crags were formed about 1000 to 1200 years ago, so that they are only about one-tenth the age of Lassen Peak.[23] The Jumbles, a chaotic avalanche deposit two and a half miles long and covering about four and a half square miles, were created much later, perhaps no more than 300 years ago.[24] Williams thought this deposit was the result of a rockfall triggered by a steam explosion that had undermined the northern dome, causing waves of shattered rock to rush northwestward at tremendous speeds. A more recent suggestion for the origin of the Jumbles is that another small dome was intruded among the Crags about 300 years ago.[25] This possible late intrusion is thought to

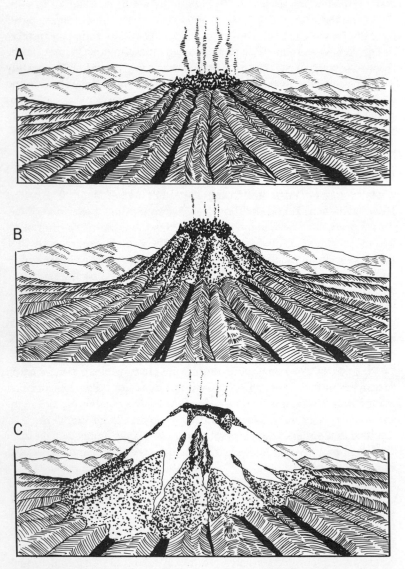

Figure 4-13. Evolution of Lassen Peak. A. A dome of viscous lava rises into the crater which had produced the "pre-Lassen" dacite flows. B. The rising dome fills and overflows the old crater. C. Crumbling fragments from the sides of the plug-dome form aprons of material around the solid mass. Lassen Peak is now complete.

have toppled an unstable formation and triggered the rockfalls and avalanches. Whatever the cause, the series of avalanches must have been appalling. Moving at an estimated 100 miles per hour, they crushed and buried everything in their path.

Steam was reported still rising in large quantities from the northern dome as late as 1854–1857.[26] This means that the volcanic life of the Crags extended over at least a thousand year period, and strongly suggests that they may not yet be extinct. The park visitor center and campground, once located on the Jumbles, have wisely been moved to safer ground.

Cinder Cone

The aptly named Cinder Cone stands about 600 feet above the flatlands near the northeast corner of the Park. Almost perfectly symmetrical, Cinder Cone is a consistent charcoal gray splotched with glassy black and rust-orange ash. The old Emigrant Trail connecting Nevada with the Sacramento Valley winds along its base and a sidetrail zigzags to its summit. The grade, about 35 degrees, is steep, but the summit is well worth investigating. Two nearly circular craters occupy the top, the smaller, deeper one contained within a broader depression. Remnants of perhaps two other crater rims are also evident, indicating that—unlike most cinder cones— this one experienced several distinct eruptive phases. In addition, extensive lava streams burst from the foot of the cone and dammed pre-existing drainage channels to form Butte and Snag Lakes.

The latest activity apparently occurred in historic time. According to the San Francisco *Daily Pacific News* of August 21, 1850, an unnamed informant actually saw "burning lava . . . running down the sides" of the volcano. The witness had reputedly ". . . been as near to the base of the cone as the heat would permit, but was obliged to retreat." Light from the eruption, the article stated, ". . . has been distinctly seen at a distance of forty-five miles." At the time of publication, the ". . . mountain had been burning for about ten days."

In a paper read before the California Academy of Sciences, Dr. H. W. Harkness summarized his interviews with "four different gentlemen" who claimed to have seen the volcano in eruption. A Dr. Wozencraft, who spent the winter of 1850–51 near Red Bluff in the Sacramento Valley, had "observed a great fire to the eastward of Lassen, which continued for many nights without change of position."[28]

Another eyewitness, Dr. J. B. Trask, also observed this night display "for many nights in succession." His vantage point was on the north fork of the Feather River, about 40 miles from the cone. The eruption must have cast a bright glare, for a party of miners at Angel's Camp in the Sierra, about 160 miles from Cinder Cone, also reported the event. Tradition holds that lava was emitted during 1850–51, but the latest flows from Cinder Cone seem to be older than 150 years. In its latest outbursts, the volcano probably erupted only fragmental material.

Exploring Lassen Peak

Of all the Cascade volcanoes, Lassen Peak is the easiest and safest to climb. Take Route 89, the main road through Lassen National Park, to the point where it crosses the mountain's southeast shoulder, just north of the Sulphur Works thermal area. The summit trail begins at a parking lot on the west side of Route 89. Starting at 8500 feet, the well-graded trail is a relatively easy two and a half or three-hour hike for persons in fair condition. At the top, the trail branches: the right-hand (northeast) path leads to the highest crag (10,457 feet); another, less well marked trail veers northwesterly across the jagged lava which filled the old crater in 1915. Past this lava, the hiker will find two bowl-shaped craters, the smallest and northwesternmost of which was opened in 1917. In clear weather, Mt. Shasta is visible 80 miles to the north.

The summit trail is usually open about July 4 and remains in use until the first heavy snows in October or November.

Chapter 4 – References

1. *DeBow, oral comm., June 10, 1973.*
2. *Loomis, 1926, p. 24.*
3. *Day and Allen, 1925, p. 178.*
4. *Ibid., p. 15.*
5. *Ibid., pp. 16–17.*
6. *Loomis, 1926, pp. 53–54.*
7. *Ibid., pp. 66–67.*
8. *Day and Allen, 1925, p. 183.*
9. *Ibid., p. 184.*
10. *Ibid.*
11. *Ibid., p. 185.*
12. *Ibid., p. 186.*
13. *Ibid., p. 28.*
14. *Ibid., p. 186.*
15. *Paul Schulz, 1959.*
16. *Williams, 1932a, p. 241; Crandell, 1972, p. c179.*
17. *Williams 1932a, pp. 300–303.*
18. *Ibid., p. 301.*
19. *Crandell, 1972.*
20. *Ibid.*
21. *Crandell, Mullineaux, and Bath, 1970, p. 84.*
22. *Williams, 1932a, pp. 346–364.*
23. *Crandell and others, 1974.*
24. *Williams, 1932; Crandell and others, 1974.*
25. *Crandell, 1974, p. 58.*
26. *Williams, 1932a, p. 347.*
27. *Harkness, 1875, p. 411.*
28. *Ibid.*

Figure 5–1. Mt. Shasta in summer, from the northwest. The front of a blocky lava flow from Shastina, right, occupies foreground. (Photo by Ed Cooper.)

5
Mt. Shasta—The "Mystery Mountain" of California

So much has been written in praise of glacier-crowned Mt. Shasta—including fantastic accounts which make its supposedly hollow interior the refuge of survivors from a lost continent—that one is tempted to take a skeptical attitude toward this over-exploited peak. But the wish to remain unimpressed must vanish at the first sight of Shasta's snow-mantled beauty.

The mountain, which rises 14,161 feet above sea level, is one of the largest stratovolcanoes in the world. Its enormous bulk has been estimated at between 80 and 84 cubic miles in volume.[1] Not only is the sheer size of the mountain overwhelming, its dominance of the surrounding Cascade landscape is complete. Towering a full 10,000 feet over rolling wooded foothills, Shasta can be seen in every direction for a hundred miles or more. Lassen Peak, visible 80 miles to the southeast, is reduced to a mere hillock by comparison.

Although other Cascade fire-mountains have their share of loyal boosters, none has attracted the bewildering variety of cults, sects and fanatical devotees as has Shasta. The village of Mt. Shasta (population about 2500), which lies at the volcano's western base, is the center for many of these off-beat religions. These groups seem to have little in common except for their conviction that Shasta is a "holy place." To such esoteric organizations as the Knights of the White Rose, the Rosicrucians, the Association Sananda and Sanat Kimara, the Radiant School of the Seekers and Servers, Understanding, Inc., and the I AM Foundation, Shasta is not merely another impressive landmark; it is a magic mountain.

Probably the best publicized legend about Shasta presents it as the home of the Lemurians, highly civilized refugees from the ancient kingdom of Mu, now submerged beneath the Pacific Ocean. These strange people, as described by those rare souls privileged to have seen them, are seven feet tall and display a walnut-sized sense organ in the middle of their foreheads. This miraculous organ enables them to communicate by extra-sensory perception and probably contributes to their ability to appear and vanish at will. A few persons have claimed to have been taken on conducted tours of the elaborate tunnel system which the Lemurians have devised within the mountain.

The most famous instance of Lemurian-related apparitions on the mountain allegedly occurred about 1930, when Guy W. Ballard, a Chicago paperhanger, encountered what he took to be a divine being high on the volcano's slopes. In his book *Unveiled Mysteries*, Ballard described meeting with one he called St. Germain, "a majestic figure, God-like in appearance, clad in jewelled robes, eyes sparkling with light and love." Reacting to his mystic experience rather like Moses after his interview with God on Mt. Sinai, Ballard came down off the sacred mountain to found a new religion, the mysterious I AM movement, largest of Mt. Shasta's many sects.

But, at least according to other local cults, the Lemurians are not the only publicity-shy race to inhabit Mt. Shasta. The Secret Commonwealth, which dwells in the subterranean cities of Iletheleme and Yaktayvia also occupy choice real estate inside the mountain. According to "authoritative sources," these Yaktayvians have fashioned vast underground caverns for their cities by their cunning use of bells. Supersonic vibrations from mighty Yaktayvian bells and chimes not only hollowed out Shasta's interior, but also supplied the citizens with heat and light. The eerie high-pitched bells also help frighten off intruders who might otherwise invade the Yaktayvians' highly valued privacy. How they manage to share quarters with the Lemurians, Atlanteans, and several other lost tribes who have also set up housekeeping inside Shasta is not known. Their mutual passion for solitude must severely conflict with the population explosion apparently taking place within the volcano.

Such beliefs represent only a part of Shastean mythology. According to other esoteric cults, Shasta is not only honeycombed by underground passageways, it is also a landing field for interplanetary travel. Flying saucers from distant points in the galaxy apparently make Shasta a scheduled stop. UFO reports, perhaps stimulated by the remarkable disc-shaped clouds that sometimes form over the summit, come in regularly from local observers.

The cause, if not the substance, of such wild surmise is understandable. For Mt. Shasta projects an unmistakable "presence," an aura of combined physical majesty and unsurpassed alpine beauty. Silhouetted against a clear blue sky, its white glaciers shimmering in sunlight or reflecting the rose and deep purple of an autumn sunset, Shasta seems quite believable as a gateway to the spirit world. Joaquin Miller's famous description of the mountain—"lonely as God and white as a winter moon"—only hints at Shasta's magnetic appeal.

While Shasta has become for some a white temple of the spirit, a lodestar for those looking for realms beyond ordinary human experience, to others it is an exceptionally attractive means of learning more about the forces that shape our earth. For the Mt. Shasta story, in purely scientific terms, is every bit as fascinating as any occult myth that has been fabricated about it.

The most obvious fact about the mountain is that it is not a single peak, but a multiple structure. From its western flank rises a secondary cone—called Shastina—that is large enough, if it stood alone, to rank as the third highest mountain in the entire Cascade chain. Only Rainier and Shasta itself exceed Shastina's 12,330-foot elevation.

The other most striking aspect of the volcano is that the summit area is relatively little eroded. Contrasted with its more northerly brothers—such as Hood or Rainier—much of Shasta's north and upper east surface has scarcely been scratched by glacier or stream cutting. Only on the south and to a lesser extent on the west and east sides has the original constructional surface disappeared. Below the Konwakiton Glacier, Mud Creek has excavated a canyon about 1500 feet deep into breccias, lavas, and mudflow deposits which compose the southeast slope. Oddly enough, erosion is much more advanced on the sunny south slope, where crags of Sargeants Ridge jut above Avalanche Gulch, the largest glacial valley present on the mountain.

Two factors contribute to Shasta's unusually fine state of preservation. First, it occupies a southerly position in the Cascade Range where the annual rain and snowfall is considerably less than on Mts. Rainier or Hood. (The nearby Klamath Mountains intercept the moisture-laden air moving inland from the Pacific before it can bring precipitation to Mt. Shasta. As a result, Shasta is much drier and has a thinner forest cover than either the Cascades to the north or the Sierras to the south.) While the annual snowline at Mt. Rainier remains at about 8000 feet, it lies above the 10,000-foot mark at Shasta. Although Shasta supports five glaciers—the largest in California—they are tiny compared to the 26 or more which bite deeply into Mt. Rainier. Erosion in general, therefore, is correspondingly less.

In addition, Mt. Shasta has erupted significantly larger volumes of lava during the past few thousand years than have many of its northern counterparts. Although parts of the edifice were repeatedly immersed in glacial ice during the Pleistocene Epoch, the volcano has since covered its flanks, especially on the north, northeast, and east sides, with a veneer of fresh deposits. Post-glacial flows of andesite lava, pyroclastic flows, and debris from dacite domes have filled in most of the gullies and cirques which Pleistocene glaciers carved in the older portions of the mountain.

How Mt. Shasta Was Built

Although it has existed for more than a hundred thousand years, Mt. Shasta is a mere infant compared to the Klamath Mountains which lie immediately to the west. These rugged peaks, formed of more ancient rocks, were upheaved into place millions of years before Mt. Shasta was born. According to Professor Howel Williams[2], glaciers may have mantled Shasta almost from its inception, for among the oldest exposed rocks are mudflows and volcanic breccias. These muddy, fragmental deposits are typically formed when hot lava mixes with meltwater from snow and ice, causing the lava to shatter into bits and pour downslope as a jumbled wet mass of boulders and mud. Such volcanic debris flows (called *lahars* after their Indonesian prototype) occurred frequently throughout the history of the volcano, suggesting the almost continuous presence of ice.

Since Mt. Shasta did not grow amid high ridges and deep canyons as did Mt. Rainier, many of the lahars were not channeled away from the volcano, but piled up in massive aprons about its base. A sequence of recent mudflows underlies the lumbering town of Mc Cloud at Shasta's southern base.

Although Professor Williams[3] recognized that Shasta was composed of two main cones, plus numerous smaller parasitic domes, cones, and vents, it was not until 1975 that the full complexity of Shasta's structure began to emerge. That summer two U.S. Geological Survey research geologists, C. Dan Miller and Robert L. Christiansen, spent several months combing the volcano's surface, including five days camped at the summit and another five days camped high on Shastina at Sisson Lake. They found Mt. Shasta consists of at least *four* distinct but overlapping cones which were built during four different eruptive cycles.

The discovery that Shasta is really four volcanoes of varying age piled atop and against each other helps explain some puzzling features. Although its shape is generally symmetrical, Shasta has some irregularities and protrusions which can not be explained by derivation from a single central vent. It has also seemed strange that the most deeply eroded and extensively glaciated parts of the mountain form its southern slopes. Because there are fewer hours of direct sunlight and less melting on the northern and eastern sides of the peaks, the largest glaciers and resulting glacial cirques in most cases occur on the shaded north and east sides, as they do on Mts. McLoughlin, Hood, Adams, and Rainier.

The most thoroughly dissected part of the mountain, the south side, is dominated by the long jagged outcrop known as Sargeants Ridge. According to Drs. Christiansen and Miller[4], this ridge is an eroded remnant of a large andesite stratovolcano built at least a hundred thousand years ago, the oldest of Shasta's four overlapping cones. The Sargeants Ridge lavas overlie the older basaltic andesites of Everitt Hill and other vents on the south side of the mountain. The last lavas erupted on the cone were hornblende-pyroxene andesites and a hornblende dacite summit dome and flow. Subjected to at least two episodes of Pleistocene glaciation, its original form has been partly destroyed.

After the Tahoe glaciation but before the Tioga glacial advance, which began about 25,000 years ago, a new vent opened on the north flank of Sargeants Ridge and built a second large pyroxene andesite cone which was later intruded by a dome of hornblende dacite. Christiansen and Miller[5] call this cone the Misery Hill volcano, for the upper part of its eroded surface is now represented by the long slope of dark, hummocky material of that name over which climbers toil on their way to the summit. In addition to numerous lava flows, and block-and-ash flows, the Misery Hill vent also produced the loosely compacted masses of orange-brown pumice which form the Red Banks, a conspicuous deposit at the head of Avalanche Gulch, on the south side. The Red Banks pumice flows were probably the final product of the Misery Hill summit vent.[6]

Post-Glacial Activity

During the 10,000-12,000 years since the Pleistocene glaciers melted in this part of California, Mt. Shasta added both the parasitic cone of Shastina and the present summit cone to its mass. An explosion crater developed about a mile and a half west of the glaciated Misery Hill cone. Viewed from the summit today, this fresh-looking structure, which contains Sisson Lake, is almost perfectly circular except where it is partly buried on the west by the younger slope of Shastina.

Shastina is centered about half a mile west of Sisson Crater. The bulk of the cone is built of pyroxene andesite lava flows, but the broad summit area (Figure 5-2) is composed of five plug domes of pyroxene-hornblende dacite[7]. Black Butte, a spectacular hornblende dacite plug dome at Shasta's western base, probably also dates from this eruptive episode. At least four of the Shasta domes produced identifiable pyroclastic flows on the west flank of the volcano, the oldest of which has a radiocarbon age of 9230 years, plus or minus 300 years.[8]

The eruptions during emplacement of these domes must have been violent, for deposits left by glowing avalanches which swept down the west side of the volcano underlie 21 square miles at its foot, including portions of the townsites of Weed and Mt. Shasta.[9] Explosions during the rise of Shastina's plug domes and the accompanying pyroclastic flows may have helped form Diller Canyon, the V-shaped gash which heads at a gap in the crater wall and slices through the west face of the cone. About a quarter of a mile wide and as much as 400 feet deep, this ravine may have been blasted out while the plug domes were being elevated, by downward-directed explosions as a result of which the crater wall collapsed to form hot gas-laden pyroclastics.[10] It is improbable[11] that the pyroclastic flows alone could have accounted for the canyon's great size as Williams thought.[12]

Among the most conspicuous surficial deposits on Shastina are a series of young-looking blocky andesite flows which issued along its northwest

Figure 5–2. Aerial view of Shastina's summit crater. The crater wall is breached on the west (left) by a deep cleft which heads Diller Canyon. The snow-covered mound occupying part of the crater is believed to be the top of a lava plug filling Shastina's eruptive conduit. (Photo by Ernest Carter, courtesy of Mary Hill.)

flank. One large flow emerged from a vent below the terminal moraine of Whitney Glacier and covered a surface underlain by deposits from pyroclastic flows, lahars, and glaciers of the older Misery Hill cone. Williams[13] estimated that the youngest flows on Shastina's north and northwest flanks were little more than 200 years old, but Miller and Christiansen[14] believe that they are all older than 9000 years. Whatever their age, they look remarkably fresh. The steep, 100-foot high margins of the blocky flows can be seen bordering U.S. Highway 97 a few miles northeast of Weed, where only a few scrub pines and sagebrush dot the bleak surfaces of "lava park."

After Shastina was built, activity resumed near the main summit. A fourth major vent opened north of the glaciated Misery Hill cone and erupted a series of short, thick blocky pyroxene andesite flows, producing the Hotlum cone, named after the glacier that clings to its north face. From a distance these stumpy, high-sided flows which compose the north and northeast flanks of the mountain resemble eroded ridges. They are, however, original constructional features which form step-like terraces just below the summit. The Hotlum cone was also invaded by a hornblende-pyroxene andesite dome, the remains of which now form the highest point on the volcano. Much decayed by their exposure to intense heat and acidic gases, these structureless andesite crags stand at both rims of Shasta's poorly defined summit crater. The crater is distinguished by a hot, acidic sulphur spring which emerges near the foot of the topmost spires, staining the adjacent snow and ground surface a dirty sulphur yellow.

The youngest part of Mt. Shasta, the Hotlum cone was erected *after* the neoglacial period which began only a few thousand years ago. The undissected Hotlum lavas postdate early neoglacial deposits that are present on the Misery Hill cone. No glacial deposits older than a few centuries are found on the Hotlum structure. The total absence of well-developed cirques or erosional gullies and the lack of much soil oxidation on the flows and other Hotlum deposits also suggest an age younger than a few thousand years.[15] Continuing thermal activity near the summit indicates that the summit dome is still cooling.

Eruptions on the flanks of Mt. Shasta have produced dacite domes and olivine-andesite flows and cinder cones on all sides of the mountain throughout its eruptive history, particularly along a linear north-south zone. Most of these parasitic structures are of Sargeants Ridge age, but some are younger.[16]

Williams thought that the pale brown pumice sprinkled over the upper slopes of the mountain might have been erupted in historic time.[17] In 1786 the French explorer La Perouse was sailing along the northern

California coast, "only four leagues" from shore. At that time he "perceived a volcano [i.e., an erupting crater] on the top of a mountain, which bore east of us; its flame was very likely, but a thick fog soon deprived us of this sight. . . ."[18] It is uncertain whether La Perouse witnessed an eruption of Lassen or Shasta, but if a mountaintop was visible it must have been the latter, which is high enough to be seen from the ocean.

Miller and Christiansen, however, found that Williams' brown pumice is derived from the Red Banks pumice flow, erupted from Misery Hill early in Holocene time.[19] They have not yet found evidence of historic activity or a likely source vent. It is possible, perhaps, that La Perouse did witness a genuine eruption of steam or other gases that did not produce enough ash to leave an easily recognizable deposit. Of the dozen or more eruptions of Mt. St. Helens between 1831 and 1857, for example, only one or two were voluminous enough to create an identifiable layer. The vent of Shasta's 1786 eruption, if there was one, may now be snow-covered or buried by slide debris.

A few feeble eruptions of steam or dust were reported as late as the 1850s. About 1855, one Nelson Harvey Eddy told of seeing "three puffs of smoke" rise from the summit of Mt. Shasta and drift southward. As he later described them, the "smokepuffs" were like those from the stack of an old-fashioned locomotive as it pulls away from a station.[20] The son of a tribal chieftain from the Shasta area reported that his father, as a young man in the 1850s had also seen smoke issuing from the top of the volcano.[21]

That Shasta's summit crater was hotter in the mid-19th century than it is now is confirmed by accounts of the first successful ascent of the mountain. In August, 1854, a climbing party from the town of Yreka found "a cluster of boiling hot sulphur springs, about a dozen in number, emitting any amount of steam, smoke, gas, etc., located on the edge of a broad snowfield just below the summit pinnacle. Captain E. D. Pearce, who led the expedition, also noted that "the ground for fifty yards around . . . [was] considerably settled and completely covered with sulphur, and the rocks are hot enough to cook an egg in five minutes."[22] Later, another group of hot springs was found on the north side of the peak.[23]

Today one small northern spring remains,[24] while those lying next to the summit spire have been reduced to a single active spring, which, in dry seasons, provides only about a pint of sulphurous hot water per minute.[25]

When the U.S. Geological Survey made aerial surveys to detect hot spots on Mt. Shasta, the infrared images taken clearly indicated thermal abnormalities in the summit area. These probably correspond to the sites of active vents reported by early climbers.[26]

Figure 5–3. Aerial view of Mt. Shasta from the west. The Whitney Glacier descends from the summit icefields and flows between the main cone and Shastina, whose crater occupies the right foreground. The Bolam Glacier covers the north (left) face of the main peak. (Photo by Austin Post, U.S. Geological Survey.)

Black Butte

U.S. Interstate 5, which circles Shasta's western base, gives the traveler a close look at Black Butte, a conical pile of black and purple andesite which stands at the highway's eastern edge near the city of Mt. Shasta. The westernmost expression of the eastwest fault which transects Mt. Shasta, Black Butte rises 2500 feet above the surrounding countryside and looks like an unusually rocky, steep-sided cinder cone. According to Williams, however, this "cone" is actually a plug dome.[27] It rose through a previously existing explosion crater, filled it, and overflowed it on almost all sides. Like those of Lassen Peak and Chaos Crags, its present slopes consist of talus and detritus which splintered from the viscous mass as it grew. Only at the top do pinnacles of solid rock show that it has a solid core. The Butte is surrounded by recent pyroclastic flow deposits.

Mt. Shasta's Glaciers

In ages past, Mt. Shasta was completely enveloped in ice. During the late Pleistocene Epoch, its alpine glaciers flowed westward into the adjacent Shasta Valley and rose up on the opposite hills to an elevation of 4000 feet. In valleys at the north base of the peak, ice attained a thickness of at least 1000 feet. Eastward-moving glaciers probably joined the large icecap that extended from the Medicine Lake highlands. Even on the sunnier south slope, glaciers rose to within 100 feet of the summits of various parasitic cinder and lava cones.[28]

Mt. Shasta's five glaciers—Whitney, Bolam, Hotlum, Wintum, and Konwakiton—are shrunken relics of their former selves. None extends downslope beyond the 9000-foot level. The largest, Wintum Glacier on the east side of the volcano, reaches down to an altitude of about 9125 feet. On the northwest slope, the Whitney Glacier terminates at about the 9850-foot level (Figure 5-4). The rate of shrinkage has apparently increased sharply during this century. In 1895 Diller calculated the length of the Konwakiton Glacier to be about 5 miles, but its present length is only a quarter of a mile. In 1934 Williams estimated that three square miles of the volcano's summit was overlain by active glaciers. By 1954 they covered only about two square miles.[29] At present the glaciers seem to be stabilizing, or even slightly gaining in size, perhaps as a response to a temporary cycle of somewhat cooler, wetter, weather (see Chapter 19).

During the summer of 1924 the length of the Konwakiton Glacier, which now terminates above a high cliff at the head of Mud Creek canyon was reduced by three-eighths of a mile.[30] Run-off from rapidly melting snowfields high on the mountain was especially large that season. Large torrents of meltwater poured into crevasses of the glacier and burst with great force from its terminus. Flowing into the Mud Creek canyon below, carrying large blocks of ice and rock debris, the swollen creek undermined the loosely consolidated canyon walls. Avalanches momentarily dammed the flood, causing water to back upstream until it surmounted the temporary earthen dams. Bursting through these obstacles, it raced down the Mud Creek valley, finally spilling out as thick sheets of fluid mud and boulders on the plains near the town of McCloud, severely damaging many homes and businesses there.

Finer silt and mud were swept on into the McCloud River and hence into the Pit and the Sacramento River. Finally, according to an anonymous undated report published by the Forest Service, debris from Mt. Shasta flowed into San Francisco Bay—whitening waters by the Golden Gate, 350 miles downstream from the volcano. Similar floods occurred in 1926 and 1931.

If such results can derive from a relatively minor glacier-outburst flood and subsequent mudflow, the mind boggles at contemplation of what havoc could be wrought should Mt. Shasta erupt during a spring thaw.

This is the secret firmly locked within the unexplored interior of this "mystery mountain." It is not the forgotten lore of the Lemurians or the fabled powers of survivors of Atlantis. It is the geologic enigma characteristic of every great dormant volcano. When will Mt. Shasta next erupt? And what will be the effect upon thousands of people living nearby?

The Medicine Lake Highland

Stretching eastward from Mt. Shasta are pine forested hills and youthful volcanic cones which culminate in the Medicine Lake Highland, 35 miles distant. Although never one of the Cascade skyscrapers like Shasta or Mt. Brokeoff, this collapsed shield volcano—which holds the shallow waters of Medicine Lake—is generally regarded as an eastern promontory of the range. Its geologic history does not belong to an account of the principal Cascade volcanoes, but for those willing to drive the narrow dirt roads which lead to the lake, it is worth a summer side-trip. (Because of heavy snowfall, the whole area is impassable to automobile traffic from fall until late spring.)

Although it never rose more than about 2500 feet above the adjoining Modoc Plateau, the Medicine Lake volcano is a huge, sprawling structure, 20 miles in diameter and dotted with many parasitic cones. The original caldera which indents the volcano's summit was approximately four by six miles; at present, however, it is not an impressive amphitheatre like that which houses Crater Lake. Its elongated summit basin has been largely filled by later eruptions from vents on the perimeter of the old caldera.

Probably more rewarding to the curious motorist are such youthful volcanoes as the nearby Glass Mountain, Little Glass Mountain (composed of two large flows of rhyolite obsidian), the Painted Pot Crater and Burnt Lava flows, and Little Mt. Hoffman. (One can drive to the summit to enjoy a spectacular panorama of the whole area, including a view of Mt. Shasta's rarely seen east side.) Volcanic activity in the

Medicine Lake region continued well into Holocene time and may even have persisted into the 20th century. Finch notes that a light shower of ashes which coated leaves of plants in nearby areas in 1910 may have originated at Glass Mountain.[31]

If one does not wish to risk his car's underpinning on the primitive logging and dusty forest service roads through Medicine Lake country, he will find an equally varied, and more accessible, display of volcanic phenomena in the Lava Beds National Monument, located a few miles to the north. (An "improved" road leads to the Monument from State Highway 139.) Of particular interest are Schochin Butte, a solitary, well-preserved cinder cone which rises above an arid plain, and the associated basaltic flows, which are riddled with miles of lava tubes and tunnels. The Modoc Indians, resisting a war of extermination waged by the U.S. Army, made their last stand here in 1872–73. For months "Captain Jack" and his men held out against superior numbers in the lava caves which border Tule Lake. At a later period in our history, thousands of Japanese-Americans were interned in the Tule Lake area.

To See Mt Shasta

If your car can endure narrow, rutted dirt roads, the best way to see Mt. Shasta is via the old Military Pass Road. The north end of the road leaves U.S. 97 about 15 miles north of Weed, beside a bronze tablet marking the Emigrant Trail. It circles the seldom-viewed east side of the mountain for 32 traffic-free miles and connects with route 89 at McCloud, a few miles east of I-5.

The Everitt Memorial Highway will take you to an elevation of 7703 feet on Shasta's southwest side. This 15-mile drive begins at the town of Mt. Shasta and ends at the Shasta Ski Bowl, where chairlifts (when operating) will carry you to 9212 feet. Although popular with skiers, the bowl area does not afford striking views of the mountain. Neither Shastina nor the actual summit are visible from here. In winter, a day lodge offers hot snacks and rental equipment.

The most-traveled (and probably technically the least demanding) route for climbing to the summit starts at the Sierra Club's Horse Camp on the southwest side. One must back-pack in about two miles from the Everitt Highway to the camp, which is located at 8000 feet. The summit trail, well marked only for the first lap, leads up over weary miles of broken rock through "Avalanche Gulch," an empty glacial cirque, to the "Red Banks," 200-foot cliffs of crumbling pumice. Once over this obstacle (the only dangerous part of the climb), the route to the summit crags is direct.

Although the vertical distance from Horse Camp to the top is only about 6100 feet, it is a long and arduous climb requiring excellent stamina. Except in winter, crampons and ropes are necessary only in the Red Banks area.

Chapter 5 – References

1. *Diller, 1895, p. 234; Williams, 1934, p. 228.*
2. *Williams, 1934.*
3. *Williams, 1932 and 1934.*
4. *Christiansen and Miller, in press.*
5. *Ibid.*
6. *Ibid.*
7. *Christiansen, written commun., 1975.*
8. *Miller and Crandell, 1975, pp. 347-348; Christiansen and Miller, in press.*
9. *Crandell, 1973, p. 28.*
10. *Christiansen, written commun., 1975.*
11. *Macdonald, 1966, p. 75*
12. *Williams, 1934, p. 236.*
13. *Williams, 1934, p. 237.*
14. *Miller and Christiansen, written commun., 1975.*
15. *Christiansen and Miller, in press.*
16. *Ibid.*
17. *Williams, 1934, p. 231.*
18. *Finch, 1930, p. 30.*
19. *Miller, written commun., 1975.*
20. *Eichorn, 1954, p. 13.*
21. *Ibid.*
22. *Ibid., p. 27.*
23. *Williams, 1934, p. 239.*
24. *Miller, written commun., 1975.*
25. *Williams, 1934.*
26. *Moxham, 1970, pp. 101-102.*
27. *Williams, 1934.*
28. *Williams, 1934, pp. 250-251,*
29. *Macdonald, 1966, p. 75.*
30. *Williams, 1934, p. 252.*
31. *Cited in Macdonald, 1966, p. 87.*

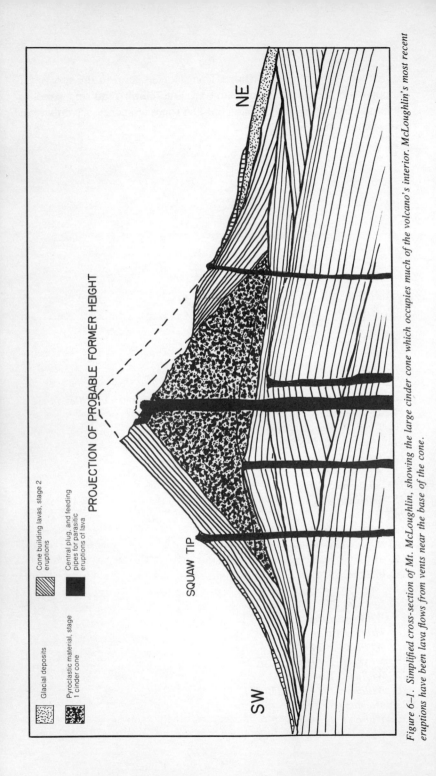

Figure 6-1. Simplified cross-section of Mt. McLoughlin, showing the large cinder cone which occupies much of the volcano's interior. McLoughlin's most recent eruptions have been lava flows from vents near the base of the cone.

Glacial deposits

Pyroclastic material, stage 1 cinder cone

Cone building lavas, stage 2 eruptions

Central plug, and feeding pipes for parasitic eruptions of lava

PROJECTION OF PROBABLE FORMER HEIGHT

SQUAW TIP

NE

SW

6
Mt. McLoughlin—Sentinel of Southern Oregon

About 70 miles north of Mt. Shasta stands the slim cone of Mt. McLoughlin, at 9493 feet the highest peak between Shasta and the Three Sisters. Little known even to most Northwesterners, except for fishermen who find excellent sport in the several lakes about its base, Mt. McLoughlin was first called Mt. Pitt, but renamed for Dr. John McLoughlin, the Hudson's Bay Company factor who generously helped American settlers at a time when both Britain and the United States claimed the Oregon territory.

The poetically christened Lake O'Woods is probably the most visited fishing spot near Mt. McLoughlin, although Four Mile Lake is the best point of departure for a summit climb. Those willing to exert the energy necessary to stand atop McLoughlin's narrow crest are rewarded by a sweeping panorama of the southern Cascades. To the west rolls a mighty sea of forested peaks and valleys, deep green close at hand, a smoky blue where they meet the horizon. The most distant ridges belong to what geologists call the Western Cascades, a deeply eroded region of volcanic rocks which are much older than those of the High Cascades, which border and partly overlap its eastern margin. McLoughlin and its fellow stratovolcanoes are all located in the more easterly High Cascade part of the range.

East of McLoughlin, somber forests extend to the curving shore of Klamath Lake, the largest body of fresh water in Oregon. Beyond it stretch the flat arid plains of Oregon's central plateau. To the south rises the white double cone of Shasta. Northward one can see the truncated mass which encircles Crater Lake. On an exceptionally clear day the snowy peaks of the Three Sisters appear dimly against the farthest horizon.

Spread out at one's feet, McLoughlin's cone provides a few surprises. To those who have previously seen the mountain only from the towns of Medford, Klamath Falls, or other settlements south of the volcano, it gives the impression of being a perfectly symmetrical cone. From the ridge that forms its present summit, however, McLoughlin is seen to be an asymmetrical victim of severe erosion. A vanished Ice Age glacier destroyed much of the northeast slope, leaving in its place a large semicircular hollow. This glacial cirque until recently was occupied by a stagnant ice field, although the ice has completely melted during the past few summers. Less than a century ago there was still an active glacier at the spot.[1]

Until the early 1970s almost nothing was known about the geology of Mt. McLoughlin. Although a prominent landmark in southern Oregon, it has neither the size nor the grandeur—at least by Cascade standards—to attract much scientific attention. The only available literature devoted to McLoughlin was a brief monograph which Arthur B. Emmons published in 1886.

Fortunately for those who would like to learn more of Mt. McLoughlin's past, the late LeRoy Maynard, then a geologist associated with the University of Oregon Center for Volcanology, spent several summers researching its history. The results of his field work—which includes a detailed map of the area—have not yet been published, but Mr. Maynard had kindly permitted his preliminary findings to be used in this review of McLoughlin's story. The text which follows is based largely on Maynard's research.

Among Maynard's most interesting discoveries about the volcano is that it underwent at least three, and possibly four, distinct stages of growth, each involving a totally different mode of eruption. Because of the large basin cut into its northeastern flank, Mt. McLoughlin's past is more clearly discernible than that of some other Cascade peaks, such as Mt. Shasta. The presence of this large cirque indicates that McLoughlin cannot be one of the younger Cascade volcanoes. It must have reached maturity some time before the last major glaciation, at least 25,000 years ago. Its exact age is unknown, but it possibly has been in existence for 100,000 years.

The Stages of Cone Building

The earliest stage of growth is problematical, since its products lie buried beneath the deposits of later eruptions. In its first *authenticated* eruptive phase, McLoughlin was highly explosive and spewed forth quantities of cinders, bombs, and ash. Localized at a central vent, these outbursts built an unusually large fragmental cone which may comprise as much as a third of the mountain's total volume of approximately 1.84 cubic miles (Figure 6-1). Judging by McLoughlin's relation to the surrounding terrain, this remarkable cinder cone *seems* to have risen to a height of about 3000 feet!

Some flows of molten rock accompanied the erection of this exceptionally big pyroclastic structure, but they were apparently confined to the lowest parts of the cone. One lava stream followed the ancestral valley of Four Bit Creek, terminating at the site of Big Butte Springs, which emerge from beneath it. Although erosion has cut deeply into the original cinder cone, no lava flows appear among the upper layers of pyroclastic material.

In the second stage of McLoughlin's development, the volcano radically changed the nature and products of its eruptions. Instead of violently blowing out pyroclastics, it began to emit voluminous but quiet streams of lava—also from a centralized summit crater. As numerous thin flows of lava poured down every side of the cone, the original cinder edifice was completely encased in clinkery andesite. McLoughlin thus became an "armored cone," with a hard outer shell of congealed lava and a soft inner core of loose fragmental material. If a glacier had not cut so deeply into its interior, we would have no way of knowing about its dual nature.

After activity at the summit crater had entirely ceased, McLoughlin began a third eruptive phase. This time copious floods of blocky andesite lava issued from vents below the summit, while fine-grained dark lavas poured from fissures along the base. Two conspicuous crags high on the west flank of the volcano, North and South Squaw Tips, now mark the vents from which exceptionally large blocky flows were erupted. These two flows merged to cover much of the southwest slope below the 7800 foot level. A much smaller but prominent flow of the same kind, the Rye Spring Flow, emerged just south of the Squaw Tip effusions, but at a lower elevation. A fourth major stream of blocky andesite issued inside the northeastern cirque and spread over glacial moraines and landslide deposits.

The dark fine-grained lavas of this period are generally much smaller in volume than the blocky flows and are restricted to the south slope of the volcano. One notable exception is a large flow which issued from two closely-spaced vents at the northwest base of the cone. This late flow, which can be seen on the road to Butte Springs, is now bordered on the north by the South Fork of Four Bit Creek.

All of these third stage lava flows are thought to have occurred after the end of the last major glaciation. Some of them remain completely unweathered, their blocky surfaces as sharp and angular as the day they cooled. Many are devoid of vegetation, extending long arms of naked rock into the thick timberlands surrounding McLoughlin's base. Recent unforested avalanche and mudflow deposits, younger even than the lava streams, are conspicuous on the north and east sides of the volcano. Maynard estimated that McLoughlin's latest lava eruptions are probably contemporaneous with the last outpourings at McKenzie Pass, and are thus about 1500 to 2000 years old (see Chapter 10).

The Puzzle of McLoughlin's Stage One Activity

It was noted above that the extraordinarily large cinder cone which forms much of McLoughlin's interior seems to stand about 3000 feet above its basement rocks. Since it is axiomatic that such loosely consolidated structures can not rise more than 1200 or 1500 feet without collapsing under their own weight,[2] the Mt. McLoughlin cinder cone presents a special problem. It is possible that some extremely short, thin lava streams helped to cement the pyroclastic mass together, thus enabling it to reach an unusual height, but none have been found among the fragmental debris exposed in the upper part of the cone. Several lava plugs did intrude the original cinder cone (perhaps after it had already been buried under younger lava flows) and these now stand as monolithic protrusions at the head of the northeast cirque.

It may be that beneath the partly exhumed cinder cone there lies a steep-sided lava shield, the result of "pre-stage one" eruptions. This hypothetical shield, if it rose 1500 to 2000 feet above the surrounding land surface, could then have formed an elevated platform on which the cinder cone was later built. With a steep shield serving as its foundation, the cone would not have exceeded the usual height limits which are imposed upon such unstable structures.

Shield volcanoes capped by large fragmental cones are common in the Oregon Cascades (see Chapters 8 and 10). Some of Mt. McLoughlin's immediate neighbors, such as Brown Mountain and Pelican Butte, offer fine examples of steep-sided shields topped and partly buried by later cinder cones.[3] Although it is presently impossible to prove, Mt. McLoughlin may, during its earliest stages of growth, have been similar in form and structure to Brown Mountain or other near-by volcanoes which closely resemble it. Alternatively, it simply may have been built over the glaciated ruins of an ancestral volcano which occupied the same site.

Mt. McLoughlin and the Cascade Icecap

The present crest of Mt. McLoughlin lies several hundred feet south of its presumed central vent. Since ice has removed not only much of the northeastern side but the former summit as well, there remains no trace of a crater. If one projects upward the original angle of incline of

McLoughlin's slopes, the lines meet at about 10,200 feet.[4] Leaving room for a modest-sized summit crater, it is probable that the volcano originally attained an altitude of about 10,000 feet, approximately 500 feet above its present top.

According to recent studies, Mt. McLoughlin is near the southern terminus of an icecap which almost buried the High Cascades during late Pleistocene time.[5] Apparently the glaciers that then mantled the volcano's northern and eastern slopes coalesced at the mountain's base with a continuous ice sheet which was there approximately 200 to 500 feet thick. Thus, except where recent lavas or landslides have moved downslope, both the northern and eastern flanks of the cone are blanketed with glacial moraines, outwash, and alluvium.

Exploring Mt. McLoughlin

Although not technically difficult, the six-mile trail to Mt. McLoughlin's summit (9493 feet) should be attempted only by persons in good physical condition and then only in late July and August after winter's snows have melted. Be sure to carry water as there is none along the trail.

From Klamath Falls, take highway 140 (west) for about 33 miles to the Four Mile Lake Road, No. 350, just west of the 31-mile post. Turn north here and proceed for 2.5 miles over rough road to the trail head located on the left hand side, where stands a sign reading Mt. McLoughlin Trail, No. 3716.

After crossing an open area and a clear stream (last source of water), the trail climbs through dense forest. It is a long 4.5 miles to timberline over increasingly steep grades and another 1.5 miles over large, angular boulders and loose rubble to the top. Above timberline, there is no real trail, only crosses and circles painted on lava blocks. At the top, there are fine views of Mt. Shasta to the south and Mt. Thielsen and the Three Sisters to the north.

If late snow drifts obscure the red "trail" markings on trees and/or boulders, mark your trail clearly; it is easy to lose one's way, particularly on the descent.

Chapter 6 –References

1. *Phillips, 1939; Montague, 1973.*
2. *Macdonald, 1972, p. 187.*
3. *Williams, 1942, pp. 19-20.*
4. *Maynard, written comm., 1973.*
5. *Crandell, 1965, pp. 348-349.*

Figure 7–1. Looking northeast across the mirror-still waters of Crater Lake. The Phantom Ship appears in the middle foreground; Mt. Thielsen's spire rises in the middle distance. (Photo courtesy of the Oregon State Highway Department.)

Crater Lake—Blue Gem of The Cascades

The calm of Crater Lake belies the cataclysmic violence which led to its creation. The enormous lake basin—five by six miles across and almost 4000 feet deep—is the hollowed out core of a giant volcano, which geologists have named Mt. Mazama. Until about 6600 years ago it rose more than a mile above the present lake rim, making it probably the highest mountain in Oregon. Then a series of tremendous explosions undermined the summit of the volcano, allowing it to collapse into a huge subterranean void.

Today, despite abundant evidence of past violence, the lake conveys a soothing impression of peace and permanence. To explore its mysteries, the visitor can follow a 1.1 mile well-graded trail to the water's edge at Cleetwood Cove; from there organized launch trips take passengers on a tour of the lake, permitting spectacular views of the geological wonders revealed inside ancient Mt. Mazama.

To appreciate the significance of what one sees from the lake or the caldera rim, it is desirable to know something of the events which produced this masterpiece. Fortunately, geologists have also found Crater Lake a fascinating subject and have been studying its history since the late 19th century; even now continuing investigations shed additional light on its origin.

The Story of Ancient Mt. Mazama

Crater Lake has existed for only a few thousand years, but the mountain in which it rests has a history going back hundreds of thousands of years. Prehistoric Mt. Mazama was roughly contemporaneous with other large stratovolcanoes which grew in the Cascades during Pleistocene time, such as Shasta, Hood, Adams, and Rainier. Rising from a basement elevation of 5000 to 6000 feet, Mazama reached a maximum height of approximately 12,000 feet above sea level.[1] Like most other composite cones in the range, Mt. Mazama erupted mainly andesitic lavas, most of which issued quietly from a number of related vents.

Since it was apparently born part way through the Pleistocene Epoch, it may have been mantled by glaciers since its inception. Glacier deposited sediments interbedded with volcanic formations can be seen in the caldera walls from bottom to top. The presence of thick layers of erosional debris lying between successive flows of andesite suggests that Mazama experienced long periods of quiescence between eruptions, during which streams of ice carved deep furrows in the mountainside. Frequently these glaciated trenches provided channels for new lava flows when the volcano reawakened.

Rising in the broad depression between Union Peak and Mt. Thielsen, Mt. Mazama gradually built a wide, gently sloping cone, notably less steep than those of Shasta or Rainier.[2] As it grew, Mazama buried at least one previously existing volcano, the Phantom Cone, part of which is now exposed inside the caldera. The triangular sails of the Phantom Ship, a tiny island near the south shore of Crater Lake (Figure 7-1), may be composed of a lava dike intruded into this ancient cone.[3]

While the main cone was gaining height by eruptions from one or more craters near the summit, many fissures opened along the flanks of the volcano. Streams of lava flowed from some of these, and parasitic cones were built at others, creating a mountain that was extremely asymmetrical. As it approached full stature, it may have resembled Sicily's Mt. Etna, which is also a vast complex of superimposed cones. Like Etna, Mt. Mazama was probably a broad, gently sloping dome, bristling with subsidiary vents (Figure 7-3).

By far the largest of the surviving satellite cones is Mt. Scott, at 8926 feet the highest point in Crater Lake National Park. Seen from the east this parasitic volcano is strikingly symmetrical, with regular slopes rising to a truncated summit. Viewed from the caldera rim, however, Mt. Scott has clearly suffered from severe glacial erosion. Its entire western face has been removed, leaving no trace of a crater. Ice streams flowing down the east-southeast slopes of Mt. Mazama, impeded in their course by the presence of Mt. Scott, inevitably cut deeply into its western slope. Since the erosion obviously occurred before the destruction of Mazama's summit, Mt. Scott must have been fully grown, if not already extinct, before the caldera was formed.

After Mt. Mazama had reached maturity, the magma within its underground feeding chamber apparently began to differentiate. As a result, instead of the andesite produced during the early eruptions, the volcano began to emit lava with a much higher silica content. Stiff, sluggish dacites were forced from fissures along Mazama's southern base. Unlike the earlier andesites, some of these dacites attained a remarkable thickness, as much as 500 to 1000 feet.[4] Humpshaped dacite domes were also extruded from the eastern foot of Mt. Scott downward to the plateau bordering U.S. Highway 97.

As dacite lava was being erupted from vents far below the summit, Mt. Mazama was becoming increasingly explosive. Large quantities of dacite pumice were blown out, and are found interspersed with glacial sediments on the upper caldera walls.[5] The presence of glacial deposits among the beds of pumice indicates that considerable time, perhaps thousands of years, elapsed between the more violent outbreaks.

Lying among and separating the layers of pumice and glacial till are blankets of *welded tuff*, a pyroclastic deposit composed of fine-grained ash and pumice dust, emplaced at such high temperatures that it was "welded" or fused together by the heat. Such formations are now recognized as the result of *glowing avalanches*, superheated masses of pumice or other fragmental material which flow over the terrain almost like a liquid. Some of these pyroclastic flow deposits contain large blocks of old lava, suggesting that Mt. Mazama was erupting with such violence that chunks of old rock were being torn from the walls of the erupting vents. Perhaps, long before the final cataclysm, Mazama's summit had been appreciably lowered by such pulverizing blasts.

The Northern Arc of Vents

Another sign that the end was approaching for Mt. Mazama was the shifting of eruptive activity from the summit crater or craters to vents on the northern slope. Either because the magma chamber had enlarged in that direction, or because a series of concentric fractures had begun to split the volcano, a long semi-circular arc of new vents opened at about the 7000 foot level. From these were erupted the most imposing lava formations to be seen today along the north caldera rim. These include a giant andesite flow, 600 feet thick, which now forms an eminence called the Watchman, located at the western end of the northern arc. Eruptions at a nearby vent built a large new parasitic cone. Now the highest elevation on the caldera rim, the remains of this andesitic volcano comprise Hillman Peak, which rises nearly 2000 feet above the present lake surface. When Mt. Mazama collapsed, the eastern half of Hillman's cone was sheared off, leaving its interior exposed in perfect cross-section.

A period of renewed glaciation followed, during which the structures just described were overridden by ice streams which extended as far as 17 miles downvalley from the present caldera rim.[6] Then, perhaps 11,000–13,000 years ago;[7] when most of the ice had melted, enormous masses of dacite lava surged upward through new vents along the northern arc.

One monstrous flow, 1200 feet thick, oozed down a deep U-shaped canyon, filling it completely and overflowing the canyon rim on either side. When Mt. Mazama later collapsed, the head of the flow was sliced off, revealing the dark gray mass, called Llao Rock, in cross-section. Rounded at the bottom, with lateral extensions near the top, it now resembles a primordial bird of prey, crouched with wings outspread atop the northern caldera rim (Figure 7-2).

Llao Rock's measurements are as impressive as its appearance. More than a mile long and one and a quarter miles wide, this single flow has a volume approximating a quarter of a cubic mile.[8]

Almost as interesting as Llao Rock are the dark glassy flows which make up Redcloud and Cloudcap, also on the northern rim. Instead of occupying a U-shaped valley like the Llao flow, that of Redcloud fills a steep V-shaped opening which at first glance seems to have been an old stream valley. Upon closer inspection, however, Redcloud's remarkable form is attributable to the fact that it filled a deep funnel-shaped explosion crater. Before the lava was extruded, strong blasts opened an almost vertically walled crater, from which quantities of dacite pumice were blown out just as in the preliminary stages of the Llao Rock eruption. The lava which welled up to build a dome over the Redcloud opening now forms an inverted triangle 600 feet high, its precipitous face exposed by the subsidence of Mazama's summit.[9]

Perhaps while the dacites were being emplaced on Mazama's northern slope, a swarm of parasitic cinder cones erupted at various points near the volcano's base. Within Crater Lake National Park there are at least 13 of these youthful cones; 11 others were built outside the Park borders.[10] Although subsidiary cones had appeared at various times during Mt. Mazama's long history, there had never been so many as were formed in early post-glacial time. All these late secondary cones, further evidence of the differentiation taking place within Mazama's magma chamber, probably helped to drain that underground reservoir and contributed another factor toward the volcano's ultimate collapse.

After the eruptions along the Northern Arc of Vents had ceased, glaciers began a new advance down the slopes of Mt. Mazama. Ice did not cover the tops of the Watchman, Hillman Peak, Llao Rock, and the Cleetwoood and Redcloud lava flows, but elsewhere the glaciers reached to elevations lower than the present rim of the caldera.[11]

The Penultimate Eruptions

Apparently a quiet interlude ensued, during which the glaciers again receded, leaving much of Mazama's lower slopes free of ice.

Then Mt. Mazama began a series of violently explosive eruptions. First, immense quantities of dacite pumice were blown high into the air from vents on the north slope. Mixed with this coarse pumice were angular chunks of old rock—andesite fragments ripped from the mountain itself. Thick layers of pumice and boulders were deposited over all the mountain, but chiefly on the north and east sides, where they now lie 50 to 100 feet deep.[12] Afterward, glowing avalances rushed down the northeast flank of the volcano, leaving a thick stratum of welded tuff. An outstanding example of this is visible near the top of the Wineglass formation on the northeast caldera wall.

Following these eruptions, another quiet interval took place. Once more the glaciers advanced, leaving their rubble atop the lump pumice and welded tuff,[13] then, perhaps about 10,000 years ago, made their final retreat. Strangely, only on the gentle south slope did they extend beyond the present caldera rim to form thin tongues of ice which covered valley floors for about a mile below the site of Crater Lake Lodge. During this interval of rest, forests once again covered Mazama's lower slopes. To the Indians who viewed the mountain at this time, Mazama probably appeared to have entered its final sleep, but deep within the earth, profound changes were taking place.

What Did Mazama Look Like Before Its Destruction?

Because of the relatively sudden and dramatic transformation of a great mountain into an enormous hole in the ground, the tendency has often been to make as good a story out of the event as possible. Therefore, greatly exaggerated estimates of Mt. Mazama's former height have circulated freely. Park visitors, told by park rangers and naturalists that Mazama was once one of the loftiest peaks in the Cascade Range, soon tell each other—and the folks back home—that it was 14,000, 15,000 or 16,000 feet high, taller even than Shasta or Rainier! Stimulating to the imagination as these guesses may be, they are not supported by the available evidence.

When Dr. Howel Williams published his study of Crater Lake in 1942, he compared the remaining slopes of Mazama's cone with those of other large Cascade volcanoes. Ignoring the parasitic cones and outcroppings along the caldera rim, Williams determined that the primary surface of Mt. Mazama is now approximately 8000 feet high on the south side, 6000 feet on the north, and at intermediate elevations on the other walls. By theoretically "cutting through" comparable Cascade peaks and im-

Figure 7–2. Crater Lake and Wizard Island. The Caldera walls on the left rise almost 2000 feet above the lake surface. The dark, massive lava flow forming Llao Rock tops the caldera rim on the right. Mt. Bailey in the middle distance. (Photo courtesy of Oregon State Highway Dept.)

posing an imaginery caldera on them Williams found that Mt. Adams (12,286 feet) came closest to matching Mazama in size and girth. Hence, he concluded that Mazama, at its maximum height, stood about 12,000 feet above sea level.

Williams cautioned that it was by no means certain that Mt. Mazama rose a full 12,000 feet immediately before the caldera-forming eruptions.[14] He pointed out that much of the former summit may have already subsided during the extremely violent outpourings which preceded the last glacial advance. Erosion, as well as subsidence, may well have appreciably diminished the volcano's original stature.

In a later report on Mazama's probable height and volume just prior to its destruction, Williams revised his previous estimates slightly downward. Emphasizing again that only on the south side did glaciers extend below the present caldera rim, he reasoned that Mazama's summit was probably occupied by a very large crater, whose irregular walls had broken down on the south, allowing ice to escape in that direction. The north and east crater rims, he believed, were probably higher than the south rim. But the north slope, dotted with parasitic cones and recently extruded domes and flows, did not permit enough ice to accumulate to form glaciers large enough to reach much below 7000 feet. This later research also indicated that some time before Mazama's collapse pumice was blasted out from vents on Mazama's northern flank, probably also helping to demolish the upper part of the mountain.[15]

Whatever Mt. Mazama's exact height before its ultimate explosion, it is likely that the mountain was then more asymmetrical than at any previous time in its history. So many satellite volcanoes occupied its lower flanks it is reasonable to suppose that many others must have grown on the now vanished upper slopes. The prolonged eruptions on the north side probably not only lowered the summit, but destroyed any glaciers that had formed there, filling their beds with flows of dacite and mounds of pumice. In any case, when the mountain collapsed, it fell eccentrically to the former summit, which lay somewhat south of the present center of the caldera.[16] The fact that the northern caldera wall averages about 2000 feet lower than the southern is probably because Mazama subsided along the deep fracture whose surface expression was the Northern Arc of Vents.

The Culminating Eruptions

We will probably never know exactly what Mt. Mazama looked like just before its fall, but we do have ample evidence of the nature and power of the outbursts which led to its collapse. From the sheets of ejecta laid down by the culminating blasts, geologists can reconstruct much of

Figure 7–3. Mt. Mazama begins the cataclysmic outburst that led to its collapse, 6600 years

what happened. Dr. Howel Williams has included a vivid recreation of Mazama's cataclysmic eruptions among his publications on Crater Lake.* In addition, a few volcanoes in modern times have had caldera-forming eruptions which in many ways paralleled that of Mt. Mazama. In 1883 the east Indian volcano, Krakatoa, staged the most violently explosive eruption in recorded history. Like Mazama, Krakatoa collapsed after expelling such enormous quantities of pumice that the peak foundered into the cavity left by the emptying of its underground magma chamber (Figure 7-4).

As with Krakatoa, Mazama's opening activity seems to have been relatively mild. Wind blowing eastward carried ash and small lumps of pumice over the arid plains of central Oregon. But, as the explosions increased in intensity, the wind veered to the northeast, transporting clouds of ash over hundreds of thousands of square miles. Near the base of the volcano, ash uniformly covered the lands with a blanket 20 feet thick, while 70 miles northeast of Mazama the initial ashfall measured a foot deep.[17] In 1883, Krakatoa's explosion clouds soared an estimated 20 miles into the stratosphere, where high winds swept them around the globe. It is possible that Mazama's cauliflower clouds rose even higher, for fine powdery ash drifted over an area of incredible extent: most of Oregon, Washington, Idaho, northern Nevada, western Montana, part of Wyoming, southern British Columbia, Alberta, and even Saskatchewan (Figure 7-5)! The ash wafting through the stratosphere must have produced brilliant sunsets throughout the entire northern hemisphere. Ancestors of the Druids in England and Gaul may have observed this atmospheric phenomenon and wondered what it portended.

Indians closer at hand experienced the paroxysm more directly. Their artifacts have been found buried beneath Mazama ash and the skeletons of some victims of the holocaust may yet be discovered.[18]

Although the desolation caused by Mazama's rain of fire was complete for hundreds of miles north and east of the volcano, the westerly winds allowed only a thin sprinkling of pumice to fall over the mountains west and southwest of the peak. In fact, an observer standing on the slopes of Union Peak, only five miles away, would probably have experienced a relatively safe, if terrifying, view of the event.[19]

Terrific as were these eruptions of frothy pumice, they were but a prelude to what followed. Perhaps after a short respite, the explosions began anew, more furiously than before. But this time the ashclouds did not shoot miles upward: instead, they frothed over the crater walls and rushed down the mountainside at dizzying speeds. When they reached

*Crater Lake: The Story of Its Origin (1941).

the glacier valleys radiating away from Mazama's cone, they divided into many branches and raced headlong into the canyons.

Although these glowing avalanches of incandescent particles did not rise high above the mountaintop, turbulent clouds of dust along their fronts and margins billowed upward for thousands of feet. Following the twisting valley of the Rogue River, one hot avalanche traveled 40 miles from its source, moving down and incinerating thick stands of timber, before coming to rest near the present village of McLeod.[20] Another seething hurricane of pumice and rock fragments descended to the north, sweeping across Diamond Lake and emptying a load of exploding pumice bombs into the valley of the North Umpqua. One arm of this avalanche was deflected westward down Lava Creek and the Clearwater River, leaving a deposit of pumice 20 to 30 feet thick.[21]

The tremendous force of these glowing avalanches is demonstrated by the fact that those which moved eastward sped over 25 miles of flat ground beyond the base of the volcano. Pumice boulders six feet across were carried 20 miles from their source, while at least one lump 14 feet long was deposited at Beaver Marsh near what is now U.S. Highway 97.[22] Similar avalanches poured southward down Annie and Sun Creek canyons, filling them to a depth of 250 feet. Southeastward they rushed down Sand Creek, continuing for more than ten miles across the flatlands beyond the base of Mt. Mazama. Some flowed into Klamath Marsh, from which masses of floating pumice were washed down the Williamson River into the Klamath Lakes.[23]

Toward the close of this explosive cycle, Mt. Mazama apparently tapped ever-deeper levels of its magma chamber. The final glowing avalanches carried large volumes of smoke-gray scoria, which formed a contrasting layer atop the pale buff and yellowish pumice flows erupted earlier. Although these scoria-bearing avalanches did not spread so far as those transporting the lighter colored pumice, on the north and northeast sides of Mazama they created the well-known Pumice Desert and inundated the wide valley of Desert Creek. Some scoria flows reached out toward the plains bordering Klamath Marsh.[24] Especially in the center of the valleys down which they moved, these avalanches of scoria laid down a conspicuous dark layer capping the more voluminous pumice deposits. The dark upper deposit is particularly evident where streams have since cut narrow gorges into the valley fills.

Long after the flows came to rest, they remained tremendously hot. Gases seething from the accumulations of pumice, some of which attained a thickness of 300 feet, produced cylindrical vents or fumaroles in the deposits. The walls of these natural flues were cemented and hardened by the hot vapors so that they became relatively resistant to later

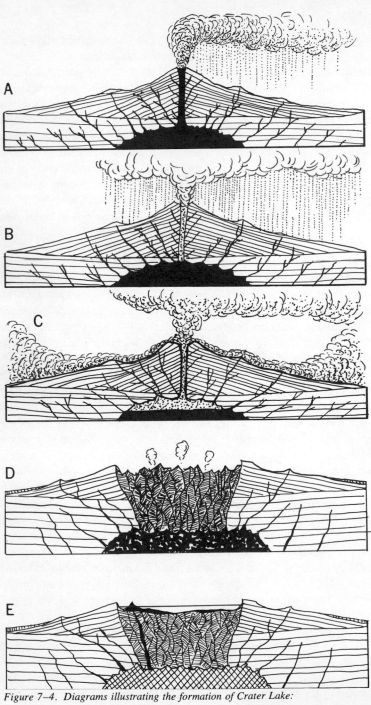

Figure 7–4. Diagrams illustrating the formation of Crater Lake:

Crater Lake 97

erosion. When rainfall and streams finally cut through the soft pumice beds, they left the hardened pipes standing as columns and spires. Outstanding examples of these "fossil fumaroles" now rise prominently along the upper walls of Annie and Sand Creek canyons.[25]

Immediately following the eruptions, each of the pumice-choked canyons extending from Mt. Mazama must have resembled a Valley of Ten Thousand Smokes. Writhing plumes of acidic gas rose from hundreds of fumaroles in the deposits; when rain fell, immense columns of steam rose from the slowly congealing masses of pumice and scoria. Adding to the acidic, smoke-filled atmosphere were the rapidly settling clouds of pumice dust which had risen above the glowing avalanches. In some places, this dust settled in accumulations 50 feet thick. Mt. Mazama, meanwhile, continued a series of weak explosions, which hurled still more pumice and fine ash into the air. Along the caldera rim, the products of these declining eruptions formed banks of fine material about 50 feet thick.[26]

When all this volcanic smog finally dissipated or drifted away, the Indian survivors of the holocaust must have rubbed their eyes in wonder. Not only was the once-green land transformed into a sea of dirty-gray pumice, but the huge mountain responsible for the catastrophe had virtually disappeared. Where a snow-capped peak once towered, there was now only a colossal depression, five to six miles wide and nearly 4000 feet deep (Figure 7-4). The dust-smeared Indian of 6600 years ago must have asked himself the same question that scientists still endeavor to answer: where did Mt. Mazama go? Was it blown apart by the earthshaking explosions? Or did it subside into a subterranean pit of its own making?

Other questions have also been raised. What, for example, enabled the avalanches of hot pumice to travel so far from Mazama's crater? How were they able to move so fast, at speeds approaching perhaps 100 miles per hour? Furthermore, how were they able to pass over the surface of

A. Mt. Mazama begins its climactic eruptions.

B. Increasingly violent explosions widen and deeper the summit crater, while the winds carry enormous quantities of ash hundreds of miles to the northeast.

C. During this second major phase of the eruptions, glowing avalanches descend Mazama's slopes while the summit area fractures and begins to sink into the void left by the rapidly emptying magma chamber beneath the volcano.

D. Mazama's summit has collapsed, forming a caldera six miles across and nearly 4000 feet deep.

E. Crater Lake today. Post-caldera eruptions have smoothed the basin floor and built Wizard Island. Rain and meltwater from snow have half filled the basin, creating Crater Lake.

Diamond Lake, 13 miles distant, and continue on for another 15 or 20 miles?

We might tackle the "easier" problems first. According to Williams, the hot avalanches achieved their astonishing mobility through (1) the momentum of their great volume and weight and (2) the continuous discharge of hot gas from the millions of molten particles they contained. Each incandescent fragment of lava in the flowing mass gave off gas under high pressure. Buoyed up and lubricated by trapped gas and air within the avalanche, propelled by the millions of minature explosions within them, the pumice flows were able to race forward even after they had reached level ground or had ploughed through forests. Behaving as superheated sandblasters, they eroded earlier pumicefall material from the upper slopes of the volcano and did not even begin to deposit their loads of rock until they entered the confines of glacial valleys five miles from the avalanche source. The formidable combination of the enormous

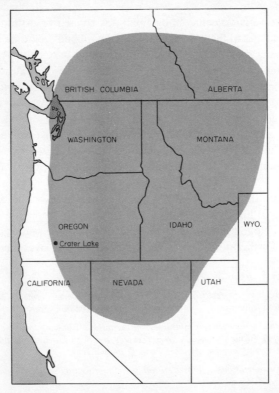

Figure 7–5. Map of the Pacific Northwest, showing area covered by the pumice eruption of Mt. Mazama. Shaded area indicates the maximum limits of ash fall.

volume, the rapidity and steepness of descent, the high gas content, intense heat, and the internal self-propulsion empowered the avalanches to travel as much as 40 miles from their source.[27] The winds of superheated air which preceded their advance must have mowed down wide swaths of timber through which the avalanches moved. The carbonized logs in the pumice flow deposits testifies to the extremely high temperature of the erupted pumice; all trees and stumps found therein were reduced to charcoal.

What Became of Mt. Mazama?

The sudden disappearance of from 15 to 17 cubic miles of Mt. Mazama's bulk is the principal mystery in the creation of Crater Lake. In 1902, J. S. Diller postulated that the rapid emptying of the volcano's magma chamber had removed support from beneath the peak, causing it to collapse. But in 1936 Smith and Swartzlow proposed that Mazama had been destroyed by explosion, arguing that Diller had underestimated the amount of old andesite fragments blown from Mazama's summit. In the most widely-accepted explanation of the volcano's demise, however, Williams suggested that a combination of several factors contributed toward the formation of the Crater Lake caldera.

Supporting Diller's thesis, Williams calculated that not more than about one or two cubic miles of the original mountain had been blown out during the culminating explosions. If Mt. Mazama had been decapitated by these blasts, one would expect to find large blocks of andesite and thick accumulations of old rock fragments littering the caldera rim and outer slopes of the volcano. To the contrary, investigators have thus far been unable to find any large boulders of old lava; pieces of old rock seldom exceed two or three inches in diameter. Together they total only a small fraction of the vanished mountaintop.

But the amount of new rock poured out during the climactic eruptions is staggering. In a revised estimate of the volume of Mazama's preliminary ashfall, Williams stated that between seven to nine cubic miles of pumice were expelled.[28] He also calculated that the glowing avalanches deposited another six to eight cubic miles of material, while the final ashfall contributed another quarter of a cubic mile of ejecta. According to Williams, then, Mazama's climactic eruptions blew out 13 to 17.25 cubic miles of fresh lava—enough to build two mountains the size of St. Helens!

Astounding as Williams' revised figures seem, he may have considerably *underestimated* the amount of new lava produced. More recent discoveries of Mazama ash as far away as Wyoming and Saskatchawan, Canada—and possibly even farther east—indicate that still another re-evaluation is necessary. Using reports unavailable to Williams and Goles in 1968, a geologist at Oregon State University recalculated the amount of ash which fell beyond a distance of 60 miles from Mt. Mazama and found that it totaled a phenomenal 31.25 cubic miles —more than five times Williams' revised estimate![29]

Adding the three cubic miles of ash deposited within 60 miles of the volcano, the six to eight cubic miles of pumice contained in the glowing avalanches, and the quarter cubic mile of ash expelled during the final eruptions, it appears that Mt. Mazama hurled out as much as 42.5 cubic miles of pyroclastics during its climactic outbursts. Most of this ash was carried by the winds hundreds, perhaps even thousands, of miles to the northeast.

No wonder that Mt. Mazama collapsed! Its underlying magma chamber had been so rapidly and completely emptied that the mountain, reduced to a hollow shell, simply caved into the void. According to Lidstrom, during the last phases of the debacle, even the inner walls of the magma chamber were apparently torn from position and blasted to the surface.[30]

To calculate the difference between the volume of new magma expelled and the volume of the vanished mountaintop, it is necessary to remember that magma in its liquid state, before being erupted, is much less voluminous than when discharged as frothy, gas-charged pumice. Williams in 1968 thought that the aggregate volume of liquid magma, plus its entrained crystals and the fragments ripped from the walls of Mazama's vents, was about ten cubic miles. But that estimate still leaves a discrepancy of from five to seven cubic miles between the volume of material blown out and the size of Mazama's missing summit.

Lidstrom's 1971 recalculation of the volume of Mazama's "preliminary ashfall" suggests that between 14.25 and 16 cubic miles of liquid magma were actually erupted. This new figure agrees closely with Williams' 1968 estimate of the volume of Mt. Mazama which disappeared. In short, the amount of material evacuated from the magma chamber roughly equals the assumed size of Mazama's former cone.

Mt. Mazama's Post-Caldera Activity

Immediately following its creation, the caldron must have been an awesome sight. Enclosed by almost vertical cliffs towering up to 4000 feet above the chaotic jumble of giant blocks which littered the caldera floor, the basin probably seethed with escaping gases and bubbling pits of mud. Yawning fissures crisscrossed the boulder-strewn floor, and avalanches of loosened rock thundered down from precipices high on the caldera walls.

The three glaciers that had descended the south side of the volcano prior to its collapse had been beheaded. Their rapidly melting remnants occupied the heads of Munson, Sun, and Kerr Valleys. The valleys themselves were almost brimfull of pumice and scoria from the glowing avalanches. When rain fell, the land surface steamed and smoked.

Stupendous as was the burst of energy required for Mazama to destroy itself, the old volcano was not yet exhausted. Because soundings along the bottom of Crater Lake indicate that the caldera floor is now relatively smooth, it seems that post-caldera eruptions of new lava streamed over the basin, filling in many of the pits and gaps in its floor. At that time, the caldera may have contained a ''lake of fire,'' similar to that in the famous lava pit of Mt. Kiluaea, Hawaii.

Apparently the caldera floor remained either too hot or too riddled by cracks and fissures to contain a large lake for many centuries after its creation. During that time several eruptions within the basin took place. For a while activity was concentrated near the southwestern edge of the caldron. Numerous lava flows piled up to erect a broad shield perhaps 1200 feet above the basin floor. When it had risen to about the present level of the lake, this young volcano inside Mazama entered a more violent phase. Explosions raised a steep, symmetrical pile of fragmental material on top of the older lava shield, building the cinder cone known today as Wizard Island.[31]

Toward the close of its activity, several flows of blocky andesite lava streamed westward from fissures near the base of the cone. Later, a second lava flow issued from the northwest side of Wizard Island, its scoriaceous crust in marked contrast to the deeply furrowed, block-laden surface of the first flows. On the east side of the cone, beneath the lake waters, lava covers about three square miles of the basin floor. But the visible lava from Wizard Island's east side comprises only a narrow strip, rising between 20 and 200 feet above the present lake surface.

Judging only by the extremely fresh appearance of Wizard Island's charcoal-gray, orange and rust-streaked slopes, the cinder cone would seem to have been created only a few centuries ago. But measurements of tree rings from timber growing on its latest lava flows indicate that they were erupted *at least* 800 or 900 years ago.[32] Granting sufficient time for soil to form on the rough lava surfaces to create a root-hold for seedlings, it is probable that Wizard Island's last outbursts occurred long before the beginning of the present millennium.

An easy climb up the 763-foot cone rewards the hiker with an opportunity to inspect one of the most interesting and best preserved explosion craters in the Cascades. It is distinguished by evidence that a miniature lava flow tried to escape through small crevices on the crater lip. Extremely thin and narrow, this tiny flow forms a black clinkery splotch on the southwest crest of the cone. Another mass of dark lava, forming a small humped dome on the crater floor, probably represents an incipient lava flow which failed to rise high enough to stream over the crater rim. Instead, it became a conduit filling and now plugs the eruptive vent.

In addition to the rounded plug which protrudes above the crater floor, the large lava boulders perched atop the narrow crater rim are worthy of comment. Six or more feet in diameter, these dark, angular blocks occur in clusters at several points along the eastern rim. It seems difficult to believe that such proportionately large blocks were blown from Wizard Island's relatively small crater, only 300 feet in diameter and 90 feet deep, especially since most of its ejecta is smaller than a man's fist. But there appears to be no other way to account for their presence. A close inspection indicates that these black monoliths did not originate as incipient spines thrust up through fissures in the crater walls.

Wizard Island is the only cone high enough to stand above the present lake surface. But recent soundings taken of the lake floor detected the presence of two additional cones. The larger of the two, Merriam Cone, lies submerged near the southern margin of the caldera. Approximately a mile across the base and 1320 feet high, it is almost precisely the same size as Paricutin, the famous Mexican volcano. Since Merriam Cone lacks a summit crater, it is thought that either material ejected during the last feeble eruptions fell back into the vent, or that a mound of lava filled the crater. At some stage of its growth, fluid lavas poured southeastward to form a level plain over the caldera floor. Later falls of cinders and ash from Wizard Island probably contributed to the relative smoothness of this area.

Like Wizard Island, Merriam Cone was probably formed before the level of Crater Lake had risen very far. The evidence indicates that few if any of the lavas comprising these cones were chilled by intrusion into cold water.

A second submerged cone lies on top of the lava field extending eastward from Wizard Island. A craterless mound of dacite, it may be a small volcano which was buried beneath later lava flows from Wizard Island.[33] Thus, during its latest eruptive cycle, Mt. Mazama produced lavas of very different types— the andesite forming Wizard Island and the dacite forming the nearby lava dome—just as it had done along the Northern Arc of Vents.

Some time after these youthful cones were built on the caldera floor, water from rain and melting snow began to fill the basin. At first a network of small pools and connecting channels must have formed. But eventually the expanding waters joined and even rose about 50 feet higher than the present level of the lake.[34] How long it took to fill the enormous caldera to approximately its present depth is not known, but there were probably many fluctuations in the water level during the past several thousand years. During the first part of the 20th century, the water dropped about 40 feet. Today, however, the National Park Service reports that water added by precipitation almost perfectly equals that lost by subterranean drainage and evaporation. Except for minor seasonal changes, the lake level now remains almost constant. With its maximum depth officially measured at 1932 feet, Crater Lake is the deepest lake in North America. The caldera walls rise from 500 to nearly 2000 feet above the lake surface. Being viewed from these elevations, plus the extreme depth and purity of the water, helps account for its extraordinary indigo color.

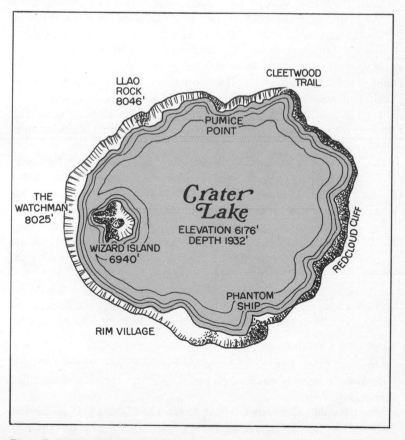

Figure 7–6. Map of the Crater Lake area.

The Future of Crater Lake

The tranquil beauty of Crater Lake makes one wish it never to change. Nature, however, does not permit even her greatest triumphs to remain unaltered for long. No matter how regrettable, the future will bring changes of unknown nature and extent. Even if old Mt. Mazama were never to erupt again, erosion will eventually breach the caldera walls and allow the lake waters to escape. Prolonged drought could diminish the lake or perhaps dry it up altogether. A return of Ice Age glaciers could grind down the encircling cliffs and level even the ruins of Mazama's cone.

But before any of these eventualities occur, it is perhaps possible that Mt. Mazama will erupt. It has been active spasmodically for hundreds of thousands of years. It has seen ice ages come and go and has remained to deposit fresh lava atop its ice-carved slopes. The fact that its latest activity, that on Wizard Island, occurred perhaps only a few thousand years ago may suggest that Mazama has not yet finished its post-caldera eruptions. Mt. Mazama may lie dormant for countless millennia, or it may revive tomorrow. Wizard Island may blaze into new life, shooting clots of red hot lava over the caldera rim or splashing them into the lake. Entirely new cones may be born on the caldera floor and may eventually emerge as a chain of islands strewn across the lake. Or more vents may open on the outer slopes of the volcano, creating additional cinder cones and lava flows.

If one compares Mazama's caldera with that of the near-by Newberry Volcano (see Chapter 9), he will see that one future possibility is that Crater Lake may ultimately be divided into two bodies of water, separated by a ridge of volcanic cones and flows. By projecting Mazama's biography far into the future, one may visualize it as someday resembling the Medicine Lake volcano, which lies about 35 miles east of Mt. Shasta in northeastern California. This caldera has been largely filled by the growth of dozens of later cones and lava domes. Although it may now seem highly unlikely, if Mazama should continue active for an indefinitely long period, it might, phoenix-like, finally rebuild its cone and once again take its place among the highest peaks in the Cascade Range.

Exploring Crater Lake

Much of Crater Lake can be enjoyed from your car. Take the 33-mile Rim Drive (one way clockwise) and stop at the roadside observation points (Fig. 7-6).

A short uphill hike eastward from Crater Lake Lodge to Garfield Peak (1.5 miles) offers a fine vantagepoint almost 1900 feet above the lake surface.

A somewhat longer (2.5 miles) and steeper trail leads from the east-side Rim Drive to Mt. Scott (8926 feet), highest elevation in the park. From the deck of a fire lookout there, one can see for 100 miles in every direction, including the entire extent of Mazama's caldera.

Cleetwood Trail (1.1 miles) descends the northern caldera wall to Cleetwood Cove, from which launch trips to Wizard Island and around the lake run during the summer season (beginning in late June or early July, depending upon snow conditions). Signs mark a parking lot on the north Rim Drive where the trail starts. Although perfectly safe if followed cautiously, these trails have been the scene of several fatal accidents involving persons who ran blindly or tried to take short cuts.

Both the Lodge and the Park Headquarters distribute maps and trail guides to numerous other points of interest in the Park.

Chapter 7–References

1. *Williams, 1942, p. 1.*
2 *Ibid., p. 30.*
3. *Ibid., p. 30.*
4. *Ibid., p. 37.*
5. *Ibid., pp. 40-42.*
6. *Ibid., pp. 60-63.*
7. *Lidstrom, 1971, p. 14.*
8. *Williams, 1942, p. 47.*
9. *Ibid., pp. 52-53.*
10. *Ibid., p. 55.*
11. *Ibid., p. 63.*
12. *Ibid., pp. 61-63.*
13. *Ibid., pp. 60-63.*
14. *Ibid., p. 66.*
15. *Williams and Goles, 1968, pp. 40-41.*
16. *Williams, 1942, p. 107.*
17. *Williams, 1941, p. 31; 1942, pp. 68-70.*
18. *Williams, 1942, p. 115.*
19. *Ibid., p. 71.*
20. *Williams, 1941, pp. 32-33.*
21. *Purdom, 1963, p. 37.*
22. *Williams, 1942, pp. 79, 95.*
23. *Williams, 1941, p. 33.*
24. *Williams, 1942, p. 83.*
25. *Ibid., p. 86.*
26. *Ibid., p. 97.*
27. *Williams, 1942, pp. 79-81.*
28. *Williams and Goles, 1968, p. 40.*
29. *Lidstrom, 1971, p. 38.*
30. *Ibid., pp. 39-68.*
31. *Williams, 1941, pp. 36-37.*
32. *Williams, 1942, pp. 116-117.*
33. *Williams, 1961, pp. 82-83.*
34. *Williams, 1942, p. 129.*

Figure 8–1. This close-up reveals the massive character of the lava plug forming Thiel-sen's summit. Repeatedly scarred by lightning, it is known as the "Lightning Rod of the Cascades." (Photo by Ed Cooper.)

8
Mt. Thielsen—Lightning Rod of the Cascades

Unique to the Oregon Cascades is a series of high pinnacles whose sheer pointed summits remind travelers of Switzerland's Matterhorn. Two of these spires can be seen from almost anywhere along the rim of Crater Lake: Union Peak (7698 feet) to the south, and Mt. Thielsen (9178 feet) 12 miles north. Still farther north in the range, between the Three Sisters and Mt. Jefferson, are the strikingly similar peaks of Mt. Washington and Three Fingered Jack. Because they all rise from broad, gently sloping bases to extremely steep summits with no trace of a summit crater, these mountains appear unlike any of the other volcanoes in the High Cascades.

There are excellent geologic reasons for the differences between such peaks as Mt. Thielsen and the more conventional-appearing cones of Hood, McLoughlin, and the Three Sisters. First of all, Thielsen, Washington, Union Peak, and Three Fingered Jack all belong to an older episode of Cascade volcanism. They may have begun life during the very late Pliocene, even though they were most active in the Pleistocene Epoch.[1] All these volcanoes were probably extinct before the last major Pleistocene glaciation, and may not have erupted within the last 100,000 years. They are thus far more extensively eroded than the younger Cascade volcanoes, many of which remained active long after the Ice Age ended.

Oregon's unusual pinnacles did not receive their peculiar form solely through glaciation, however. The nature and sequence of the eruptions which built them are equally responsible for their obelisk-like profiles. Since each of the cones under discussion apparently underwent the same three main stages of growth, what holds true for one seems to be equally valid for the others. Thanks to investigations by Diller in 1902 and Williams in 1933, Mt. Thielsen is the best studied of the group of "Matterhorn" shaped volcanoes, and makes a good representative choice.

Mt. Thielsen rises above the east shore of Diamond Lake; above the opposite shore is Mt. Bailey, a volcanic contemporary of Thielsen, but much less eroded. Thielsen's eastern slopes extend down to the basaltic plateau of central Oregon, while southward they end against a complex of basaltic volcanoes.[2]

Figure 8–2. Evolution of a typical High Cascade volcano:

A. After relatively quiet outpourings of lava construct a broad shield, a cone of fragmental ejecta begins to form in the summit crater.

B. The pyroclastic summit cone, which now overlaps the older shield, is invaded by a large viscous plug and a swarm of dikes. Parasitic cinder cones build along the flanks of the shield.

C. Erosion cuts deeply into the volcano, demolishing most of the summit cone and revealing the central plug. These simplified drawings illustrate the general development of such Oregon volcanoes as Thielsen, Washington, Union Peak, the North Sister, and Three Fingered Jack. (Based on drawings by Howel Williams, 1962.)

The first eruptions of Mt. Thielsen produced fluid streams of basalt which formed a broad, gently-sloping shield. Long flows poured northwestward, but to the immediate north the lavas were blocked by those advancing from the nearby Howlock volcano. Lavas moving southward spread for an average distance of about five miles.[3] After many thousand years, Thielsen's shield, when completed, resembled an enormous inverted saucer, 5000–6000 feet high, with a base 11 miles in diameter and a crater at least a mile and a half across. At this stage of its development, Mt. Thielsen was not only wide and flat-topped, but its angle of slope averaged only about five degrees. The early lavas evidently were fluid and few exceeded a thickness of five or 10 feet. Additional eruptions of lava from fissures along the base also contributed to the mountain's low profile.

Thielsen's appearance began to change rapidly, however, as its eruptions became increasingly explosive. A large pyroclastic cone developed within the summit crater and eventually filled it completely and overflowed onto the outer slopes of the shield. Several thin flows of basalt helped build this cone, which ultimately raised Thielsen's height to perhaps 10,000 feet, nearly a thousand feet above its present crest.

After the summit cone had been built, its interior was riven by numerous cracks produced by the invasion of dense, black or dark green basalts. When solidified, they formed a swarm of nearly vertical walls averaging about six feet in thickness. These *dikes* are probably responsible for preserving what is left of the glaciated summit cone. Harder than the surrounding fragmental rocks they penetrated, the dikes resisted the encroaching glaciers and reinforced parts of the cone.

The final phase in the formation of Mt. Thielsen was the intrusion of two huge plugs, each about half a mile in diameter, into the summit cone. One rose near the eastern wall of the old crater, and the other, which now forms Thielsen's most prominent spire, was pushed into place close to the western crater rim.[4]

These massive intrusions disrupted the layers of pyroclastic material composing the summit cone, tipping the bedded tuffs almost at right angles to their former position. Williams concluded that the plugs must have been unusually viscous, perhaps almost solid, when emplaced.[5]

A third, much smaller, plug was erupted at the southern foot of Mt. Thielsen. Now called "Summit Rock," its relation to other Thielsen lavas is obscured by overlying glacial sediments.

Mt. Thielsen was brought to its present needle-like state by erosion that stripped away the loose pyroclastic material surrounding the plugs and dikes. Once glaciers had demolished the summit cone—and also eaten part way into the plugs themselves—meltwater and rivers carried away the resultant detritus to give the mountain its distinctive Matterhorn appearance. The western plug formed the volcano's present apex, while the other plug and a swarm of dikes formed a complex of lesser summits falling away to the east. Figure 8-2 illustrates the evolution of Mt. Thielsen from a broad rounded shield to its current craggy state.

Thielsen's high spire attracts countless lightning bolts. It has been struck so often that the mountain is known as "the lightning rod of the Cascades." Over the years repeated electrical charges have formed on the summit rocks a peculiar substance called fulgurite. Derived from the Latin term for thunderbolt, fulgurites form coatings on rock surfaces or small carrot-shaped tubes inside the rocks. These "lightning tubes" are created when the intense heat fuses the crystals present in volcanic rock.

On Mt. Thielsen, the fulgurites appear as brownish-green glass which resemble greasy splotches of enamel paint. Sometimes the fulgurites are also found lining small holes and crevices in the rock. According to climbers' reports, they are mostly confined to the top five or 10 feet of the highest pinnacle.[6]

Mt. Bailey

Mt. Thielsen's close neighbor, across the shallow waters of Diamond Lake, is broad-shouldered Mt. Bailey. Although probably about the same age, it is much less eroded than Thielsen. Even so, glaciers have obliterated much of its former summit and excavated large cirques and gullies along its flanks. These erosional "windows" reveal enough of Bailey's internal structure to show that it, too, is a shield volcano surmounted by a fragmental cone.

Mt. Washington

Motorists crossing the barren lava wastes at central Oregon's McKenzie Pass cannot fail to notice the massive summit pinnacle of Mt. Washington. From some angles Mt. Washington's spire is sharp enough to be another Cleopatra's Needle; from others it bears a general resemblance to Sugarloaf Mountain which guards the famous harbor of Rio de Janeiro.

Like Thielsen, Mt. Washington was composed in three different stages. The first built a wide shield, the second a summit cone of fragmental ejects, and the third a huge basaltic plug which was injected into the upper cone. Mt. Washington also became extinct far back in the Pleistocene, so that glaciers have had time to ravage the upper part of the mountain, leaving only the towering obelisk of its central plug. Dikes and ridge-like portions of the destroyed summit cone radiate away from this volcanic neck much as they do at Mt. Thielsen.

Three Fingered Jack

Northernmost of the "Matterhorn" type of Cascade volcano, Three Fingered Jack (7841 feet) is as picturesque as its name. Williams' investigation of Three Fingered Jack revealed that its development almost exactly paralleled that of the other eroded volcanic necks which it so closely resembles.[7] Like that of Union Peak and Mt. Washington, its present summit consists of a large central plug with attendant radial dikes.[8] Because the dikes surround the main spire, it sports several crag-like eminences. From the east it is seen along its long axis and appears as a saw-toothed ridge. To climbers, the inhospitable northeast face presents an almost vertical wall of rotten, crumbling rock. Even the snowfields at

Figure 8–3. Several of central Oregon's "Matterhorn" peaks appear in this aerial photograph. Mount Washington is in the foreground, Three Fingered Jack in the middle distance, and Mount Jefferson on the far horizon. (Photo by Delano Photographics.)

the base tilt at angles of 50 to 55 degrees.[9] A thick conspicuous band of lightcolored pumice cuts almost horizontally through the steep lava cliffs, making a strong contrast to the reddish, brown, and gray pyroclastics which comprise the upper part of the volcano.

Because of its irregular shape, Three Fingered Jack looks rather different when seen from various points of the compass. Although it shows only a single spire from certain directions, from the southeast it displays the trio of separate peaks which inspired its homely sobriquet. The highest is on the east so that the westward-descending order of lesser summits gives the mountain an awkward hump-backed appearance.

Viewing Mt. Thielsen

Because of its sheer, crumbling spire Mt. Thielsen is a fairly difficult rock climb, which should be attempted only by experienced mountaineers. To enjoy a good view of the peak, drive to Diamond Lake, either from the Crater Lake Road to Bend (across the buff-colored Pumice Desert) or from Highway 97 along 138 (west). Mt. Washington and Three Fingered Jack are also difficult ascents which should be undertaken only by experienced climbers.

Chapter 8 –References

1. *Williams, 1933, p. 198.*
2. *Ibid., p. 195.*
3. *Ibid., p. 201.*
4. *Ibid., p. 204.*
5. *Ibid., p. 206.*
6. *Purdom, 1963, p. 31.*
7. *Williams, 1957.*
8. *Taylor, 1968, p. 29.*
9. *Cummins, 1964, p. 52.*

Newberry Volcano— "Lunar" Training Ground For Astronauts

Newberry Volcano is not actually part of the Cascade Range—it lies about 40 miles east of the chain, just south of Bend—but it so closely resembles its western neighbors that it seems to belong to the Cascade province.

If Crater Lake did not exist, Newberry might have become Oregon's only national park. For this enormous shield volcano—20 miles in diameter and approximately 80 cubic miles in volume[1]—possesses some of the same remarkable attributes which make Crater Lake so famous. Like Mt. Mazama, Newberry has lost its former summit, so that the top of the mountain is now occupied by a huge depression. Although slightly smaller than Mazama's caldera, that of Newberry contains not one but two lakes—Paulina and East Lakes. Instead of only a single volcanic cone, like Wizard Island, visible in the caldera, Newberry can boast of many recent cinder cones, lava flows, and domes of glistening black obsidian. Judging by the dozens of parasitic vents and flows both within and without the caldera, its activity during the past few thousand years has been far more frequent and varied than that at Crater Lake.

The best place to get a comprehensive view of Newberry's attractions is the crest of Paulina Peak (7985 feet), the highest elevation on the caldera rim (Figure 9-1). To the south Paulina Peak's slopes descend to the basaltic flatlands of central Oregon; its northern face is an almost vertical cliff which plunges 1500 feet to the caldera floor below. Except for the latest eruptive deposits, which remain stark and unweathered, the caldera is heavily timbered. Four by five miles in diameter, it forms an irregular oval with its major axis trending east-west. Hemmed in on most sides by cliffs rising up to 1500 feet, the caldera is drained by Paulina Creek, which has cut a narrow gorge through the sunken western wall. East Lake has no known outlet and maintains a water level about 40 feet higher than that of Paulina Lake.[2]

The two lakes are separated by numerous lava flows topped by several large cinder cones. Most conspicuous of these is the appropriately named Central Pumice Cone, literally the central feature of the caldera. This mile-wide 700-foot-high cone is not the former peak of the volanco which sank to its present position. Instead, it was built long after the caldera was formed and sits on top of a post-caldera basaltic lava flow.[3] Its 250-foot-deep crater is notched on the northwest side, possibly indicating the presence of a fault in that direction.

Besides the several steep-sided pyroclastic cones which were built along both the north and south margins of the caldera, the most prominent formations are several large flows of obsidian, which look like coal that spilled over the caldera floor. Easily the most impressive of these is the Big Obsidian Flow, which was erupted about 1350 years ago over an older glowing avalanche deposit.[4] Issuing from a fissure near the south wall of the caldera, it spread over a square mile before erecting a hummocky dome over the erupting vent. Its blocky surface furrowed by giant "wrinkles" formed as it moved forward, the Big Obsidian Flow terminates in abrupt margins 100 feet high. It is quite a feat to scale the front of this lava, whose sharp crust challenges even the toughest bootleather. Other recent obsidian flows, such as that which poured from crevices on the north caldera wall about 1700 years ago and partly encircled the Central Pumice Cone, are only slightly less formidable.[5] After these glassy masses had cooled, the prehistoric Indians of central Oregon found that the obsidian made excellent arrowheads, which they apparently bartered with other tribes of the Northwest.

On the northern caldera wall is The Fissure, a deep gash that rises from the shore of East Lake. According to some reports, it marks the terminus of the Northwest Rift Zone, a 20-mile-long crack in the earth which extends from Newberry northwestward to beyond Lava Butte on U.S. Highway 97.[6] The East Lake Fissure may have erupted fountains of molten rock, known as "fire curtains," such as are common on the flanks of Mt. Etna and the volcanoes on the island of Hawaii. Along its margins are found heaps of scoria, fused particles of congealed lava, and thin glassy flows, which may have resulted from the falling spray of lava. They are among the latest eruptive products of Newberry Volcano.[7]

Although it is generally covered with forest, parts of the Newberry shield have been created so recently that they seem too bleak and inhospitable to belong on this planet. Some U.S. government officials must have shared this impression, for sections of the volcano's outer slopes were chosen as a training ground for astronauts.[8] The stark, pumice-dusted surfaces were thought to offer a rough approximation of what lunar explorers might expect when they landed.

Figure 9–1. This view from Paulina Peak on the south wall of Newberry Caldera shows, left to right, Paulina Lake, Central Pumice Cone, and East Lake. A light snowfall emphasizes the wrinkled surface of the Big Obsidian Flow (right center). (Photo by Delano Photographics.)

Newberry Volcano is so geologically new it has undergone little erosion; there are no cirques or deep canyons cut into its sides. Only inside the caldera can one read the story of Newberry's evolution. But even here none but the most recent developments are on view. The vast summit depression is still not deep enough to expose the lavas erupted in the volcano's youth.

The Growth of Newberry Volcano

Although the entire surface of Newberry Volcano was apparently formed after the Pleistocene ended, the volcano undoubtedly began to erupt hundreds of thousands of years earlier. It is simply too big—roughly the volume of Mt. Shasta—to have been built during the past 10,000 years. Its first known eruptions, from a single summit caldera which enclosed many other vents, were of fluid basalts. Streaming many miles from their source, these thin flows gradually constructed Newberry's 20-mile-wide shield. After reaching a height of about 2000 feet above the encircling plain, the volcano began to discharge thick sheets of pasty rhyolite, which alternated with emissions of the highly liquid basalts. Although most flows issued from centralized vents, many others poured through fissures near the base of the shield, thus increasing its diameter.[9] Eventually, Newberry became the largest shield volcano in Oregon, standing at least 5000 feet above its original foundation. At that time extremely broad and gently sloping, the volcano rose a full 1000 feet higher than its present elevation of nearly 8000 feet.[10] If its pyroclastic eruptions erected a steep fragmental cone on top of the shield, as did Newberry's older counterparts like Mt. Thielsen and the North Sister, it may have attained a maximum height of 10,000 feet.

When the volcano had assumed almost its present dimensions, it began to erupt much more violently. The products of these explosions and flows, displayed in the upper walls of the caldera, record in stone Newberry's later activity. They reveal that as the volcano grew older, it erupted a wide variety of lava types, mixing andesite and basalt with rhyolite and dacite.*

The oldest rocks visible in the caldera wall are rhyolites, which presumably overlie the earlier basalts. Because the caldera is so large, some layers of material do not appear on all four walls. Many eruptions were confined to only one side of the volcano. On the other hand, some of the late eruptions were powerful enough to spread flows and debris over the entire central part of the shield. A platy andesitic basalt forms a layer from 20 to 300 feet thick on all sides of the caldera.[11] Equally well distributed are a bed of red scoria and layers of beige to brown tuff which rests upon it. These tuffs were apparently erupted under water, which explains their finely graded and bedded appearance. They fell into place as a sticky rain of mud which was fluid yet cohesive enough to drape uniformly over the pre-existing topography. This deposit is significant because it establishes the time when the volcano's gradually subsiding summit had formed a depression large enough to contain a lake. The tuffs, which accumulated to depths of 10 to 150 feet, probably represent at least 150 different eruptions.[12] Because they are in some places separated from the Mazama ash of 6600 years ago by intervening lava flows and pyroclastics, the air-borne mud must have been ejected some time before Mazama's climactic outbursts. It follows that a caldera formed at Newberry Volcano long before Crater Lake came into being.

After the tuffs, but before the Mazama ashfall, glowing avalanches similar to those which preceded the destruction of Mazama's cone were erupted. One of these hot avalanches, which filled a channel-like depres-

---

*Geologists have compiled detailed chronicles of the nature and sequence of the late eruptions, (Williams, 1935; Higgins and Waters, 1968; Higgins, 1973), but only the major events, as revealed by the strata they left, are outlined here.

sion on the east slope of the volcano, may have issued from a fracture caused by the subsidence of the eastern caldera wall. The temperature of this avalanche was extremely high, for the pumice bombs, obsidian shards, and blocks of old lava which it had ripped from its conduit are welded together throughout.[13]

The most striking results of Newberry's late "pre-caldera" activity are immense floods of rhyolite lava which poured southward from fissures near the top of the volcano. These dark rhyolites, 1200 feet thick, now form Paulina Peak, the highest remnant of the original south slope. They, too were emplaced before 6600 years ago, for they are overlain by 10 to 20 inches of Mazama ash.

Creation of the Newberry Caldera

While these late eruptions were taking place, the summit depression indenting Newberry's shield was probably developing. A series of concentric faults allowed large portions of the summit area to sink into the underlying magma. As the summit broke up, downfaulting continued until the caldera attained its present size. Subsidence of the summit blocks was particularly extensive on the west side, where the caldera walls have sunk almost out of sight.[14] Paulina Creek has cut a narrow gully through this gap in the western rim, and drains Paulina Lake. Had this gap not been formed, the water level within Newberry's caldron would today be much higher and there would probably be a single lake instead of two.

Although Newberry Crater experienced many violent explosions during the closing stages of its caldera formation, none of these eruptions approached the cataclysmic force of those which preceded the creation of Crater Lake. Although much pumice mantles the shield, no great piles of ejecta comparable to those at Crater Lake are anywhere to be found. What then, caused the disappearance of Newberry's former summit? Williams suggests that the quiet but rapid outflow of basaltic lava from vents low on the flanks of the volcano drained the central reservoir and so withdrew support from beneath the summit. The upper part of the cone then collapsed into the underground cavity.[15]

Other geologists have since forwarded alternate theories to explain the origin of Newberry's caldera. One recent hypothesis[16] states that the tremendously divergent kinds of lava which Newberry erupted during its late stages of growth precludes the existence of a subterranean magma chamber such as Williams envisioned. According to Higgins, the extreme differentiation of Newberry's lavas suggests that instead of drawing magma from a single cavern-like hollow beneath the earth, Newberry tapped various parts of a netlike complex of magma-feeders that lay at different depths beneath its cone. Widely separated pockets or pools of magma were tapped at different times, thus accounting for the great variety of lavas produced during the late eruptions. The contents of the hypothetical pools were released by fault movement, which simultaneously cracked and downfaulted the volcano's summit. Although this hypothesis explains the wide range in the type and chemical composition of Newberry's lavas, it does not tell us why such extensive concentric faulting of the summit area should have occurred in the first place.

Whatever the cause of its formation, Newberry caldera has been the scene of much subsequent activity. Besides building several large fragmental cones and pouring out the obsidian mentioned above, vents within the depression produced widespread falls of ash and pumice. The most important of these pyroclastics is called Newberry ash number 2. This includes a main pumice fall which the winds carried 20 to 40 miles east of the caldera, and at least five later deposits of fine ash, which are confined to within three miles of the caldera. The age of the main pumice sheet, seen on the caldera rim as thick white bands of glassy fragments, has been assigned at least two conflicting dates. According to one source, it is about 1720 years old, give or take 250 years.[17] According to another, it is within 60 years of being 1270 years old.[18] This 500 year discrepancy may result from the fact that the wood and charcoal used in radiocarbon dating the pumice were not taken from exactly the same stratigraphic positions. The problem is further complicated by the results of a recent hydration analysis of Pumice Cone itself. The cone has generally been assumed to be coeval with the main pumice fall, but the hydration method suggests it is 6000 years old.[19] Whatever age the pumice may be, the Big Obsidian Flow is clearly younger, for it lies on top of the pumice beds.

Also younger than the main pumice fall are the heaps of loose scoria and flows of andesite and basaltic lava which form the topmost layers on the north and east caldera walls.[20] These were erupted from numerous local vents and fissures, probably along fault lines associated with the caldera subsidence. Additional recent ejecta are abundantly strewn over Mazama ash on the south and west rims as well.

Two of the youngest cones inside the caldron are the inelegantly named Red Slide and Sheep's Rump, respectively located high on the north and northeast caldera walls. The former was built above the north shore of Pauline Lake, toward which it sent a basaltic flow, while the latter rose above the northeast corner of East Lake. Both are composed of basaltic fragments and may have contributed some of the ejecta which blanket the late pumice and ash deposits. The East Lake Fissure may also have spouted its molten fountains close to the time when these young cones were erupting.

Late Eruption on the Outer Slopes

While these eruptions of basalt, andesite, and rhyolite were occurring within the caldera, activity was equally intense on the outer slopes of the volcano. The Newberry Shield is often locally referred to as the "Paulina Mountains" as if it constituted a separate mountain range in itself. There is some justification for this local nomenclature, for there are no less than 200 miniature volcanoes on Newberry's flanks.[21] Most of these cinder cones range in height from 200 to 400 feet, although a few rise 500 feet above the basaltic surface on which they were built. Most have diameters of between a third and a quarter of a mile, although the largest exceed half a mile. The majority have shallow, saucer-like summit depressions, but some, such as Lava Top and Kawak Buttes, retain steep-sided craters 200 to 300 feet deep. Flank eruptions either concentrated at a single vent and formed cinder cones, or occurred along fissures and built long ridges, such as the Devil's Horn.[22]

The age of these 200-odd parasitic cones, which stand out like knobs on Newberry's gentle slopes, vary considerably. The oldest are partly submerged beneath the latest shield-building lava flows and the youngest are free even of the most recent Newberry pumice.[23]

After they had erected their pyroclastic cones, many of these satellite vents erupted streams of basalt and andesite. Tongues of lava flowed between and around the cones, leaving a network of intermingling flows. Most of them emerged from the bases of cinder cones, but others issued from nearby fissures. Both pahoehoe and aa lavas were erupted, some of which retain extremely fresh-looking surfaces and sharply defined margins. Like the cinder cones, the lateral flows are of diverse ages. Williams estimated that probably all the postcinder cone flows are less than 1000 years old.[24]

In addition to the cones and lava flows, parasitic eruptions extruded three small domes of rhyolite on Newberry's western flank and two large rhyolite and obsidian domes, East Butte and China Hat, on the extreme eastern flank. All are older than the Mazama ashfall.[25]

The East Lake Fissure

Extending for 20 miles northwest from the Newberry Shield is the East Lake Fissure. It seems to begin at the vertical scar on the north caldera wall above East Lake and to terminate beyond Lava Butte, 10 miles south of Bend on Highway 97. During the past few hundred to few thousand years, many different eruptions have occurred along this line of crustal weakness. Between 5800 and 6400 years ago at least eight flows of basalt poured from the fissure, overwhelming nearby timberlands. The Lava

Cast Forest Flow, so called because the molten rock engulfed standing trees, incinerated them, and formed hollow molds of their trunks which erosion has since exposed, is a favorite stopping-place for tourists. Despite its recent appearance, it seems to be 6150 to 6380 years old. Several other aa lava flows which emerged from the Northwest Rift Zone, such as the Lava Cascade Flow, Gas-Line Flow, and the Forest Road Flow, appear to be only 200 to 300 years younger.[26]

The most voluminous outpouring from the 20-mile-long fault occurred near its northern terminus. The site is marked by impressive, 500-foot-high Lava Butte, which rises at the edge of the main highway into Bend. Steep-sided, beautifully symmetrical, with a deep, perfectly preserved summit crater, Lava Butte is one of the most accessible examples of a cinder cone to be found near the Cascades. Because of its archetypal form and convenient location, the University of Oregon Center for Volcanology has established a research area and exhibit there. A paved road spirals to the summit, where a small museum displays colorful illustrations of the local geology. From the crater rim visitors can peer into a pit where lava once bubbled and from which sprayed fountains of molten rock.

Lava Butte received its name from the floods of lava which poured from an aperture at its southern base. This flow, or series of several flows, spread over 10 square miles, damming the course of the ancestral Deschutes River. After being displaced by the thick floods of aa lava, the Deschutes cut a new course around the flow margins, creating spectacular waterfalls and rapids.

Some geologists believe that prior to building its fragmental cone, an earlier vent at the site of Lava Butte erupted streams of basaltic lava.[27] If this is correct, the present cone represents the second major stage of activity, a pyroclastic episode between two distinct phases of effusive activity. Another geologist has suggested that if Lava Butte had not, figuratively speaking, squandered its resources by pouring out lavas over territory so far removed from the main crater, it might have been able to construct a cone high enough to match that of Bachelor Butte.[28]

Whatever Lava Butte's potential might have been at some point in the past, in its present stage it affords an excellent lookout for surveying the volcanic wonderland of central Oregon. From the huge, knobby mass of the Newberry Shield 20 miles distant, to the snow-glistening peaks of the Three Sisters on the western skyline, the whole region is a volcanologist's paradise.

Chapter 9 – References

1. Williams, 1935, p. 256.
2. Ibid., p. 257.
3. Higgins, 1973, p. 470.
4. Peterson and Groh, 1969, p. 78.
5. Williams, 1935, p. 274; Peterson and Groh, 1969, pp. 78-81.
6. Peterson and Groh, 1965, p. 9; 1969, p. 75.
7. Higgins, 1973, p. 471.
8. Peterson and Groh, 1965.
9. Williams, 1935, p. 259.
10. Williams, 1962, p. 44.
11. Higgins, 1973, p. 460.
12. Ibid., pp. 462-468.
13. Ibid, p. 468.
14. Williams, 1935; Higgins, 1973.
15. Williams, 1935; 1962, p. 44.
16. Higgins, 1973.
17. Ibid., p. 471.
18. Peterson and Groh, 1969, p. 76.
19. Friedman, 1971, p. A117.
20. Higgins, 1973, p. 460.
21. Ibid., p. 472.
22. Williams, 1935, pp. 278-279.
23. Higgins, 1973, p. 472.
24. Williams, 1935, p. 280.
25. Higgins, 1973, p. 474.
26. Peterson and Groh, 1969, p. 76.
27. Peterson and Groh, 1965, p. 9.
28. Brogan, not dated, p. 6.

Figure 10–1. *Three Sisters in summer, from the southeast. Note the wrinkled surface of the youthful lava flow (foreground). At least a half dozen active glaciers are visible in this scene. (Photo by Delano Photographics.)*

10
The Three Sisters — Oregon's Volcanic Playground

Throughout most of the length of the Cascade Range, large volcanic peaks are spaced about 40 to 80 miles apart. This distribution of the higher peaks allows a particular mountain to reign visually over a wide domain, of which it is unmistakably the chief topographical feature. In central Oregon, however, the usual pattern is broken. Instead of a single snowy cone dominating the immediate countryside, a whole cluster of closely grouped volcanoes creates an impressively crowded skyline (Figure 10-1).

Viewed from the hills near Bend, the prominent elevations, from south to north, include symmetrical Bachelor Butte, craggy Broken Top, the South, Middle, and North Sisters (all over 10,000 feet) and Belknap Crater. Most of these peaks remain snowcapped even in summer, while the Sisters themselves bear at least a dozen active glaciers. Farther north are the pinnacles of Mt. Washington and Three Fingered Jack.

Nowhere in the range has there been a greater number and variety of recent eruptions than in the vicinity of Oregon's Three Sisters.[1] From the oldest, highly eroded spires of Mt. Washington and the North Sister to the smooth, almost unmarred summit cones of Bachelor Butte and South Sister, the skyline view offers a lavish display of volcanoes old and new.

Because of its scenic beauty and (at least nominal) protection by the Federal Government, the Three Sisters Wilderness is increasingly well known as a year-round recreational area. A ski resort on Bachelor Butte attracts a throng of winter visitors, while summer sports enthusiasts find excellent camping and hiking opportunities along the 240 miles of developed trails which criss-cross the region. Scented pine forests, flowering meadows, and mossy-banked streams add to the charm of this natural playground. West and south of the Sisters are 37 alpine lakes, ranging in size from small tarns to respectable bodies of water suitable for fishing, swimming (if one can tolerate the chill) and boating.

Motorists following the Cascade Lakes Highway southwest from Bend can stop conveniently at many of these scenic glacial ponds, some of which are bordered by cliffs of glistening obsidian or flows of treeless blocky lava. Nature here presents a vivid contrast: luxuriant alpine parklands surrounded by bleak monuments to the earth's past violence.

The Geology of the Three Sisters Area

When he published the first geological reconnaissance of the Three Sisters region in 1925, Dr. Edwin T. Hodge concluded that these mountains were but remnants of a once vastly larger volcanic cone that had collapsed in Miocene or early Pliocene time. The broad arc of peaks that runs from Broken Top through Devil's Hill, the Wife and Sphinx, Husband, Little Brother, and North Sister seemed to outline an ancient caldera rim. Observing the long slopes leading outward from the ragged arc, one might easily imagine them projected upward to an enormous central cone. Hodge called this theoretical ancestor of the Sisters Mt. Multnomah. He concluded that it had been engulfed, in much the same way that ancient Mt. Mazama had collapsed to form the caldera in which Crater Lake lies.

In the 1940s Professor Howel Williams, the dean of Cascade volcanologists, examined the Three Sisters and associated peaks. He concluded that each of the volcanoes in question is a totally separate entity.[2] While several cones may be parasitic to the larger peaks, none of them represents survivors of a demolished older structure.

The North Sister

The oldest mountain in the area is the steep, rugged North Sister (10,085 feet). Considered the most difficult climb of the three chief peaks, its summit consists of almost sheer cliffs of disintegrating rock (Figure 10-2). Profoundly eroded, its original constructional surface has vanished, leaving no trace of a crater.

With a base 15 to 20 miles in diameter, the North Sister was once one of the mightiest volcanoes in the Oregon Cascades, at least 11,000 feet high.[3] Williams' investigations also revealed that the cone was built in three distinct stages, almost duplicating the three-part development of Thielsen, Washington, and similar early-Pleistocene volcanoes of Oregon. First, the North Sister formed a wide basalt shield that eventually rose about 4000 feet above its foundation. Then, when it had attained a height of some 8000 feet above sea level, quiet effusions of fluid basalt gave way to explosions, which erected a large fragmental cone in its large summit crater. When finished, this fragmental summit cone stood about 3000 feet above the underlying shield. Glacial erosion has since scooped out large sections of this cone, so that its composition is clearly displayed. It consists of shattered lava blocks, derived from older plugs and flows, as well as pumice, scoria, bombs, and cinders. In addition, slaggy flows of vesicular basalt issued from both the central vent and from fissures along the sides of the cone. Compared with those that built the shield, most of these later flows are notably thin. An exposure south of the Thayer Glacier, for example, shows that 50 superimposed flows make up a cliff only about 120 feet high.

Figure 10–2. Glacial erosion has stripped the North Sister (foreground) of a third of its original bulk. Small remaining glaciers continue to carve basins into the deeply denuded cone. The white mass of Collier Glacier, the largest in Oregon, originates on the Middle Sister (right background). Bachelor Butte is seen to the southeast (left) and South Sister appears directly behind North Sister's summit (center). (Photo by Austin Post, U.S. Geological Survey.)

During its late stages of activity, the North Sister apparently erupted from numerous secondary vents bordering its summit area. Pyroclastic deposits and lava streams now overlie each other in irregular fashion, as exposed by later erosion. Some of these unconformities may have been caused by erosion during long intervals between eruptions, but Williams believes that most are probably the result of activity from various subsidiary craters.

In its last stage of growth, the North Sister also resembled Thielsen and Washington. The summit cone was invaded by swarms of dikes, more numerous than those found on any similar Cascade peak. Now exhumed by glacial erosion, dozens of vertical or oblique lava walls ranging in width from a few inches to 25 feet radiate away from the summit. Finally, a massive "steep-sided plug of . . . brown-crusted, greenish lava" welled upward into the main conduit, thrusting aside and displacing many of the earlier dikes and fragmental dsposlts.[4] Completely filling the volcano's throat, this 300-yard-wide plug now forms the two summit pinnacles, known as the Middle and South Horns.

As in the cases of Mt. Thielsen, Union Peak, and other mountains of comparable age, glaciation removed a quarter to a third of the North Sister's original volume. During maximum glaciation, ice entirely covered the peak, extending north and east to elevations of about 4000 feet; some glaciers stretched 15 miles westward to an elevation of 1000 feet.[5] Judging by its extremely denuded state, North Sister had probably ceased to erupt well before the last major glacial advance. The fact that it retains more of a conical shape than do the thin spires of Thielsen or Washington is probably due as much to its greater size as to the possibility that it remained active to a significantly later date.

At least some of the many irregular mounds and protrusions cluttering the North Sister's flanks probably represent the eroded remains of various satellite cones. One of the most prominent of these is the dissected Little Brother, reproducing in miniature the development of its parent.

Other conspicuous and deeply eroded landforms, which are likewise miniature replicas of the North Sister, abound in the area. West of the Middle and South Sisters is The Husband, notable for the unusual fluidity of its early lava flows, some of which reached as far as the Western Cascade boundary. The Husband is also remarkable for its two enormous summit plugs. The southern plug measures 600 by 200 yards; the northern one is three quarters of a mile along its major axis and 300 yards along its minor and stands 800 feet high.[6] Although these protrusions may have been conduit fillings, they probably rose above the original vents as steep-sided lava domes.

The Wife, Sphinx, and Burnt Top also form secondary outcroppings along the central Cascade skyline. All belong approximately to the North Sister's main period of activity[7] and all have had their original features effaced by glacial cutting.

Broken Top

One of the largest volcanoes in the Three Sisters constellation is Broken Top. Once a shield volcano capped by a summit cone appreciably higher than its present 9175 feet, Broken Top is now a semi-circular amphitheatre, open to the southeast. Its former summit, entire southeast slope, and most of its interior have completely disappeared. In addition, at least four more cirques indent other sides of the volcano, so that its core is largely laid bare. Like the North Sister and the inner walls of Crater Lake, Broken Top provides superb "inside views" of how a large volcano is put together; in its interior, one can see layers of pumice, ash, bombs, basalt blocks, and lava flows. As at Crater Lake, the strata are brilliantly colored, showing bands of red, purple and black scoria alternating with yellow, brown and orange tuffs.[8] A conspicuous stratum of white pumice is strikingly interbedded with chunks of black basalt.

Williams found that Broken Top first erupted flows of basalts and basaltic andesites. Later flows, exposed higher on the cone, are more siliceous, the topmost flow on the eastern flank being the only obsidian found among the older volcanoes. In its maturity, Broken Top became extremely violent and hurled out lava bombs as much as eight feet long. The summit cone, built mostly of fragmental material, was finally mantled with thin lava flows. It was then intruded by dikes and two conduit-filling summit plugs.[9]

The most formidable of Broken Top's concluding eruptions produced a series of glowing avalanches. Probably emerging from a vent on the volcano's northeast slope, some of these incandescent flows swept eastward down the canyon of Tumalo Creek, overflowing its banks and emptying into the valley of the Deschutes River about a mile and a half south of Bend. Most of the hot avalanches raced northeastward to cover almost the whole of the Bend quadrangle west of the Deschutes River (see map). These avalanches left deposits of welded pumice and ash, between 20 and 50 feet thick, over much of the flat country that now underlies the town of Sisters. In all, the glowing avalanches blanketed an area of more than 200 square miles.[10]

If a comparable eruption were to occur today, many lives would be endangered. Since Bend's expanding suburbs, as well as several other towns and villages, are built atop glowing avalanche deposits, only a total evacuation of the affected area could ensure the inhabitants' safety should a similar outburst threaten.

The Middle Sister

Smallest of the trio of volcanic siblings, Middle Sister (10,047 feet) has few distinctions. Were it not for its height and glacial covering it would merit little attention. In general outline, the Middle Sister is a regular cone, the eastern face of which has been stripped away. It thus resembles a half-dome rising above the thick lava accumulations of its predecessors in the area. The Hayden and Diller Glaciers continue to enlarge the amphitheatre excavated in its eastern slope and probably obscure the site of its former central conduit.[11] The Middle Sister thus has neither a crater, like the South Sister, nor impressive summit pinnacles, like the North.

The Collier Glacier, which descends from Middle Sister's north shoulder, flows north-northeastward directly across the North Sister's western flank, into which it has cut a broad channel. The glacier is distinguished by large lateral moraines which seem to have been formed in late post-glacial time. After several decades of shrinking, the glacier seems recently to have stabilized. If the present cooler climatic trend continues, it may again advance to its former terminus at Collier Cone.

The South Sister

The highest and best preserved of the three major peaks, the South Sister (10,358 feet) retains an almost perfectly circular summit crater. In spring and summer melting snow forms a small crater lake, the highest body of water in Oregon.

Although its form is generally conical, the South Sister has a complex history. Its base consists of a broad basaltic shield, perhaps contemporaneous with that of the North Sister. The original shield was later almost buried beneath a steeper cone of andesite and dacite, which composes the bulk of the mountain. Two basaltic cones form the present summit area; glaciers had largely destroyed the elder structure before the younger cone was built slightly to the west of its predecessor.

The South Sister not only erupted a great variety of lava types, it also built numerous parasitic structures along its flanks. Many of these features have been glaciated, but the latest appear completely unweathered. In post-glacial time a series of vents and fissures opened along the volcano's southeast slope. First, large quantities of dacite pumice were ejected and formed a thick sheet over the entire vicinity. Then, beginning at an elevation of about 8000 feet and moving progressively downward for a distance of three miles, masses of obsidian and dacite surged out of the fissures. Two thick flows crept down the east side and reached the base of the mountain; their deeply wrinkled surfaces can be seen in Figure 10-1. Most of the dacite and obsidian erupted during this phase was too stiff and viscous to flow away in streams. Instead, it piled up to form a chain of steep-sided domes whose black, glassy crusts were shattered by pulses of new lava from below.

The massive obsidian domes along the South Sister's southeast base bristle with sharp spires, huge angular blocks, and other chaotic surface features. Some, which formed as low as the 5500 foot level, are easily seen from the Cascade Lakes Highway near the shores of Devil's Lake.

The South Sister underwent at least three distinct glaciations. Little evidence remains of the oldest, but during the last glacial stage, which ended approximately 10,000 years ago, a vast icecap buried the High Cascades, covering all but the highest ridges and peaks and merging with alpine glaciers descending from the Sisters. Ice streams flowing down the South Sister's southern slope filled adjacent valleys to a depth of 500 feet.[12] Neither the central ice field nor its related glaciers, some of which were 19 miles long, extended beyond the High Cascades platform; in the Sisters area few of the glaciers descended below 3600 feet.

A more recent glacial episode deposited fresh moraines and outwash between elevations of 7000 and 9000 feet on the high peaks. Radiocarbon ages of associated lavas and ash deposits indicate that these moraines were formed less than 2500 years ago and belong to what is sometimes called the "Little Ice Age" or Neoglaciation. The last minor glacial advance culminated near the end of the 19th century.[13]

The small, generally shallow cirques cut into the southeast surface of the South Sister's present summit cone (Figure 10-1) may have formed during one of these Neoglacial periods. The latest glacial advances did not last long enough to breach the crater walls, where strata of black scoria, almond-shaped bombs up to a yard long, and flows of dark, scoriaceous basalt lie undisturbed along the inside rim. Two depressions on the crater floor, one east-southeast of the other, may mark the vents through which the last eruptions occurred. According to Williams, the latest activity may have taken place within the last 1000 years.[14]

Glaciers have cut more deeply into the north face of the volcano, where 1200 feet of layered basalts are exposed just below the summit. Three main terraces of lava, perhaps belonging to the elder summit cone's eruptive cycle, are interspersed by steep hanging icefields said to slant at 50 degrees.[15] Existing glaciers seem too small to be responsible for these erosional features, which were probably carved during an earlier glacial advance.

Considering the fresh appearance of the volcano's summit area, it seems strange that there are no known reports of recent activity. Most of the other Cascade volcanoes with comparably youthful craters have records of observed eruptions—or at least escaping steam—during historic

Figure 10–3. The northeast face of Bachelor Butte. Except for the small glacier-filled cirque just below the summit, this young volcano is almost unmarred by erosion. A recent parasitic cinder cone appears at the center right. (Photo courtesy of the U.S. Forest Service.)

time. It should be remembered, however, that central Oregon was but sparsely settled until about 70 or 80 years ago. Although early explorers, such as Peter Skene Ogden, Captain J. C. Frémont, and John J. Newberry, a scientist with the Williamson Railroad Survey, passed through the region between 1826 and 1855, there were few permanent residents until several decades later. The town of Bend was not founded until about 1900. Thus, even if some mild expulsions of steam or ash did occur, it is likely that no one with an interest in recording such events was present to observe them.

Bachelor Butte

Bachelor Butte (9065 feet) is a charmingly symmetrical cone which rises at least 3000 feet above the surrounding woodlands a few miles south of Broken Top (Figure 10-3). It is familiar to thousands because of the popular ski resort located on its northern slope. Except for a small glacial cirque on its shaded northern side, it is virtually unmodified by erosion. The blocky, basaltic lava flows, which cover much of its surface, appear completely unweathered, suggesting that the visible part of the volcano was constructed in post-glacial time.

Williams remarked, "no one who sees the barren flows of basalt which poured from fissures on the northern flank and spread in branching tongues into Sparks Lake can doubt that they must have escaped only a few centuries ago.''[16] Most of the Bachelor's flows, however, were erupted before Mt. Mazama showered a layer of fine pumice over the whole region about 6600 years ago. [17] Some of Bachelor Butte's parasitic cinder cones, which cluster about its base, may postdate the Mazama ashfall.

Climbing Bachelor Butte along the edge of the shallow trench which its one surviving glacier has excavated is an educational experience. The forces which sculptured the larger Cascade volcanoes are here revealed in miniature. Although this unnamed glacier is tiny by Cascade standards, it is vigorous and hard-working. Lavas at the margin of its bed appear as fresh as if they had just congealed. But where the glacier has over-ridden them and cut below the surface, the ice has ground seemingly indestructible lava blocks into a fine, charcoal-gray flour, easily carried away by streams issuing from the glacier's snout. The transformation of solid rock into gritty dust is particularly dramatic at the glacier's terminus, where a large semi-circular ridge, concave toward the glacier-front has been deposited. Although some climbers mistake this formation for a cinder cone, it is the glacier's terminal moraine.

Just below the summit, the glacier has uncovered what seem to be solidified feeding pipes of former eruptive vents. Some of these may have fed lava flows, others may represent conduit fillings from explosive eruptions. No single crater now occupies Bachelor Butte's summit. Instead, there are several more or less circular small depressions, which may mark the site at which lava sank back into the supplying vents at the close of the volcano's latest eruptions. Or, the funnel-shaped hollows may simply be miniature explosion craters which were active at diverse times. Significant accumulations of pyroclastic material, however, seem to be absent from the summit area.

The well preserved state of Bachelor Butte suggests that it may now be resting between outbursts. Its Holocene activity possibly indicates that it is still in the cone-building stage and may eventually grow significantly in size and height.

That internal heat still exists within the cone is made clear by the numerous fumaroles or ''hot spots'' which appear on its northern slope. In winter, subsurface heat melts the overlying snowpack in places to create deep cylindrical ''wells,'' which resemble manholes in the snow. No steam or other gases are visible, but these north-side thermal areas present a hazard to unwary skiers, some of whom have reputedly plunged into them. Whether comparable melt-pits exist on other, less frequented, sides of the mountain is not known.

Cones North of the North Sister

In a north-south alignment between the large cones of the North Sister and Three Fingered Jack, at least 125 separate eruptive centers have blazed and died in post-glacial time.[18] These recent vents built cinder cones several hundred feet high, covered the surrounding countryside with thick mantles of ash and pumice, and—most impressively— poured out immense streams of lava whose surfaces are so fresh and unweathered that they look as if they had congealed only yesterday. Lava issuing from a cinder cone near Sand Mountain dammed the McKenzie River to form Clear Lake, now a favorite Cascade fishing spot. Ghostly forests, denuded of branches, can be seen still standing in the depths of the lake. The cold waters must act as an effective preservative, for, according to radiocarbon dating from wood samples taken nearby, the forest was drowned about 3000 years ago.[19]

Remarkable volcanic displays greet the traveler on his way over Mc-Kenzie Pass, which traverses the central Cascades between Bend and Eugene. Following the devious but generally east-west trending Mc-Kenzie River valley, the highway crosses lava fields covering an area of 85 square miles—a forbidding desert of black, jagged basalt. Several major vents contributed lava; the most important were Belknap Crater, Little Belknap, and the Yapoah cinder cone. From the Dee Wright observatory, built of and atop the basaltic flood, one can enjoy a sweeping panorama of the several volcanoes involved. To the south stands the white massif of North Sister, its base dotted with recent peripheral cones. One of them, Yapoah Cone, emitted the particular flow on which the observatory sits. Northward rises the eroded volcanic neck of Mt. Washington, on whose glaciated lower slopes the Belknap volcanoes were erected.

Most of the visible lava was erupted from Belknap Crater and its two principal satellites, Little Belknap and South Belknap. The main Belknap cone (6869 feet) was constructed in the wide depression between the opposing slopes of the North Sister and Mt. Washington, whose lavas probably underlie Belknap's broad shield.

Belknap's lava shield is topped by a 400-foot high cinder cone, indented by three summit craters of varying size, aligned in a north-northwesterly direction.[20] The northernmost and smallest vent apparently erupted some lava, for part of the crater wall is breached by a small flow. The much larger south crater emitted large quantities of ash which drifted over an area exceeding 100 square miles.[21]

Later, fissures near the summit split Belknap's cone, and from these issued copious streams of basalt, which inundated the entire shield. Most of this lava is of the blocky or scoriaceous type, although some true pahoehoe crusts were also formed. The collapse of lava tubes, and the breaking up and "peeling back" of cooling lava crusts as the fluid interior of the flow moved forward, make these basalt surfaces unusually chaotic and virtually impossible to cross.

Despite their fresh appearance, some of the Belknap lavas are surprisingly old. About 2900 years ago basalt lava erupted from Little Belknap, a vent about a mile east of the main crater. These hummocky, virtually treeless flows surround two prominent *steptoes* or "islands" of older volcanic rock, leaving them as isolated outcroppings amid a sea of black basalt. Williams described these Little Belknap effusions, with their crusts often broken into jumbled piles of sharp rock, as "reminiscent of a shattered ice jam." The final lavas from Little Belknap filled the crater, leaving a craggy mound of red clinkery rock, from which collapsed lava tubes diverge radially.[22]

The next major overflow occurred about 1800 years ago at South Belknap, a subsidiary cone on the south flank of Belknap Crater.[23] Moving over the older Belknap flows, the South Belknap lava streamed southward to McKenzie Pass, where it banked against the margins of a solidified flow from Yapoah Cone, which was emplaced about 2900 to 2600 years ago.

The largest and last outpouring took place about 1500 years ago from fissures located near the base of the main Belknap shield.[24] Simultaneously, explosions blew quantities of ash from the northern of the two principal summit craters. The blocky basalt flowed 12 miles westward where it plunged onto the McKenzie canyon floor, altering the course of the McKenzie River. The lava spread across the riverbed, damming it and creating an extensive swamp—Beaver Marsh—upstream.[25] Today the McKenzie disappears into the permeable sediments along the flow margins and runs underground until it reappears at Tamolitch Falls.

Other Recent Eruptions

Because such an abundance of new cones and lava flows characterize the area north of The Sisters, only two of the most notable will be mentioned. Four-in-One-Cone, as its name implies, consists of a row of four closely-spaced, almost identical cinder cones, which, about 2600 years ago, had their northeast crater walls breached by extensive lava flows. It must sit astride a fault zone, for it is part of an alignment of 19 similar cones.[26]

Collier Cone, on the flanks of the North Sister, may be the most recently active volcano in the group. Its eruptive history is long and complex. Not only did its explosive eruptions create a mile-square plain of desolation, known as the Ahalapam Cinder Field, it also produced a series of lava flows which extended three miles to the northwest and eight and a half miles to the west.

Standing in the path of the Collier Glacier, Collier Cone blocked that ice stream's advance during several recent glacial resurgences. As late as 1924 Collier ice rode high on the side of the cone. At an earlier period, when the glacier was at least 200 feet thick at its terminus, water from its

Figure 10–4. Map of the Three Sisters region, showing locations of the major cones.

melting surface flowed into the crater of Collier Cone and covered much of the crater floor with outwash. Stream gravels were simultaneously deposited in the lava gutters and other flow features surrounding the cone.[27] Today the Collier Glacier has retreated far up the flanks of the North Sister, leaving behind a conspicuous glacial moraine which borders the cinder cone.

The Volcanic Future of the Three Sisters Area

Because of the number and variety of post-glacial eruptions in The Three Sisters vicinity it seems hardly possible that all of the recent vents are extinct. In the past few thousand years, old volcanoes have reawakened and many completely new ones have been built. The brief period of quiescence during historic time (which in this part of Oregon goes back less than a century) is probably only a hiatus in what will prove to be a long future of intermittent volcanic activity. Which one of the many cones, fissures, blow-holes, or craters will next break into new life? Perhaps an entirely new mountain will one day be erected before our eyes, as was the famous Paricutin, which was born in a Mexican cornfield in 1943. The Three Sisters region is as likely as any in the whole range to stage a spectacular volcanic renaissance.

Exploring the Three Sisters Areas

A panoramic view of the Three Sisters and their satellites can be seen from your car along Highway 97 for miles both north and south of Bend. The short paved road to the summit of Lava Butte, a few miles south of Bend, affords an unobstructed view of the entire region. Watch for the roadside marker.

The Cascade Lakes Highway leaves 97 at Bend and leads west southwestward to skirt the base of South Sister before rejoining Highway 97 near LaPine. Although this route provides access to the many scenic lakes that dot the sparsely timbered highland, the road does not actually take you *on* any of the Sisters. The closest approach is to the south flank of South Sister at Sparks and Devil's Lakes. For a summit climb it is necessary to backpack approximately six miles along a trail which leads from Century Drive to the Green Lakes basin, at the eastern foot of the volcano.

If you want to climb one of the major peaks but do not have time for the extra day's backpacking required to reach a base camp at any of the Three Sisters, follow the Cascade Lakes Highway to Bachelor Butte, 22 miles west of Bend and turn left at the sign indicating Bachelor Butte Ski Area. Keep to the left until you reach the upper parking lot.

Follow a dirt logging road, which begins near the lower end of the chair lift, past the upper terminus of the lift. Scramble over large lava blocks bordering the shallow glacial cirque on Bachelor's northeast face. Just below the summit you will find a relatively flat area from which the "trail" to the crest is visible. Allow two to three hours one way for a 2600 foot gain in altitude. On a clear day the summit view is spectacular: northward are all Three Sisters, glaciers, lava fields, dozens of lakes, dense forest, Mt. Washington, Three Fingered Jack and Mt. Jefferson. When the weather is cooperative, Mt. Hood, 100 miles distant, is also visible.

Chapter 10 – References

1. Williams, 1962, p. 49.
2. Williams, 1944.
3. Ibid., p. 41.
4. Ibid., pp. 42-43.
5. Ibid., p. 41.
6. Ibid., p. 44.
7. Ibid., pp. 44-45.
8. Ibid., p. 46.
9. Ibid., pp. 45-46.
10. Williams, 1957.
11. Williams, 1944, p. 48.
12. Ibid., p. 51.
13. Taylor, 1968, p. 5.
14. Williams, 1944, p. 51.
15. Hyslop, 1971, p. 21.
16. Williams, 1944, p. 52.
17. Williams, 1957.
18. Taylor, 1965, p. 144.
19. Taylor, 1968, pp. 8-9.
20. Williams, 1944, p. 56.
21. Taylor, 1968, p. 21.
22. Williams, 1944, p. 57.
23. Taylor, 1968, p. 20.
24. Ibid., pp. 21, 24.
25. Taylor, 1965, p. 131.
26. Taylor, 1965, p. 141; 1968, p. 18.
27. Taylor, 1965, pp. 143-144.

11
Mt. Jefferson—
Guardian of the Wilderness

Mt. Jefferson, the second highest peak in Oregon, is surrounded by a primitive wilderness which makes access difficult. A popular hiking trail leads to Jefferson Park on the mountain's northwest side, but the closest one can approach by car is via a gravel logging road (No. 1044) that connects with Highway 22 and comes within four miles of the peak. As a result, Mt. Jefferson is usually seen only from a distance; the stretch of U.S. Highway 97 between Bend and The Dalles affords good views of the east side.

Despite its inaccessibility, Jefferson has frequently appeared, anonymously, as a splendid backdrop in national advertisements for Detroit's new cars. The awkward fact that few luxury models can get near the mountain is not a deterrent when the peak's suitability for advertising is so obvious.

Mt. Jefferson is unusually photogenic for several reasons. One is its considerable height. Surmounting the Cascade divide 40 miles south of Mt. Hood, Jefferson rises to 10,495 feet. Another contributing factor is its sharp, pointed summit, which from the southeast is as picturesquely horn-like as those of Mts. Thielsen or Washington. A third is the abundance of glacial ice, which keeps the peak white and glittering throughout the year. The Whitewater Glacier covers much of the east side, extending even below timberline. Jefferson Park, with its clear rivulets and profusion of wild flowers, also provides an exceptionally attractive setting which photographers have used advantageously to frame their pictures of this severely glaciated volcano (Figure 11-1).

Mt. Jefferson first entered the literature of the West when Lewis and Clark sighted it from near the mouth of the Willamette River. Named to honor the great president who sponsored their expedition, Jefferson was the only High Cascade peak christened by the explorers.

Perhaps because neighboring Mt. Hood is higher and more visible from Oregon's population centers, very little has been published about Mt. Jefferson. The only printed report devoted exclusively to the volcano is that by Edwin T. Hodge,[1] a former professor of geology at the University of Oregon. Thayer[2] analyzed the chemical composition of lavas in the Jefferson area, but included few comments about the sequence in which they were erupted. In a U.S. Geological Survey Bulletin suggesting ways to exploit the economic potential of the Mt. Jefferson Wilderness, Walker, Greene, and Pattee[3] cite a few general facts about the peak. Greene[4] adds little specific information; Condie and Swenson[5] provide extensive analyses of lava samples from the volcano, which they found remarkably uniform in its mineralogy.

Fortunately, Kenneth G. Sutton, a geologist associated with the University of Oregon's Center for Volcanology, has recently completed (1975) a reconnaissance study of Mt. Jefferson's volcanic and glacial history.[6] The following discussion relies heavily on Sutton's unpublished thesis.

The Geology of Mt. Jefferson

Mt. Jefferson was built atop a rugged terrain averaging 5500 to 6500 feet in altitude; its cone is thus no more than a mile high, although some andesite flows extend several miles into adjacent canyon bottoms to elevations as low as 3000 feet. Condie and Swenson[7] estimated that Jefferson is composed about equally of pyroclastics and lava flows, but Sutton's investigations led him to conclude that pyroclastics make up only 20 to 25 per cent of the volcano's bulk. What appear to be pyroclastic deposits are typically the shattered and fragmented bases of lava flows.[8]

Because Mt. Jefferson is probably the most deeply eroded high stratovolcano in Oregon, the sequence of events which built its cone is clearly evident. Like Mt. McLoughlin, Jefferson began as a highly explosive vent and erected a large fragmental cone, which glacial cutting has since exposed. The most extensive exposure of Jefferson's pyroclastic core occurs in the West Milk Creek Cirque, where a Pleistocene glacier cut deeply into the western side of the volcano.

The original pumice cone was later completely buried under sheets of basaltic andesite, which attained an aggregate thickness of at least 2000 feet. These flows, designated the main cone lavas, are now exposed in the West Milk Creek Cirque, where they overlie the earlier pyroclastic deposits. Glaciated remnants of the Main Cone flows also appear along the west and northwest flanks of the mountain, in the east wall of the Russell Glacier valley, beneath the terminus of Jefferson Glacier, in the ridge between the main summit and the North Complex (a later secondary cone), and in the bergschrund wall of Waldo Glacier.

These main cone lavas, some of which moved seven miles or more into nearby valleys, are relatively thin high on the mountain. On the northwest flank and in the east wall of the Russell Glacier valley, the lavas slant toward the north at about 20 to 30 degrees and range from five to 40 feet in thickness. Some eastward-flowing lavas apparently poured down steeper slopes of 30 to 45 degrees; most of these are about 15 to 20 feet thick.

Figure 11–1. Mt. Jefferson from the northwest, Jefferson Park in the foreground. (Bob and Ira Spring photo.)

Lava flows now forming the north ridge between Jefferson Park Glacier and the Whitewater Glacier slant towards the north and west, indicating that there must have been an eruptive center to the east of the present main ridge near the bergschrund of Whitewater Glacier. The glacier has apparently obliterated all traces of that subsidiary vent.

The voluminous main cone lavas are in striking contrast to the pyroclastic deposits which preceded them. If explosive action accompanied the principal outpouring of lava, it did not leave any recognizable deposits. Nor are there any known mudflow (lahar) deposits among the aa and block lava flows.

The apparent absence of avalanche and mudflow material among the early pyroclastics and main cone lavas indicates that these were erupted during a climatically mild interval of the Pleistocene when the volcano was mostly free of ice. After the main cone basaltic andesites had been emplaced, however, glaciers formed on Mt. Jefferson and caused local erosion of the peak, evidence of which can be seen in the east wall of the Russell Glacier valley. Following this relatively minor glaciation, Mt. Jefferson began a new cycle of activity which produced andesite flows with a much higher silica content and which differed mineralogically and chemically from the more fluid lavas which form the bulk of Jefferson's cone. These second stage flows were notably thicker and must have moved more sluggishly than the basaltic andesites. One 150 foot-thick andesite flow covered a 25 to 35 degree slope that had been cut in the earlier basaltic andesites by a glacier in the Russell Glacier valley. In one sequence, revealed in the bergschrund wall of Russell Glacier, a silicic andesite flow overlies glacial deposits that in turn lie atop the main cone lavas.

Although Pleistocene glaciation has left only small remnants of these second stage flows, they locally cap the main peaks and ridges of Mt. Jefferson. A mass of this silicic andesite, approximately 100 feet thick, now forms the present summit of the volcano.

Because of a resemblance to the spires of Mts. Thielsen, Washington, and Three Fingered Jack, it had previously been assumed that Mt. Jefferson's Matterhorn-like peak is an eroded plug, a conduit filling that had been exposed by erosion.[9]

But the fact that this topmost lava cap slants from the west to east indicates that it was erupted from a (now vanished) source west of the present summit. Mt. Jefferson's original crater, therefore, lay above the present west Milk Creek Glacier, at an altitude perhaps as high as 12,000 feet. The severe glacial erosion which followed eruption of the second stage lavas destroyed at least a third of Jefferson's original cone, removing the summit and almost the entire western half of the mountain.

As a result, what was once part of the volcano's eastern slope became the present crest.

An area of intensely altered rock visible in the West Milk Creek Cirque walls may represent the approximate location of the vent which produced the second stage lavas. North of this area which was chemically altered by heat and volcanic acids is a mass of light gray lava which at some time intruded the main cone lavas. Other second stage lavas flowed north and eastward from the summit area and now cap the cliffs north of the Whitewater Glacier. The crumbling banks of talus lying between the north and south summit horns, known as the Red Saddle, are also the shattered remains of second stage lavas.

During the period when the second stage lavas were being erupted, two sizable parasitic cones formed on the flanks of Mt. Jefferson. One of these secondary cones, called the North Complex, is located near Jefferson Park. Erosion has stripped its original surface, revealing lava dikes which once fed flows. In post-glacial time, the creek issuing from the northwest part of the Whitewater Glacier has cut further into the exposed lava flows so that their original form and relationship has been almost obliterated.

Another secondary vent opened two miles almost due south of Jefferson's summit, through which a viscous dome of reddish-brown dacite emerged. No lava flows have been found associated with the dome, now known as Goat's Peak.

Somewhat more fluid eruptions of silicic andesite issued from fissures along the south flank of Mt. Jefferson. A hypersthene andesite flow from the topmost part of the eastern fissure traveled toward the south-southeast and Goat's Peak before it cascaded over a ridge and poured south-eastward. Remains of this flow presently form the east ridge of the V-shaped valley to the north of Shale Lake at an elevation of 7600 feet. Portions of the same flow are visible southwest of Waldo Glacier, where the flow underlies the cliffs near the glacier.

An extensive lava formation in the Mt. Jefferson vicinity, known as the Santiam basalts, was formed at some point before the last major glaciation. Like Jefferson itself, the Santiam basalts have a normal magnetic polarity, which means that they were emitted since the last significant reversal of the earth's north-south magnetic poles approximately 770,000 years ago. According to Thayer[10], the Santiam basalts fill the North Santiam River valley to a depth of 1800 feet. Because there is no contact between these basalts and the Jefferson lavas, it is impossible to determine their relative ages.

After the last Pleistocene glaciers melted, several pyroclastic cones and related intercanyon basalt flows were erupted south of Mt. Jefferson.

Two of the most prominent of these are the Forked Butte Cinder Cone with its associated flow in the valley of Cabot Creek, and the Bear Butte lava flow which descended the valley of Jefferson Creek. Another Holocene pumice cone, not recognized until recently, is located about a quarter mile northeast of Goat's Peak. Although eroded, it retains a conical form; from its southeast flank a lava flow extends eastward. According to Sutton's analysis, these gray Holocene flows are definitely basalt.

Age and Volume of Eruptions in the Mt. Jefferson Area

The deeply eroded lavas composing the Western Cascade sequence west of Mt. Jefferson are several million years old. By contrast, all the lavas in the Mt. Jefferson vicinity are younger than the last magnetic reversal and were therefore erupted during the last 770,000 years. The earliest of these, the Minto lavas, formed a broad plateau of coalescing shield volcanoes that were thoroughly glaciated before the Jefferson lavas were extruded. Both Jefferson's main cone and second stage lavas are younger than the Minto group, but all were apparently erupted before the major glaciation known locally as the Jack Creek drift glaciation, which occurred between about 40,000 and 110,000 years ago. The Forked Butte lava flows are younger even than the last glacial advance, equivalent to the Fraser glaciation, which ended approximately 10,000 years ago. The latest cinder cone activity has been tentatively dated at 6400-6500 years old.[11]

The lava formations in the Mt. Jefferson area steadily decrease in volume according to age. The Minto lavas are the most voluminous, approximating 23.4 cubic miles; the main cone lavas are about five cubic miles, while those of the second stage are less than one cubic mile in volume. The Santiam basalts represent about two cubic miles and the Forked Butte lavas only eight tenths of a cubic mile.

Thus, although Mt. Jefferson is the most imposing topographical feature in this part of the High Cascades, it represents only a minor amount of lava compared to the abundant flows from shield volcanoes and fissure eruptions in the area. This volumetric ratio is typical of the central Oregon Cascades, where some individual basaltic flows with little topographical relief but large areas have volumes two or three times greater than a high-standing stratovolcano.[12]

Judging by its severely eroded state, the absence of post-glacial eruptive deposits or any fumarole activity, Mt. Jefferson may be extinct. Future activity may occur at cinder cones or fissures in the mountain's vicinity, but Jefferson itself does not seem a prime candidate for the honor of being the next Cascade volcano to erupt.

Chapter 11 – References

1. *Hodge, 1925.*
2. *Thayer, 1937 and 1939.*
3. *Walker, Greene, and Pattee, 1966.*
4. *Greene, 1968.*
5. *Condie and Swenson, 1973.*
6. *Sutton, written comm., 1975.*
7. *Condie and Swenson, 1973, p. 3.*
8. *Sutton, written comm., 1975.*
9. *Hodge, 1925.*
10. *Thayer, 1937.*
11. *Scott, 1974, cited in Sutton, 1975.*
12. *McBirney, Sutter, Naslund, Sutton, and White, 1974, p. 589.*

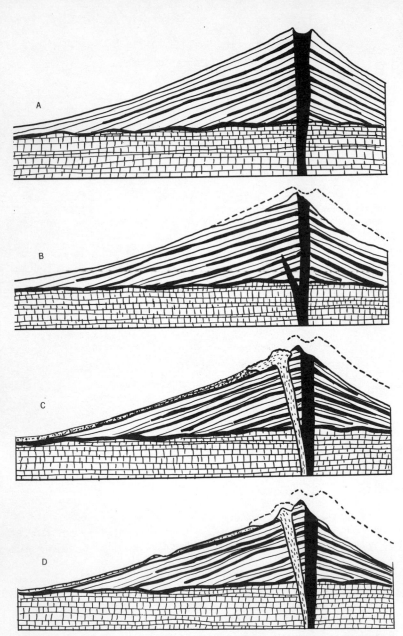

Figure 12-1. Simplified cross-sections through Mt. Hood, showing four stages in the volcano's development: A. Mt. Hood at the time of its maximum height (about 12,000 feet). Dark lines indicate lava flows; dotted areas represent pyroclastic deposits. B. After extensive glaciation. The dotted line above the cone indicates the former contours of the volcano. C. Eruption of the large hornblende andesite plug-dome and formation of the debris fan on the south slope. D. Mt. Hood today, after erosion has removed much of the plug and debris fan. (Based on drawings by W. S. Wise (1966) and used here with Dr. Wise's permission.)

12
Mt. Hood, Oregon's Most Popular Volcano

When the pioneers' covered wagons lumbered over the dry sagebrush plains of eastern Oregon on their way to the Willamette Valley, the travelers' first sight of Mt. Hood's glittering white spire promised a land of fresh, snow-fed waters, cool evergreen forests, and a long-hoped-for respite from the arid deserts which stretched between the Rockies and the Cascades. The Cascade barrier had yet to be crossed, either via the Columbia River or Barlow Pass, which skirts Hood's southern base, but at last the end was in sight.

Although perhaps not greeted so fervently today, the mountain is a delightful sight to the descendants of those hardy people. Viewed from Portland, Mt. Hood seems a classically symmetrical cone terminating in a sharp peak. Seen from other directions, however, the volcano is highly asymmetrical. Eroded by glaciers which have stripped away much of its original bulk and reduced its height by 1000 feet, Mt. Hood nonetheless is one of the most beautiful mountains in the world. Its proportions are so ideal that it appears much loftier than its 11,245 feet.

As the second most often climbed snowpeak in the world—the first being Japan's sacred volcano, Fujiyama—Hood attracts thousands of alpinists, hikers, and other sportsmen. Because some slopes remain snow covered throughout the year, it is the site of an international summer ski school and competition.Best known of Mt. Hood's man-made attractions is Timberline Lodge, at the 6000-foot level on the mountain's south side. Constructed of native materials handicrafted in Indian and wildlife motifs, the luxurious and picturesque lodge makes a good point of departure for exploring the mountain. A snow-cat ride from the lodge offers an easy journey to the 9000 foot level.

For climbers above the terminus of the snow-cat tour, a natural goal is Crater Rock, the visible top of a solidified lava column extending deep within Mt. Hood. The nearby "Hot Rocks," the base of Steel Cliff, and the depression behind Crater Rock are the sites of the largest solfataric field in Oregon. Here the lavas have been altered to soft corroding masses, colored pink, white, orange, and yellow. These "hot spots" are also the source of a powerful sulphur odor which the climber can smell from sometimes a mile away. Even after centuries of cooling, Crater Rock is encompassed by numerous fumaroles, steam jets, gas vents, and other spots too hot to touch. The temperature in many vents is approximately that of the boiling point of water at this altitude[1] and the venturesome must be careful to avoid scalding,

When the escaping clouds of vapor and gas condense to form clouds of "smoke," which curl about the mountain top, the lodge frequently receives phone calls from anxious Portlanders to whom the "smoke" seems to harbinger a new eruption. Except for a brief period in 1907, however, these columns of vapor do not seem to imply increased volcanic activity. But they are reminders that Mt. Hood's fires are not extinguished. This volcano, in fact, is the only one in Oregon for which we have a well authenticated record of observed eruptions.

Although H. R. Coombs does not include Mt. Hood in his *Catalog of Active Volcanoes in the United States*, there does seem to be evidence of several minor eruptions between about 1846 and 1865. Additionally, there was at least one other eruption just before the period of historical observation.

Shortly before Lewis and Clark made their famous journey to the Pacific Ocean (1804-1806), Mt. Hood exploded violently. This eruption deposited a layer of ash at least six inches thick at timberline on the mountain's southwest side. The ash blanket was also identified at Tilly Jane Camp, on the northeast side, where it is about four and a half inches thick. The ash did not come from Mt. St. Helens, which was also active at about the same time. The ash particles coarsened toward the summit of Mt. Hood, but were absent at a point midway between it and Mt. St. Helens,[2] indicating that Mt. Hood was the source of the eruption.

The Rev. Samuel Parker, a moderately reliable source for the earlier historic activity of Mt. St. Helens, wrote that he had heard of Indian reports of volcanic displays on Mt. Hood: "Tilki, the first chief of the La Dalles Indians, who is a man of more than ordinary talents, said he had frequently seen fires in the fissures of rock [on Mt. Hood.]"[3] Other accounts, equally vague and unsubstantiated, refer to "fire" and/or "smoke" issuing from the mountain.

A. Perrey, the authoritative Belgian seismologist who kept month-by-month reports of earthquakes and volcanic eruptions world-wide, noted that Mt. Hood was active in 1853, August, 1854 (again a year when Mt. St. Helens was repeatedly in eruption), August 15-17, 1859, and September 21 to October 8, 1865.[4] Although Perrey seems to be accurate, his notations are brief and his sources generally unknown. It is not until 1859 that we have a relatively detailed account of an eruption on Mt. Hood. Regrettably, one of the two known descriptions of the phenomenon was not printed until nearly a half century after the event. Writing in the *Everett* (Wash.) *Record* of May 17, 1902, W. F. Courtney, an Oregon pioneer, recalled that:

> The eruption took place during the later part of September, 1859 . . . . We were camped on Tie Ridge about thirty-five miles from Mt. Hood. . . . . It was about 1:30 o'clock in the morning . . . when suddenly the heavens lit up and from the dark there shot up a column of fire. With a flash that illuminated the whole mountainside with a pinkish glare, the flame danced from the crater. . . . For two hours, as we watched, the mountain continued to blaze at irregular intervals, and when morning came Mt. Hood presented a peculiar sight. His sides, where the day before there was snow, were blackened as if cinders and ashes had been thrown out.[5]

Courtney adds "That was the only time that I ever saw flames issue from the crater, but I was a member of a party at one time when we encountered hot cinders on the mountainside." The sighting of actual "flame" and finding "hot cinders" indicates that fresh, possibly molten magma was discharged at this time (1859).

Corroborating the reliability of Courtney's late account, the Portland *Weekly Oregonian* of August 20, 1859, also reported that "The Pride of Portland" was then in eruption. Although the *Oregonian* gives an earlier date for the activity than did Courtney, it seems likely that both accounts refer to the same event. After 43 years Courtney may understandably have forgotten the exact month involved. Under the heading "Eruptions of Mt. Hood," the *Oregonian* stated:

> On Wednesday last, the atmosphere suddenly became exceedingly hot about midday. In the afternoon the heavens presented a singular appearance; dark, silvery, condensed clouds hung over the top of Mt. Hood. The next day several persons watched the appearance of Mt. Hood until evening. An occasional flash of fire could be distinctly seen rolling up. On Thursday night the fire was plainly seen by every one whose attention could be drawn to the subject. Yesterday the mountain was closely examined by those who have recently returned from a visit to its summit, when, by the naked eye or a glass, it seemed that a large mass of the northwest side had disappeared, and that the immense quantity of snow which, two weeks since, covered the south side,

Figure 12–2. Aerial view of the southeast side of Mt. Hood. Crater Rock rises above an ice field in the semi-circular basin just below the summit. White River Glacier (slightly left of center) is cutting into the margin of the large debris fan which flowed down the volcano's south slope (left of glacier) while Crater Rock was being emplaced. Newton Clark Glacier occupies part of the volcano's east flank (extreme right). (Photo by Austin Post, U.S. Geological Survey.)

had also disappeared. The dense cloud of steam and smoke constantly rising over and far above the summit, together with the entire change in its appearance heretofore, convinces us that Mt. Hood is now in a state of eruption, which has broken out within a few days. The curious will examine it and see for themselves.[6]

The *Oregonian*'s claim that "a large mass of the northwest side had disappeared" and that the wholesale melting of snowpacks occurred on the south flank must be no more than editorial exaggeration. At least, no evidence of massive rockfalls or mudflows dating from this period has been recognized. The *Oregonian*'s emphasis on heat, humidity, and other atmospheric phenomena sounds supiciously as if some of the "eruption" clouds could be accounted for by an unusually heavy condensation of the steam and gas effusions which normally rise from Crater Rock. Courtney's observation, from a high ridge much nearer the mountain than is Portland, that Mt. Hood's snowcap was "blackened as if cinders and ashes had been thrown out" rather than extensively melted is certainly the preferred explanation of any sudden change in the mountain's appearance.

Six years later, on September 26, 1865, the *Oregonian* again reported an eruption. "It is some time since we have had an excitement about old Mt. Hood belching forth, but on Saturday last the active puffs, in dense black smoke, were witnessed by hundreds of people in this city. The fumes appeared to rise from the deep gorge in the southwestern side, and were so thick as to literally obscure the view of the summit at times." Since the source of the "dense black smoke" was a "deep gorge," apparently low down on the southwestern flank of the mountain, the phenomenon described could have been a forest fire. However, the reference to "puffs" rather than billows or columns of smoke hints at a mildly explosive ejection of vapor, similar to the manner in which Mt. St. Helens expelled "puffs" of steam and ash in 1854 (see p. 186).

The same issue of the *Oregonian* also carried a plausible eyewitness report which tends to rule out the theory that a forest fire was mistaken for an eruption. John Dever, of Company E. First Regiment, Washington Territory Volunteers, was stationed at Vancouver, where he stood duty during the early morning of September 21. He wrote the Portland newspaper that:

> Between the hours of 5 and 7 o'clock, and as the morning was particularly bright for this season of the year, my attention was naturally drawn towards the east. . . . Judge, then, of my surprise to see the top of Mount Hood enveloped in smoke and flame. Yes, sir, real jets of flame shot upwards seemingly a distance of fifteen or twenty feet above the mountain's height, accompanied by discharges of what appeared to be fragments of rock, cast up a considerable distance, which I could perceive fall immediately after with a rumbling noise not unlike distant thunder. This phenomenon was witnessed by other members of the guard.[7]

Dever, like Courtney in 1859, saw clouds of "smoke" and "flame" issue from near the volcano's summit rather than from a "deep gorge" far down the mountainside, as the *Oregonian* reported. It is possible that two widely-spaced vents were active during a short period of time. Dever's clear and precise description of flying shards of rock thundering downslope could apply only to a genuine eruption.

The California historian, H. H. Bancroft, was also aware of the 1865 activity. In a private manuscript he emphasized that Mt. Hood was *"certainly"* in eruption from September 23 through October 8 of that year.[8] Although Bancroft dates the initial outburst two days after Dever witnessed lava fragments being hurled from the crater, he was nonetheless convinced of the reality of the explosion.

Plummer cites another eruption in 1869.[9] The fact that it is unsubstantiated does not necessarily mean that some minor activity did not occur, but no other written account of it seems to have survived. Except for the wreaths of "smoke" that frequently rise from Crater Rock to encircle the peak, the only 20th century incident involving a volcanic flareup is that witnessed by a camping party in August, 1907. A member of the U.S. Geological Survey, A. H. Sylvester, was bivouaced at Government Camp, five miles south of the summit, when he noticed increased clouds of steam rising from Steel Cliff, slightly east of Crater Rock. Later that day (the 28th) his companions saw a dense column of "smoke" or steam rise from Crater Rock and extend high above the mountain's summit. This emission of vapor lasted throughout the day.[10]

When night fell a member of the party, with the aid of field glasses, observed a glow from behind Crater Rock which he described as "looking like a chimney burning out." The next morning the White River, which originates from a glacier between Crater Rock and Steel Cliff, was suddenly swollen from a gentle stream to a rushing watercourse triple its previous volume. Since weather conditions could not account for the abrupt increase in the river's flow, Sylvester concluded that volcanic heat had partly melted the White Glacier.

The presence of fresh volcanic deposits at various locations on the mountain adds credibility to these 19th and 20th century reports. Not only has an ash eruption been scientifically dated at about 1800, but, if we are to believe a report in the *Geological News Letter*, even more recent ejecta have been found. According to this study, trees on the north side of Mt. Hood, near Cloud Cap Inn, have been charred by contact with hot pyroclastics. Cores taken from timber growing at Photographer's Rock, which forms a cliff in front of the old inn, reveal a series of closely spaced tree rings which formed about 150 years ago. Deefeldorfer's article states that ash and pumice lie three feet deep in the vicinity of the alleged vent, which is described as "choked" by accumulations of brick-red scoria. Older Mt. Hood lavas surrounding the supposed vent have been extensively shattered. A second and possibly younger opening is said to be located a few hundred yards downslope to the southwest. According to Deefeldorfer, the scoria from this vent "is very probably the youngest rock in Oregon.''[11] However, some geologists familiar with the Cloud Cap area seriously question the presence of a recently active vent there.[12]

Mt. Hood's Geologic History

Although Mt. Hood has long been one of the two most frequently climbed mountains in the world, its geology was little understood; until the past decade it has kept the secrets of its geologic peculiarities. One of the features of the volcano which especially puzzled the experts is the unexpectedly smooth southern slope, which heads at the craggy mass of Crater Rock. Another peculiarity which makes Mt. Hood seem unlike most other Cascade volcanoes is that it appears to be constructed largely of pyroclastic material. While Mt. Rainier, Mt. Jefferson, Mt. Adams, and the Sisters are built mainly of lava flows interbedded with infrequent layers of pyroclastics, Mt. Hood, especially on its smooth south side, seems to be made up primarily of pyroclastics. Except for the lava fields on the north flank below Cloud Cap Inn, there is little solid lava exposed anywhere.

Many theories have sought to explain Mt. Hood's unique features. One hypothesis held that the volcano poured liquid lava down its northern slope while it blew out only fragmental ejecta onto its opposite side.[13] Because it was obviously a lava plug filling an old conduit, Crater Rock was assumed to mark the original opening of the volcano. The bulky formations on either side of it (Steel Cliff and Hawkins Ridge) were thought to be remnants of the original crater walls. The steep summit cliff above Crater Rock was clearly the north rim. Because the southern side was made of loose material, it was conjectured that glaciers had pushed over the southern crater wall and the resultant debris was distributed downward to form the remarkably smooth south slope.[14]

A more elaborate theory held that about 2000 years ago Mt. Hood's crater was still intact and held a lake about 800 feet deep, similar to but larger than that now contained in the summit crater of the South Sister (see p. 128). Some time before 1700 years ago, as determined by radiocarbon dating from wood buried by the eruption, Mt. Hood exploded, shattering the southern crater wall and pouring immense volumes of water and melting ice onto the mountainside below.[15] The consequent avalanches and mudflows thus formed the smooth southern slope.

Interesting hypotheses like these were held until about 1965, when Dr. William S. Wise, professor of geology at the University of California at Santa Barbara, provided a more cogent explanation of Mt.

Hood's unusual aspects.[16] Dr. Wise's various reports on Mt. Hood's geologic history form the basis for much of which follows:

When the present Mt. Hood volcano began to erupt, perhaps relatively late in the Pleistocene, the surrounding Cascade topography was apparently very much as it is now. The average elevation in this area twenty miles south of the Columbia River is and was about 4500 feet, but individual peaks stood at least 2000 feet higher. The streams which now originate from Mt. Hood's glaciers—the Zigzag, Sandy, White, and Hood Rivers—were already present, although they then occupied V-shaped canyons. The Pleistocene glaciers were yet to remodel them into U-shaped valleys.

As Mt. Hood grew it gradually buried an ancestral volcano, which had built a sizable cone late in the Pliocene. Although much eroded, the older volcano had left a thick accumulation of olivine andesite lavas. Two of the ancestral flows—as much as 1000 feet thick—are now exposed on the northwest flank of Mt. Hood below the Sandy Glacier.[17]

During the first 10 years of its existence, the new volcano may have grown to a height of several thousand feet.[18] The early lavas flowed down ancient river canyons and some traveled as far as eight miles from their source. A few individual flows were 500 feet thick and half a cubic mile in volume.[19] These flows, the oldest eruptive products yet recognized on the mountain, now form several long ridges extending from the base of the cone. By the usual processes of erosion, the streams they displaced hundreds of thousands of years ago have since cut new canyons on either side of each flow, leaving them freestanding landforms. This "reversal of topography" occurs on nearly every Cascade volcano which has been subjected to long-term erosion.

After the first voluminous outpourings of lava had ceased, Mt. Hood's eruptions became less frequent and more explosive. Much of the upper 4000 feet of the cone is built of pyroclastics interbedded with relatively thin lava flows. About a third of the total mountain[20] is composed of loosely compacted fragmental material, which may explain why the mountain is now so deeply eroded. Among the large Cascade volcanoes only Mt. St. Helens is formed of a higher percentage of pyroclastics.

A few thick flows were erupted from vents at 8000 feet or above. Remnants of these form Barrett Spur and Steel Cliff. The latter, a massive outcrop east of Crater Rock, is so thick that it may have filled a high-lying glacial basin. Andesite flows typically exceed a depth of 50 feet only on gentle slopes (less than eight degrees) or when they are contained in canyons.

Expanding glaciers repeatedly sheathed the rising volcano, so that as hot rock was emitted onto icefields large mudflows poured into valleys heading on the mountain. Some mudflows left thick deposits near the volcano's base. Others may have emptied into the Columbia River, 20 miles distant.

At its zenith, Mt. Hood stood 12,000 feet high,[21] a full 8000 feet above its Cascade foundation. With a base spreading over 92 square miles, the cone attained a volume of 45 cubic miles.[22] No other volcano in Oregon, except Mt. Mazama far to the south, could match it in bulk or height. To the north, only Mt. Adams and Mt. Rainier were larger.

After Mt. Hood had reached its maximum size, eruptions apparently ceased at the summit crater. Two new vents opened on the north and northeast flanks of the mountain. From these poured the most extensive

Figure 12–3. Summit of Mt. Hood from the southeast. Crater Rock is visible at the extreme bottom left. Bare patches in the snow (center and bottom of photo) are sites of fumaroles and hot rocks from which steam and other gases continually escape. Note the climbing party skirting the open crevasse near the foot of the summit ridge. Steel Cliff at the extreme right. (Photo courtesy of the U.S. Forest Service.)

lava flows in the volcano's later history.[23] Some flows traveled 15 miles into the upper Hood River Valley. The plug of one satellite vent forms The Pinnacle, a sharp spire to which three flows can be traced. The second vent, near Cloud Cap Inn, has been covered by moraines from Eliot Glacier so that the actual source of the four 100-foot thick flows it produced cannot now be seen. As noted in the section on Mt. Hood's historic eruptions, some of Hood's latest volcanic activity is said to have occurred in this vicinity.

By the onset of the Fraser Glaciation, about 25,000 years ago, Mt. Hood may have been as symmetrical as is the present Mt. St. Helens. But during the last advance of Pleistocene glaciers the mountain formed the center of an icecap which almost completely covered the volcano and extended far down adjacent valleys, particularly on the north and east sides. The grinding ice removed a thousand feet from the sides and top of Mt. Hood, transforming it from a smooth cone into the four-faceted horn it is today.

A few lava masses resisted the glaciers and remain as outcrops on the mountain's flanks. Barrett Spur and Cooper Spur on Hood's north and east sides survive to demonstrate the relative hardness of some lava flows. If one traces a line from the top of either of these ridges toward the summit one can visualize how much of the pre-Fraser cone has vanished.

Glaciers scoured the peak so thoroughly that they exposed the original eruptive conduit, now a column of solidified lava. Recent investigations suggest that Mt. Hood's primary crater was located to the *north* of the present summit ridge (in what is now thin air), rather than at the site of Crater Rock as had been formerly supposed.[24] Unfortunately the conduit plug is virtually inaccessible among the precipices and ice-falls of the north summit face.

At the close of the Fraser period, the glaciers retreated to their present high altitudes, where they continue to carve cirques into the mountainside. Mt. Hood's 11 glaciers remain effective eroding agents, each year removing countless tons of material from the ever-diminishing cone.

Solution to the "Problem of the South Slope"

Until about 2000 years ago the south flanks of the mountain, though perhaps to a lesser extent, shared the craggy, ice-scarred contours of the other two sides. It was then that the old volcano reawakened and produced those unusual features which for so long baffled the experts. After a sleep of many centuries, Mt. Hood blasted out a new crater high on the south side, at about the 10,000-foot level. Lava again welled up into the opening, but it was too pasty to flow out in coherent streams, as had the earlier andesite lava. Instead it oozed out to form a large plug dome, similar in structure to that of Lassen Peak. Pushing through accumulations of snow and ice, the rising dome shattered and crumbled, producing hot avalanches of angular boulders up to 20 feet in diameter. Mixing with melted snow and the ash blown out by accompanying explosions, the semi-molten fragments generated numerous mudflows which swept down the mountainside and engulfed an ancient forest.

Apparently the lava plug continued to grow over a period of several hundred years, sending wave after wave of debris downslope. Eventually the entire south and southwest side of the mountain was buried under the recurring mudflows. The volume of new lava erupted totaled at least three-fourths of a cubic mile, an amount that compares favorably with the copious lava flows of the volcano's youth. Then, as the supply of underlying magma diminished and gas pressure continued to mount, repeated explosions undermined and further shattered the extruded dome. The plug was reduced to a quarter of its maximum height of 1000 feet. Finally, as the eruptions gradually ceased, erosion removed all loose material, leaving the solid core of hornblende andesite which we know as Crater Rock. The hornblende-bearing rocks in Steel Cliff and other nearby ridges were probably also formed during this cycle of activity.[25]

Continued gas pressure produced occasional explosions of ash for several centuries more. These late eruptions contributed to the demolition of the plug dome by blasting a trench around it. The most extensive of the recent eruptions, that of about 1800, added a layer of ash more than six inches thick to the upper cone. The observed explosions in 1846 (?), 1859, and 1865, apparently left only minor ash and/or cinder deposits, since buried in snow or borne away by meltwater.

Indian Lore

A discussion of Mt. Hood would be incomplete without some notice given to the wealth of Indian legends it inspired. The most famous of these, the "Bridge of the Gods" myth, belongs to the chapter on Mt. St. Helens (see Chapter 14), but the one accounting for the supposed "Chief's Face" to be viewed amid the crags and shadows on Mt. Hood's north side is equally significant and more poignant. Both legends illustrate that the peak, which now seems benign in its airy lightness, was in former times the incarnation of divine anger and the realm of spirits hostile to man.

According to a popular version of the Chief's story, Mt. Hood once towered so high that when the sun shone on its south side a shadow stretched north for a day's journey. It was majestic but also fearsome, for inside dwelt demonic spirits who sent forth streams of liquid fire to destroy the Indians' homes. One night a particularly brave chief had a vision. A voice told him that if he were to save his tribe he must conquer the evil forces that inhabited the mountain, lest they totally annihilate his people. Accordingly, the courageous warrior climbed to the top of the mountain where he found a gaping hole from which issued fire and smoke. Hurling bolders into the opening in the hopes of killing the evil spirits who lived below, the chief was horrified when they were thrown back, heated red-hot. For many days the chief and the fire-monsters kept up the stone-throwing contest. Then, during a respite in the battle, the Chief looked downward to the land he had left. His heart cracked in grief: the once-fertile valleys were desolate, choked with lava and ash. The rivers had dried up, the forest burned, and the people and animals fled. The chief's courage forsook him and he sank to earth, to be buried by fresh streams of liquid rock. Today his sorrowful profile, with its distinctive scalp lock, can be seen halfway down the north side of the mountain.

Although some of the chief's people had taken refuge on hills above the devastated valleys and thus survived, the stricken land offered so poor a living that their children never attained the parents' former stature. Thus the Indians must remain small people until another brave leader comes who can overpower the evil spirits who remain hidden within the volcano.[26]

How to See Mt. Hood

Driving the Mt. Hood loop provides some excellent views of the peak and its fellow Guardians of the Columbia, Mt. St. Helens and Adams. Highway 26, through Sandy, enters the Hood National Forest at Zigzag. Much of the west side of this highway parallels the old Barlow Road, the first to cross the Oregon Cascades. Near Government Camp, named for the contingent of U.S. Army Rifles who wintered here in 1849, take the road to Timberline Lodge, which affords a direct view of Crater Rock, Steel Cliff, and the recent debris fan. Only experienced climbers should attempt the summit, but snow-cats regularly transport sightseers to the 8000-9000 foot level.

To see the north side of the mountain, return to Highway 26, turn off on Highway 35 (toward Hood River), and take a side trip to Cloud Cap Saddle, location of rustic Cloud Cap Inn, the oldest building on the mountain. A short hike up from this 6000 foot elevation are viewpoints of Eliot Glacier, the second largest in Oregon. Looking northward across the Columbia River bluffs toward the Washington Cascades there is an incomparable panorama that includes St. Helens, Adams and Rainier (102 miles distant).

Return

Return to 35 and Hood River, where you take the Columbia River Highway back to Portland and Interstate 5. Include a stop at Cascade Locks where the legendary Bridge of the Gods once spanned the Columbia rapids. On the trip back, Multnomah Falls and Crown Point State Park are worth a special stop.

Chapter 12—References

1. *Phillips, 1935, pp. 44-46; Ayeres and Creswell, 1951, pp. 33-39.*
2. *Lawrence, 1948, pp. 22-23.*
3. *Parker, 1846, p. 337.*
4. *Holden, 1898.*
5. *Steel, 1907b, p. 135.*
6. *Ibid., p. 136.*
7. *Steel, 1906, p. 23.*
8. *Holden, 1898.*
9. *Ibid., p. 26.*
10. *Sylvester, 1908, pp. 524-25.*
11. *Deefeldorfer, 1967, p. 69.*
12. *Crandell and Wise, written comm., 1973.*
13. *Wise, 1964a, p. 17.*
14. *Ibid., p. 21.*
15. *Lawrence and Lawrence, 1959, pp. 11-12.*
16. *Wise, 1966; 1968; 1969.*
17. *Wise, 1964a, p. 13; 1969, pp. 993-94.*
18. *Wise, 1964a, p. 15.*
19. *Wise, 1968, p. 81.*
20. *Wise, 1969, p. 993.*
21. *Wise, 1966, p. 17; 1968, p. 81.*
22. *Wise, 1969, p. 993.*
23. *Wise, 1964a, p. 19.*
24. *Wise, 1968, pp. 85, 92.*
25. *Wise, 1966; 1968.*
26. *Clark, 1966, pp. 15-16.*

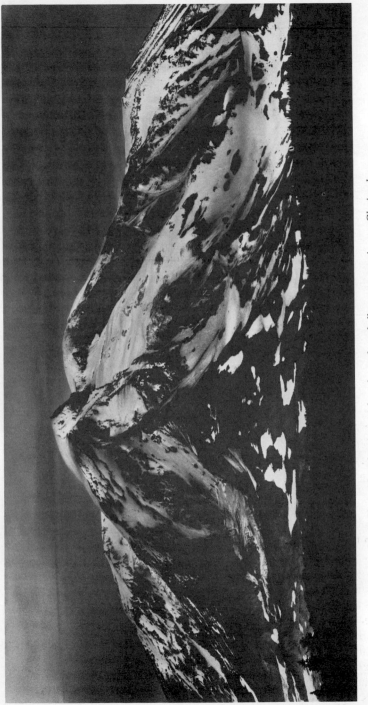

Figure 13-1. Mt. Adams' rugged southwest face challenges mountaineers. Glaciers have eroded Adams' elongated cone into complex cliffs and cirques. (Telephoto by Ed Cooper.)

13
Mt. Adams—The Forgotten Giant Of Washington

Mt. Adams is the second highest peak in the Pacific Northwest, its 12,286 feet exceeded only by Mt. Rainier. Unlike its much younger neighbor, Mt. St. Helens, which rises above a gently rolling mountainscape 40 miles to the west, Adams is surrounded by a rocky labyrinth of jagged ridges, deep glacier-cut valleys, and barren lava wastes. It is old, weather-beaten, and asymmetrical.

Instead of tapering gracefully to a sharp point like Mt. Jefferson, or sweeping grandly to a truncated summit like Rainier, Adams is broad, massive and squat (Figure 13-1). Its almost flat summit robs the mountain of the soaring quality which characterizes St. Helens and Hood. A critical hiker once described Adams as "unimaginatively designed." Despite its aesthetic failings, Adams' vast size lends the peak an impressive dignity. Its very lack of regularity may indicate a volcanic history more complex and interesting than that of its more symmetrical companions.

Rather than a single cone, Adams appears to be a group of several superimposed cones all leaning one upon the other. When viewed from the southwest, Adams is revealed as a long humped ridge with a north-south-trending axis (Figure 13-2). Its heavily glaciated slopes are irregularly eroded into deep gullies separated by high cleavers. On the east side the Klickitat Glacier has carved an enormous amphitheatre deep into the volcano's side. Two large ice streams descending from the summit ice fields feed this unusually destructive glacier, whose mile-wide cirque is the second largest of any active glacier in the Cascade Range. Only that of the Carbon Glacier on the north flank of Mt. Rainier is larger.

Rising over a thousand feet above the floor of Hellroaring Canyon, the fittingly named Ridge of Wonders on Adams' southeast slope affords breathtaking views of the Mazama and Klickitat Glaciers. No trails lead to this rugged highland, but hikers who venture there are rewarded by an incomparable view of the mountain's precipitous eastern cliffs, lava dikes, icefalls and crumbling piles of volcanic rock. Avalanches of ice, snow and rock frequently thunder down the volcano's steep eastern face.

As a result of its isolated position relatively far from towns or cities, Mt. Adams has not been "developed" as a tourist mecca as have its more famous neighbors. Accessible only by unpaved logging or Forest Service roads, Adams' flower-strewn meadows and mossy parklands retain much of their pristine beauty. Only overgrazing by sheep and cattle not properly supervised by the Forest Service, threatens to spoil the Elysian Fields that surround this rugged peak. On the debit side, this general neglect of the mountain means that its geology is little understood. No thorough study of its eruptive and erosional history has yet been published. We do not know when Adams began to build its massive structure or when it last erupted. Unlike some other Cascade volcanoes, Adams has no record of an historic eruption. Steam and other gases still issue in small quantities from summit crevices, however, and the crater is heavily laden with sulphur and alum deposits.

Indian Legends and Early History

According to the Columbia River Indians, Mt. Adams was one of three mountains that smoked continuously, the others being Hood and St. Helens.[1] Like his brother mountain, Wyeast (Hood) across the Great River, Adams (Pahto or Paddo) was the son of the Great Spirit. Like Wyeast he also courted the fair St. Helens (La-wa-la-clough), the damsel of the trio. When St. Helens preferred Adams to Hood, the latter struck his northern brother so mighty a blow that his head was utterly flattened. This fraternal battle, lost by Adams, explains the somewhat ungainly and bulbous appearance of the volcano. Intimidated by his pugnacious brother, Adams never again dared lift his head in its former dignity and pride.

The story of how Mt. Adams received its rechristening by white men is only slightly less fantastic than the Indian legends about its allegedly romantic past. Although Lewis and Clark sighted the peak as early as 1805, they mistook it for St. Helens and consequently made no attempt to bestow an appropriate name upon what they took to be "the highest pinnacle in America." Since Vancouver had not seen the mountain, it escaped the fate of its more westerly fellows and did not already bear the name of yet another 18th century British diplomat. In the period 1830–1834 Hall J. Kelley, an enthusiastic American patriot, led a movement to call the Cascades the "Presidents' Range." All the major peaks were to bear the last names of former U.S. presidents. Oregon's Three Sisters and California's Shasta were to be Madison and Jackson, while Hood and St.

Helens were to be renamed Adams and Washington. Adams, apparently unknown to Kelley, was not included in his plan.

Implementing Kelley's project, one Thomas J. Farnham, working only from inadequate maps, inadvertently interchanged the Kelley names for Hood and St. Helens. Inexplicably, Farnham made a major error in latitude and placed "Adams" on his map a fully 40 miles east of St. Helens and north of Hood. As mountaineer Ray Smutek recently commented, "In what has to be one of geography's greatest coincidences, there was a mountain there to accept the name."[2] Ironically, Adams was the only name in the Kelley-Farnham scheme that took, and it was applied to a mountain whose existence they never suspected.

The Summit Sulphur Fields

In the 1930s Mt. Adams acquired the dubious distinction of becoming the only high Cascade volcano to have its crater invaded by commercial speculators. It is paradoxical that Adams, one of the most solitary of major peaks, should first attract not for scenic but for industrial reasons. The extensive sulphur fields atop the volcano proved irresistible to the spirt of American enterprise. In 1929, a businessman from the Columbia River village of White Salmon filed mineral claims covering the 210-acre summit plateau. A trail suitable for horses and mules was constructed on the relatively easy south slope and a diamond core drilling machine was laboriously hauled to the crater. In 1932, when active mining at the summit began, hundreds of pack-train trips were made up and down the mountain. By 1959, when the last assessment work was done, the cost of getting the sulphur down off the mountain became prohibitive and the mines were abandoned.

Although hydrogen sulphide gas issues from several other Cascade vents, such as Hood and Rainier, sulphur fields comparable to those on Mt. Adams were not formed. In investigating the causes of Adams' unique sulphur deposits, Fowler concluded that as the sulphide gas rose from deep within the mountain it was forced to pass through the loose collections of cinders and ash that filled the bottom of Adams' crater. As it did so, free sulphur was deposited in the highly porous rocks. The chilling effect of Adams' summit ice cap, 210 feet thick, also helped in the rapid deposition of sulphur amid gaps in the loosely compacted summit rocks. Eventually not only the crater floor but large areas outside the crater rim became impregnated with the mineral.[3]

By similar processes, alum and gypsum deposits 20 to 30 feet thick were formed high on the mountain. In shades of red, green, purple, and white, the multi-colored gypsum contrasts brilliantly to the prevailing dark grays and blacks of Adams' lavas.

The Geologic Story

So little has Mt. Adams been studied that most of its past remains a mystery. In general, the lava fields that surround the volcano, with their fresh-looking crusts and extensive tubes, caves, and tree-casts, appear much more youthful than most of those near Mt. Hood, but from the severe erosion that the peak has undergone it is clear that the main cone was built long before the last major glaciation. Like Baker and Rainier, it is composed chiefly of andesitic lava flows with relatively few pyroclastic deposits.

In one of the rare items published on Adams' eruptive history, Kenneth Hopkins briefly summarized some of the late events on the mountain's south slope. The relatively little eroded south side of the volcano, that by which most ascents are made, is the only part of the cone not covered by glaciers. Suksdorf Ridge, a prominent buttress extending southward from near the summit to about the 8000-foot level, is the outstanding feature of the southern flank. Hopkins' investigation of the ridge showed it to be the site of repeated eruptions during late Pleistocene time. The ridge, he found, is composed of andesite lava flows which poured from fissures located at an altitude of about 9500 feet. Some of these andesite flows extended downslope for approximately eight miles, where they interfingered with streams of olivine basalt simultaneously being erupted from peripheral vents near the base of the mountain.[4]

Judging by their relation to the main cone, these Suksdorf flows began only after Adams had probably attained its maximum height. It is possible, however, that the summit cinder cone may have been built in post-glacial time. Most of the Suksdorf lavas, as well of the associated basalts, are now overlain by glacial till from the Fraser Glaciation, indicating that they were emitted at least ten and possibly more than 20,000 years ago.[5]

Mt. Adams continued to erupt lava from various points along its flanks even after the Pleistocene glaciers had permanently disappeared. Hopkins' 1969 report notes that some lava flows, with rough comparatively unweathered surfaces, appear not to have been glaciated at all. Young flows of this kind occur on the south, east, north and northwest slopes of the volcano. The most recent eruption of lava from Mt. Adams seems to be a narrow four and a half mile-long blocky flow which was extruded from the vicinity of South Butte. The oldest trees on this flow began growing about 300 years ago. Granting sufficient time for enough soil to accumulate on the lava's blocky, inhospitable surface, Hopkins estimates that this stream can be no more than 1000 or 2000 years old.[6] If soil formed on the lava surface in a matter of decades after its emplacement, this south-side flow may be considerably younger.

In addition to flank eruptions of recent lava, Mt. Adams is distinguished by numerous parasitic cinder cones, vents, and "blow-holes" that encircle its base. Although some of these satellite cones appear to have been overridden by Pleistocene glaciers and reduced to rubble, others look surprisingly fresh. Little Mt. Adams is an uneroded cinder cone perched atop the Ridge of Wonders on Adams' southeast side. Its circular crater of reddish scoria is perfectly preserved. From a distance, the seemingly vertical crater walls resemble an ancient Roman stadium. On Adams' north side, Potato Hill, which rises about 800 feet above the lava plain, is another strikingly symmetrical cone. Except for Mazama and Shasta, few other Cascade peaks have so many parasitic volcanoes dotting their flanks.

The extreme broadness and flatness of Mt. Adams' summit is apparently not due to the collapse of a once higher peak. Hopkins has looked for, but not found, evidence of summit collapse such as occurred

Figure 13–2. In this aerial view, Mt. Adams' smooth south slope (left) contrasts with the eroded east (right) side. Note the icefalls spilling from the summit glacier into the canyons carved into the volcano's east flank. Part of the west side of the summit cinder cone (formation left of summit icecap) seems to have slid down the mountain's steep western face. The Mazama Glacier occupies the left center foreground; right center is the Klickitat Glacier and beyond it the Rusk. Mt. Rainier stands about 50 miles to the north. (Photo by Delano Photographics.)

at Mt. Rainier (Chapter 15). The abnormal breadth of Adams' top apparently results from the fact that the mountain is actually a complex of overlapping cones. Instead of building a towering pile around a single central conduit, as Rainier and Hood appear to have done, Adams seems to have erupted—at different and widely spaced intervals—from several principal vents along a major north-northwesterly trending fissure.[7]

Supporting the thesis that Adams is constructed of several interrelated cones is the fact that the mountain has not one but several recognizable summits. At the 11,500 foot level the long south slope terminates in a false summit, known to climbers as "Piker's Peak." This may represent the top of one major cone. From this summit to the foot of the last is a plain nearly a half mile across. The topmost cone is steep, with slopes of about 35 degrees. Judging from photographs of this summit formation it is a small pyroclastic cone standing above the summit plateau. Its snow-filled crater appears to have been breached on the west side, as if part of the crater wall had slid down the steep western face of the mountain. Since Fowler discovered that the summit rocks are composed of ash and other fragmental material—indicating that explosive action completed the final stages of cone-building—it may be that late explosions caused the collapse and avalanching of part of the summit area.[8]

In this respect it should be remembered that the largest avalanche in the recorded history of Mt. Adams—the Great Slide of 1921—originated on the west side at about 1000 feet below the summit. On that occasion an enormous mass of rock and ice fell a vertical mile to inundate 6000 acres of the western slope. This slide may have been only the latest in a series of rockfalls that undermined the west face of the summit cone. Judging by the fact that active steam jets were discovered near the source of the avalanche three years after the event, it is possible that the rockfall was precipitated by a small steam explosion similar to that which presumably caused the 1963 rockfalls on Little Tahoma (Chapter 15).

Present Thermal Activity

Mt. Adams is a dormant volcano, with no record of an historic eruption, but it is not yet dead. The presence of heat deep within the mountain is indicated by the steam and hydrogen sulphide gas which still issue from crevices within and around the crater. Such emissions, however, appear to be diminishing. Fowler found steam issuing from only one place, a fumarole on the south crater wall, but he observed that hydrogen sulphide rose from every fissure bounding the crater. At times the odor of sulphur was strong enough to be detected as far as six miles from the mountain top. Many climbers since then have reported being nauseated by the strong odor of sulphur.

In 1924 Judge Fred W. Stadler observed "a group of steam vents west of the summit and less than 1000 feet below it, in a canyon to the south of the so-called west summit and above White Salmon Glacier."[9] Probably because this area is difficult to reach and off the main climbing routes, these steam jets have not been reported since. When Phillips explored the summit he could find no steam emission, but did discover a small vent about one quarter mile north of the summit in the center of a large snowfield. This fumarole felt "slightly warm" and had a recorded temperature of 38 degrees Centigrade, (100.4° Fahrenheit) the lowest temperature his thermometer could register.[10]

When Moxham conducted an infrared survey from an airplane over Mt. Adams, he could detect no evidence of abnormal temperatures. He concluded that either the previously reported fumaroles had disappeared or were of too low temperature to be detected by infrared process.[11] Thermal activity on this ancient volcano thus seems to be waning.

The Goat Rocks Wilderness

A few miles directly north of Mt. Adams, along the serrated crest of the Washington Cascades, lie the deeply eroded remains of a much older stratovolcano. This cluster of ridges and sheer cliffs—appropriately named Goat Rocks after the bands of mountain goats which ramble over its precipices—offers a stunning example of what all the lofty Cascade volcanoes may one day become were they never to erupt again. For the Goat Rocks volcano was once a towering peak which closely resembled the present large volcanoes of Washington in height, form, and rock type.[12]

The Goat Rocks mountain goes back much further in time than any of the Cascade peaks which still retain their conical forms. Goat Rocks volcanism began with a major Cascade uplift—during the Miocene Epoch, perhaps 15,000,000 years ago—and continued through the Pliocene into early Pleistocene time, when it finally ceased. The Goat Rocks volcano has thus been extinct for as long as 2,000,000 years, which left it vulnerable to the destructive forces of glacial erosion. The highest present elevation in the Goat Rocks Wilderness, a federally protected area 18 miles long and 12 miles wide, is 8201-foot Mt. Curtis Gilbert. Geologically speaking, the most interesting part of Goat Rocks is Black Thumb. This broken ridge, 1.5 miles long and half a mile across, has been eroded from the central plug or conduit filling of the original cone.[13]

Judging from the thick accumulations of fragmental material under-lying the Rocks, the volcano—in its prime—was extraordinarily explosive. Bedded pyroclastics 2200 feet thick are now exposed beneath the ridge from Tieton Peak to Bear Creek Mountain. These deposits, called the Devil's Horn pyroclastics, are nearly horizontal layers of pyroxene andesite tuff and represent products from the initial explosive eruptions of the volcano. Water-laid strata are interspersed between massive beds of white rhyolitic tuff, the latter of which contains abundant examples of carbonized wood. According to Ellingson, the Goat Rocks volcano was probably responsible for most of the andesitic debris of the middle part of the Ellensburg Formation near the town of Yakima.

When looking out over the ruined foundations of a mountain that once stood perhaps as high as St. Helens or Hood, it is tempting to reconstruct the vanished majesty of that peak in the mind's eye. At the same time, it is sobering to reflect that this prehistoric colossus was brought to its present state, not by some spectacular explosion or collapse, but by the inexorable forces of erosion that even now work to level the younger Cascade counterparts we see today.

Exploring Mt. Adams

No paved roads reach Mt. Adams, but narrow, rutted dirt roads take one as far as timberline. Drive to Trout Lake either from Randle via the Trout Lake-Randle road (123-N84) or from Vancouver, Washington, via Highway 14 along the north bank of the Columbia River. From Trout Lake drive north, turning off the surfaced highway in about 1½ miles onto road N80. Timberline is 12.8 miles, but a more scenic goal (not decimated by overgrazing sheep) is Bird Creek Meadows, crossed by numerous rivulets and carpeted with a profusion of alpine flowers. Turn off N80 toward Bird Creek Meadow Picnic Area about 1.1 miles beyond Mirror Lake and Mirror Lake Campground.

Although there are no beaten paths, the hiker can find his way eastward to Little Mt. Adams, Hellroaring Canyon, and the Ridge of Wonders with spectacular views of the Mazama Glacier. For more information on hiking routes, see *102 Hikes in the Alpine Lakes, South Cascades, and Olympics*, published by The Mountaineers.

Chapter 13—References

1. *Gibbs, 1855.*
2. *Smutek, 1972.*
3. *Fowler, 1936.*
4. *Hopkins, 1969.*
5. *Ibid.*
6. *Hopkins, written comm. 1973.*
7. *Ibid.*
8. *Fowler, 1936.*
9. *In Phillips, 1941, p. 42.*
10. *Phillips, 1941.*
11. *Moxham, 1970.*
12. *Ellingson, 1969, p. 15.*
13. *Ibid.*

14
Mt. St. Helens—The Northwest's Most Violent Volcano

Because of its almost perfectly symmetrical cone, graceful Mt. St. Helens (9,677 feet) has long been known as the Fujiyama of America. In the early spring of 1980, however, it acquired a new distinction: the only currently active volcano in the 48 contiguous states.

Beginning on March 20 a swarm of earthquakes, some registering as high as 4.8 on the Richter scale, shook the mountain, alerting geologists to the possibility of an eruption. Only a week after the seismic activity began, an explosion — the first since 1857 — tore through the ice-filled summit crater and expelled a cloud of steam and fine powdery ash, derived from pulverized rock in the old plug that sealed the volcano's central conduit. Described by some scientists as "a volcano in a hurry," St. Helens produced a rapid-fire series of increasingly violent detonations that took only a few days to enlarge the original vent into a gaping crater more than 1700 feet across and 500 feet deep. Explosive eruptions were frequent, some lasting over an hour and ejecting columns of black ash 11,000 feet above the mountaintop.

Officials from the U.S. Forest Service, Geological Survey, and numerous universities flocked to southwest Washington to observe, measure, and interpret the phenomenon. Residents of Spirit Lake at St. Helens' northern foot and at various logging settlements within a 12-mile radius of the mountain were evacuated, their household goods later removed in a caravan of moving vans. With hundreds of tourists swarming into the area, complicating the problem of public safety, Governor Dixy Lee Ray declared a state of emergency. The National Guard was summoned to control traffic and maintain order.

Earthquakes continued to jar the volcano, sending avalanches of rock and ice tumbling downslope and opening large crevasses on the five glaciers mantling the upper cone. By April 2-4, harmonic tremors — rhythmic undulations which differ from the usual sharp jolt of most quakes but which are characteristic of erupting volcanoes — were de-

Figure 14–1. Mt. St. Helens during a steam and ash eruption in April, 1980. Note the ash dropping from the steam clouds. A growing crater between the false and true summits altered the traditional cone shape of the mountain during these eruptions. (Photo by Charlotte Casey.)

tected, apparently indicating that fresh magma, molten rock moving underground, was approaching the surface. Charcoal gray ash not only shot skyward but rolled in thick waves down St. Helens' once glistening white slopes, transforming them to a sinister black. Winds swept the ash as far northeast as Spokane, 300 miles away.

Because St. Helens is geologically very young — its entire visible cone probably having been constructed during the last millennium — geologists were not entirely caught off guard by its sudden reawakening.

Studies of deposits laid down by past eruptions suggested that it was certain to erupt again, possibly before the end of this century.[1] A voluminous eruption of tephra, consisting mostly of pumice lapilli and extending many miles northeastward from the cone (layer T) occurred about 1800.[2]

Indian legends, as well as the geologic evidence, reflect the immediacy of St. Helens' fiery past. Of particular interest is the "Bridge of the Gods" story, in which the three guardian peaks of the Columbia, Hood, Adams, and St. Helens, play leading roles. The Klickitat Indians, who recognized St. Helens' volcanic nature in their name for her — Tah-one-lat-clah ("Fire Mountain"), have a popular version of the legend. According to their tale, a mighty natural bridge of stone once spanned the Columbia River near the present town of Cascade Locks. Territory north and south of the bridge was ruled, respectively, by Pahto and Wyeast, supernaturally powerful braves who were sons of the Great Spirit. Unfortunately for the continuing peace of the region, both young chiefs fell in love with a beautiful but indecisive maiden who could not make up her mind which of the two heroes she preferred. The maiden, incidentally, had once been an ugly old hag whom the Great Spirit had miraculously transformed into a white-clad virgin of incomparable loveliness. Competing for the recently metamorphosed beauty, Pahto and Wyeast waged war with catastrophic results. Hurling fire and hot rocks at each other across the river, they devastated the countryside and made the very earth tremble. Convulsive shocks caused the sacred "Bridge of the Gods" to collapse into the Columbia River Gorge, so angering the Great Spirit that he changed his querulous sons into the two "Masculine" Guardians of the Columbia. Wyeast became Mt. Hood, Pahto became Mt. Adams, while the feminine cause of the cataclysmic battle became lovely Mt. St. Helens.[3]

The legend's reference to St. Helens' miraculous transformation from a dark and ugly form into one of snowy beauty may possibly reflect tribal memories of a time when the volcano was too low in elevation to maintain a permanent snow cap. Too recent to be forested or to have its contours smoothed by snowfields, it then may have resembled a slag heap of black lava. The relatively sudden growth of the summit cone and the simultaneous covering of previously irregular slopes with fields of pumice would have considerably improved the mountain's appearance. After reaching a certain height, St. Helens could support a year-round blanket of snow, thus qualifying it as a fitting symbol of the irresistible Indian maid. It should be noted, of course, that the massive landslide, which apparently gave rise to the Bridge of the Gods legend, was not simultaneous with the emplacement of St. Helens' summit. In looking for humanly understandable reasons for the volcanic "conflict" between Adams and

Hood, with the presumably resultant earthquake that caused the rockfalls which produced the Columbia Cascades, the Klickitat legend conflated and perhaps reversed time sequences to give the tale a psychologically attractive cause-and-effect relationship.

The Geologic Story

Youthful as it is, Mt. St. Helens has a complex history. The modern cone stands atop and partially conceals the eroded remnants of an older volcano which, judging by the amount of debris it scattered for miles over the countryside, was one of the most explosive peaks in the Pacific Northwest. The oldest recognized products of this ancestral cone are a pumice layer dated at 37,600 years and a weathered mudflow deposit about 36,000 years in age.[4] Glacial sediments containing fragments of the earlier mountain are between 18,000 and 14,000 years old[5] and reveal that St. Helens experienced at least one episode of glaciation. The chief difference in the make-up of these two superimposed cones is the chemical composition of their lavas. The earlier vent consistently erupted a characteristic variety of dacite and andesite until about 2500 years ago. Then the lava content rather abruptly changed to olivine basalt, dacite, and pyroxene andesite[6] of which the present St. Helens is mostly built.

Although now almost buried beneath the recent cone, the ancestral St. Helens has left impressive evidence of its past energy (Figure 14-6). Conspicuous blankets of pumiceous ash extend for hundreds of miles from the volcano; valleys heading on the cone are filled with thick accumulations of explosion rubble. A recent detailed study of the Pine Creek valley on the southeast side of Mt. St. Helens revealed that during the past 18,000 years the volcano has repeatedly erupted glowing avalanches of hot gas and pyroclastic debris, explosion-shattered rock fragments, as well as widespread showers of air-borne pumice.[7]

Perhaps the most extensive and best studied of these airfall pumice deposits is that called Y. Rather than the product of a single outburst, the "Y set" represents at least 10 separate eruptions, two of which covered thousands of square miles with a distinctive ash.[8] The winds carried one ash cloud to the northeast, where it mantled the site of Mt. Rainier National Park, 50 miles distant, with yellowish brown pumice up to 18 inches in depth.[9] Traces of this ash have been recognized as far northeast as Banff Park in Alberta, Canada.[10] Another ash lobe extends southeast from Mt. St. Helens and is found at least as far away as eastern Oregon.[11] The Y pumice as a whole was erupted between 4000 and 3000 years ago, but the two most extensive layers are closely bracketed by radiocarbon dates of 3500 and 3350 years.[12] The total volume of material blown out during the Y producing eruptions may have approximated 2.5 cubic miles.[13]

In addition to countless eruptions of air-borne material between about 18,000 and 2500 years ago, the ancestral St. Helens was also characterized by the emission of glowing avalanches. These incandescent debris flows, sometimes accompanied by voluminous ash clouds, repeatedly swept down the flanks of the volcano and left thick fills in the adjacent valleys. The avalanches, which were apparently erupted at temperatures ranging from 300 to 500 degrees Centigrade, consisted of both frothy pumice and solid rock fragments. The dense rock debris may have been derived from viscous domes and spines which were shattered by explosion as they were being elevated.[14] The ancestral Mt. St. Helens may have been composed primarily of dacite domes which intruded a collection of cones built of fragmental material. If, late in its development, the old St. Helens was a single cone with a central dome, it probably had a crater open to the southeast which discharged into an "avalanche valley" at the head of Pine Creek.[15]

Until about 2000 years ago lava flows seem to have played a relatively minor part in St. Helens' development, but mudflows probably occurred intermittently throughout the volcano's existence. During the past few thousand years several particularly voluminous mudflows streamed many miles down valleys west and south of the volcano. Between 2500 and 3000 years ago one large mudflow inundated the Lewis River valley for a distance of at least 40 miles. About 2000 years ago similar mudflows traveled as far as 30 miles down the Toutle and Kalama River valleys. According to Hyde some may have reached the Columbia River![16]

Building the "New" St. Helens

The graceful form of Mt. St. Helens thus rises above a thick accumulation of avalanche debris, explosion rubble, and mudflow deposits erupted by its predecessor. (The older vent, in turn, lies upon a gently folded plateau of Tertiary sandstone, mudstones, and ancient volcanic rocks.) Some time after the first century A.D., the nature of St. Helens' eruptions changed radically. About 1900 years ago fluid streams of pahoehoe lava flowed down the south flank of the mountain and cascaded into the Lewis and Kalama River valleys. Some moved as far as eight or nine miles from their source.[17] The best known of these smooth, ropy flows is the Cave Basalt which filled a stream valley cut into earlier pyroclastic deposits.[18] Named for the elaborate system of passageways, chambers, and tunnels which honeycomb its interior, the Cave Basalt is a favorite haunt of Washington state spelunkers.

The "new" St. Helens also grew through the extrusion of at least two large dacite domes and the production of glowing avalanches similar to those erupted by the ancestral volcano. During the past 600 years "hurricanes'' of incandescent debris repeatedly raced down the volcano's slopes and moved down valleys within a 10-mile radius of the cone.[19] Some were accompanied by searing clouds of gas and fine ash. About 500 years ago this eruptive cycle culminated in a series of rough, aa flows of olivine basalt.[20]

Explosive activity reached a climax about 450 years ago when immense quantities of pumice and fine ash were blown high into the air. This airfall pumice, which forms a whitish layer (called W) and is several inches thick many miles northeast of the volcano, was the most extensive since the Y ash erupted more than 3000 years earlier. These pyrotechnics heralded the rise of the present summit dome. Lava oozed from the newly cleared central vent and gradually a dacite mass, hundreds of feet high, grew atop the volcano. Crumbling debris from the growing dome avalanched down the mountain's slopes and buried the sites of earlier flank eruptions. Today talus from the summit plug so completely mantles the upper cone that outcrops of solid rock above 6000 feet are rare.[21]

Low-temperature explosions opened a new crater at the top of the dome. Several of these outbursts were laterally directed and blasted out a V-shaped notch in the southeast crater wall. The force of these blasts may have aided in excavating the narrow ravine which extends down the east slope of the cone and ends in a chaotic fan of broken fragments torn from the crater rim.[22] The Shoestring Glacier presently descends from the crater ice fields through this gash in the mountain. As the summit dome rose into position, glowing avalanches again rushed down all sides of the volcano, followed by flows of andesite which emerged from fissures along the lower slopes. No lava streams appear to have issued from the summit crater itself.

Some of the late flank eruptions of lava were also preceded by avalanches of pyroclastic material.[23] These *may* have contributed to the mudflows which reportedly helped to dam the Toutle River and enlarge Spirit Lake. According to Lawrence and Lawrence, the last significant rise in the lake level apparently took place shortly before A.D. 1550. After this episode of intense volcanism, St. Helens seems to have been relatively quiescent. Although more eruptions probably occurred—Indian legends suggest that the mountain was ''smoking'' continuously—they were perhaps relatively minor compared to those of the 16th century. Judging by timber growth on the north side of the volcano, there was not another exceptionally heavy fall of pumice until about 1800.[24]

Near the turn of the last century a new vent was blown open high on the northwest slope of the volcano.[25] Large volumes of pumice were discharged and fell to a depth of eight to 12 feet on the mountain's northern slope (Figure 14-6). Winds, again blowing toward the northeast, carried ash an astonishing distance from the crater. Known as layer T, the 1800 St. Helens ashfall extended along a northeasterly axis for hundreds of miles over central and eastern Washington, northern Idaho, and western Montana.[26] Since samples of layer T have been found near the Canadian border, it seems probable that ash drifted over both British Columbia and Alberta, as had the northeasterly lobe of layer Y more than 3000 years before.

After the initial explosions of pumice lapilli, a dacite dome rose to fill the eruptive vent. Following this activity, fissures opened lower down on the volcano's northwest and south flanks. From these peripheral vents streams of andesite issued.[27] According to Verhoogen and Lawrence one such blocky stream then emerged from beneath the Toutle Glacier at the 6000-foot level. This rough flow is distinguished by several isolated groves of trees which stand like green oases on its otherwise arid surface. Because he thought that the flow carried a load of fertile glacial sediments on its back when it issued from under the glacier, Lawrence dubbed it the "Floating Island" lava flow. Recent investigations, however, indicate that the patches of "soil" atop the lava crust were formed when small hot avalanches were spasmodically discharged from above onto the flowing lava.[28]

The Historic Eruptions

The period of volcanic activity following 1800 brings us to the most fascinating part of Mt. St. Helens' eruptive history—that recent enough to be recorded by literate European and American eyewitnesses. Because of their intrinsic interest, these early reports are quoted below in full. Only where they are obviously derivative or unduly repetitious are they significantly abridged.

Although the great eruption of 1800 preceded the appearance of Caucasian settlers in the area, Indian lore, apparently based on the event, was later passed on to white explorers. In his narrative of an expedition to Oregon territory, published in 1845, Charles Wilkes reported interviewing a 60-year-old chief of the Spokane tribe, named Cornelius or Bighead, about an eruption that had occurred "some fifty years ago, before [the Indians] knew anything of white people, or had heard of them." According to Chief Cornelius, when he was about 10 years old he was

suddenly awakened by his mother, who called out to him that the world was falling to pieces. He then heard a great noise of thunder overhead, and all the people crying out in great terror. Something was falling very thick, which they at first took for snow, but on going out they found it to be dirt: it proved to be ashes, which fell to the depth of six inches, and increased their fears, by causing them to suppose that the end of the world was actually at hand."[29]

ERUPTIONS AND DORMANT INTERVALS AT MT. ST. HELENS SINCE 2500 B.C.

A.D.

1980 — Tephra eruptions.
1900 — Dormant interval of 123 years.
1857 — Last recorded pyroclastic eruption.
     — Eruptions of pyroclastics, domes, lava flows.
1800 — Pyroclastic eruptions (T), mudflows.
     — Apparent dormant interval of ca. 150 years.

1700 —
     — Pyroclastic flows (avalanches).
     — Dome eruption, mudflows.

1600 —
     — Apparent dormant interval of ca. 100 years.
1500 — Airborne pyroclastic eruptions (W), pyroclastic flows.
     — Pyroclastic flow.
1400 — Lava flows, pyroclastic flow.
     — Pyroclastic flows.
1300 — Dome eruptions (?)
1200 —
1100 — Apparent dormant interval of 400-500 years.
1000 —
900 —
     — Airborne pyroclastic eruption.
800 —
700 —
600 — Apparent dormant interval of 400-500 years.
500 —
400 —
     — Airborne pyroclastic eruptions, mudflows.
300 —
200 — Airborne pyroclastic eruptions.

SCALE
CHANGE

A. D.

```
        100 — Lava flows.
          0 —
B. C.
        100 — Pyroclastic flows, mudflows.
            — Pyroclastic flows.
        200 —
        300 — Pyroclastic flows, airborne pyroclastic eruptions, mudflows.
        400 — Airborne pyroclastic eruptions, mudflows.
            — Lava flows.
        500 — Apparent dormant interval, 400-500 years.

SCALE
CHANGE
       1000 — Repeated eruption of large pyroclastic flows, domes, and airborne pyroclastics; mudflows.
       1500 — Apparent dormant interval of ca. 400 years.
            Intermittent eruptions of large-volume airborne pyroclastics (Y),
            pyroclastic flows, eruptions of domes; mudflows.
       2000 —
B. C.  2500 — Apparent dormant interval of 4,000 years.
```

As the above chronology indicates, the *known* eruptions (many deposits may not yet have been recognized or have left no trace) of about the last 4000 years can be grouped into four periods: 2500 to 1600 B.C., 1200 to 800 B.C., 400 B.C. to 400 A.D., and from 1300 A.D. through the first half of the 19th century.

Building of the "modern" St. Helens began about 400 B.C. with a new behavior pattern characterized by eruptions of many different types and of different kinds of rock in rapid succession. In the last 2500 years the volcano has erupted dacite, andesite, and basalt in the form of pyroclastic flows (hot avalanches), domes, lava flows, and airborne pyroclastics (tephra).

During the past four millenia dormant intervals have typically lasted a few centuries or less. St. Helens' 1980 activity fulfilled geologists' expectations that the volcano would erupt before the end of this century.[78]

Figure 14–2. Chart outlining major volcanic events at Mt. St. Helens since 2500 B.C.

The geologist James D. Dana was with Wilkes' expedition and it is probably to Cornelius' story that he refers when, in 1849, he stated that "an account is on record of ashes falling fifty years since."[30] As the Spokane Indians lived in northeastern Washington, but frequently traveled south and west to trade and fish, the erupting peak could have been almost any of the northern Cascades. Mt. Hood is known to have erupted about that time, but St. Helens is the crater most likely to have produced so extensive an ash fall. That of 1800—known as layer T—is several inches thick many miles from the volcano.

It is not until 1835 that we have an authenticated *eye-witness* account of St. Helens' activity. In March of that year Dr. Meredith Gairdner, who was then official physician for the Hudson's Bay Company at Fort Vancouver, observed an eruption of the volcano. Unfortunately for science, this brilliant 26-year-old doctor from Edinburgh had to forego his proposed climb of the volcano. He was already ill with tuberculosis, which caused his death in Hawaii two years later. He did, however, send an undated letter to the *Edinburgh New Philosophical Journal*, which appeared in January, 1836.

> We have recently had an eruption of Mount Saint Helens, one of the snowy peaks of the Marine Chain on the north-west coast, about 40 miles to the north of this place [Fort Vancouver]. There was no earthquake or preliminary noise here: the first thing which excited my notice was a dense haze for two or three days, accompanied with a fall of minute flocculi of ashes, which, on clearing off, disclosed the mountain destitute of its cover of everlasting snow, and furrowed deeply by what through the glass appeared to be lava streams. . . . I believe this is the first well ascertained proof of the existence of a volcano on the west coast of America, to the north of California on the mainland. At the same season of the year 1831, a much denser darkness occurred here, which doubtless arose from the same cause, although at that time no one thought of examining the appearance of this mountain.[31]

Shortly after Gairdner sailed for Hawaii, the American missionary Samuel Parker arrived at Fort Vancouver. Although he noted that the volcano was still active, "down to the present . . . [sending] forth smoke and fine cinders to a considerable distance,"[32] he did not himself witness the eruptions of either 1831 or 1835. Oddly enough, Parker's secondhand version of the 1831 activity corresponds almost verbatim to that of J. Quinn Thornton, a judge of the Oregon Supreme Court, who claimed a "Dr. Gassner, a distinguished naturalist of England" as well as "gentlemen connected with the Hudson Bay Company" as authorities for his report.[33] Gairdner's researches no doubt stand behind both accounts: In the 1846 edition of his *Journal* Parker wrote,

> . . . there was in August 1831, an uncommonly dark day, which was thought to have been caused by an eruption of a volcano. The whole day was nearly as dark as night, except a slight red, lurid in appearance, which was perceptible until near night. Lighted candles were necessary during the day. The atmosphere was filled with ashes of wood, all having the appearance of having been produced by great fires, and yet none were known to have been in the whole region. The day was perfectly calm, without any wind. For a few days after, the fires out of doors were noticed to burn as though mixed with sulphur. There were no earthquakes.
>
> By observations which were made after the atmosphere became clear, it was thought the pure white perpetual snow of Mount St. Helens was discolored, presenting a brown appearance, and therefore it was concluded that there had been a slight eruption.

In a footnote, Parker adds "I have been creditably informed that lava was ejected at that time from St. Helens." All this sounds very much like Gairdner's 1836 report to the Edinburgh *New Philosophical Journal*, including its emphasis on discoloration of the snow and the suggestion that lava flows occurred. Both eruptions seem to have produced billowing, ash-laden clouds which darkened the skies and showered volcanic ejecta for miles over the countryside. All accounts agree that the 1831 activity produced a more severe plague of darkness, even to the point of necessitating candles during the daylight hours.

Gairdner's reference to "what appear to be lava streams" and Parker's conviction that "lava was ejected" must be taken with caution, since the eruptions were viewed from a considerable distance. In the popular imagination a volcanic outburst without rivers of molten lava streaming down the mountainside is unthinkable. There is, however, definite evidence that lava flows did occur at some point *after* the great eruption of 1800.

By counting the annual growth rings of trees affected by the event, Lawrence concluded that the "Floating Island" lava flow must have occurred "two or three years" after the 1800 fall of pumice.[34] Hopson notes that andesitic lava flowed from vents on both the northwest and south sides of the volcano following the 1800 pumice fall,[35] but Crandell cautions that none of these flows have yet been correlated with a specific recent eruption.[36] It is perhaps possible, but not by any means certain, that at least some of St. Helens' youngest lava flows occurred during the observed eruptions of 1831 or 1835. The problem of dating the latest flows is further complicated by Peterson and Groh, who state that "a small, black andesite flow" was extruded "around 1838"[37]—not a date given for any known historic eruption.

The "Great Eruption" of 1842-43

Although there is some uncertainty about the precise dates,* in the late fall or early winter of 1842 St. Helens entered into a violent eruptive phase that continued intermittently for 15 years. Since there were by then a few more settlers, including several literate missionaries in the area, this is the period for which we have the most extensive record. Even so, because of the absence of any scientifically-trained observers and the near impenetrability of the wilderness that surrounded the volcano, the surviving accounts in private journals, letters and diaries are tantalizingly brief.

Although eyewitnesses disagree on the exact date when St. Helens resumed activity, their impressions concur: the initial explosions were sudden, violent, and began without warning. According to J. L. Parrish, a Methodist missionary who conveyed his observations to Judge Thornton, "no earthquake was felt, no noise was heard."[39] From Parrish's vantage "ten miles below Salem" it was a silent if awe-inspiring spectacle: "He saw vast columns of lurid smoke and fire shoot up; which after attaining to a certain elevation, spread out in a line parallel to the plane of the horizon, and presented the appearance of a vast table, supported by immense pillars of convolving flame and smoke." Fifty years later, in a letter to the editor of a short-lived mountaineering publication, *Steel Points*, Parrish added further details:

> upon looking at the mountain we saw arising from its summit immense and beautiful scrolls of what seemed to be pure white steam, which rose many degrees into the heavens. Then came a stratum just below those fine huge scrolls of steam, which was an indefinite shade of gray. Then down next the mountain's top the substance emitted was black as ink.[40]

Parrish's description corresponds well to established volcanic phenomena: the inky black cloud nearest the vent was most permeated with dark ash, while the billowy white "scrolls" at the top were probably columns of water vapor. Parrish also described how the ash-fall changed the volcano's appearance:

> The next day after the eruption I was out on French Prairie where I had a good view of the mountain, and I noticed that she had changed her snowy dress of pure white for a sombre black mantle, which she wore until the snows of the ensuing winter fell upon her.

*S. F. Emmons with his famous reference to a "French Canadian voyageur" who reported that "the light from the burning volcano was so intense that one could see to pick up a pin in the grass at midnight near his cabin," established the inaccurate date of "the winter of 1841-42" as the time of the great eruption.[38] Later geologists and historians frequently repeated his error.

Another, less well-known account, preserved in F. G. Plummer's remarkable article on Northwest volcanism, is that of the Rev. Gustavus Hines, "an early missionary to the Columbia River country." Like Parrish, he emphasizes the vast dimensions of the eruption cloud that suddenly burst from St. Helens' snowy cone.

> . . . in the month of October [sic] 1842, St. Helens was discovered all at once to be covered with a dense cloud of smoke, which continued to enlarge and move off in dense masses to the eastward, and filling the heavens in that direction, presented an appearance like that occasioned by a tremendous conflagration viewed at a vast distance. When the first volume of smoke had cleared away it could be distinctly seen from different parts of the country that an eruption had taken place on the north side of St. Helens, a little below the summit, and from the smoke that continued to rise from the chasm or crater, it was pronounced to be a volcano in active operation. When the explosion took place the wind was north/northwest and on the same day and extending from thirty to fifty miles to the southeast there fell showers of ashes or dust, which covered the ground in some places so as to admit of its being gathered in quantities.[41]

Like that of Lassen in 1915, St. Helens' 1842 ash fall was extensive, if not heavy. In Captain J. C. Frémont's journal for November 13, 1843, he wrote that "on the 23rd of the preceding November [Nov. 23, 1842], St. Helens had scattered its ashes, like a light fall of snow, over The Dalles of the Columbia, 50 miles distant [actually about 65 air-line miles]. A specimen of these ashes was given to me by Mr. Brewer, one of the clergymen at The Dalles."[42] Parrish also reports that "the ashes fell at The Dalles to the depth of half an inch, so I was informed by the missionaries stationed there."[43]

One of these missionaries later published an anonymous memoir in which he described the eruption's effect on The Dalles community:

> On a pleasant evening, in the month of November 1843 [sic] the missionaries at The Dalles were favored with a visit. . . . About the time these friends arrived at the mission, a dark, heavy cloud was seen rising in the direction of Mount Saint Helens. No special remark was excited by this fact, but, on going to the door the next morning, the missionaries were surprised to see the ground, the trees, the grass—everything—sprinkled with ashes. A dark cloud shrouded the sky. It seemed to rain; but the clouds were not dropping water. Something descended gently to the earth, in form like fine sand,—in color, it appeared like ashes. Its odor was that of sulphur. The Indians said it had descended in larger quantities toward Mount Saint Helens. Soon the mystery was solved: that mountain had broken forth in a splendid eruption, and the winds had wafted its ashes to the door of the missionaries.[44]

Although the date given for this occurrence is a year later than the

Figure 14–3. This romantic painting of Mt. St. Helens during a night eruption, by Canadian artist Paul Kane, correctly shows the active crater located considerably below the volcano's summit. (Reprinted by permission of the Royal Ontario Museum, Toronto, Canada.)

accepted one, it is undoubtedly a reminiscence of the outburst of November 22, 1842,* referred to by Frémont and described by Hines and Parrish. Climbing a hill near the Columbia River from which they commanded a sweeping panorama of St. Helens, Adams, and Rainier, The Dalles missionaries noted that—in striking contrast to the snowy repose of the other peaks—St. Helens tumultuously sent up dense masses of steam and ash: "Amid this group of lofty mountains, Helens threw out its dark cloud of smoke. Its fires seem smothered, but the issuing volumes of smoke and ashes contrasted impressively with the sparkling snow of the surrounding peaks."

From these similar accounts, it appears that the November outbursts occurred during a temporary reversal of the usual Cascade wind patterns. The prevailing westerly or southwesterly winds had carried most of St. Helens' prehistoric eruption clouds northward so that the ash fell heaviest north of the peak. In 1842, however, the north-northwesterly currents caused a "rain" of ash to extend far south and east

---

*The Rev. Henry Bridgman Brewer, another missionary at The Dalles, places the date of the ash-fall on Nov. 25, 1842. His diary for that date records that "This morning was memorable for the shower of sand supposed to come from Mt. St. Helens or Hood."[45] If the eruption began Nov. 22 (as Parrish twice insisted) or Nov. 23, it is remarkable that ashes did not fall until—or were still falling on—the morning of the 25th.

of the volcano, covering Fort Vancouver as well as The Dalles. At a distance of 65 miles from the crater, the gently drifting ashes reportedly "reeked" of sulphur but were not perceptibly hot.

After the initial explosions, St. Helens seems to have remained in an almost continuous state of eruption for many weeks or even months throughout the winter of 1842–43. On December 13, 1842, another Methodist missionary, John H. Frost, from a viewpoint on the Columbia River near Vancouver, observed "a column of smoke to ascend from the N.W. side of Mt. St. Helens, towards the top. . . . It has been ascertained since that it was an actual volcanic eruption. I know not that it has as yet emitted anything but smoke. Have learned since that ashes have been thrown out in great abundance, even as far as The Dalles."[46]

Earlier in December another spectacular outburst was observed nearer at hand from the Cowlitz Mission, in what is now Washington State. On December 5, 1842, Father J. B. Z. Bolduc, wrote to his superiors in Quebec:

> To the northeast and southeast are two mountains whose height I still do not know, but which are at least 4,000 [a 10,000-foot underestimate for Rainier!] They are snowcovered, even in the greatest heat of summer. One of them—the one toward the southeast—is in the shape of a cone, and is opposite my dwelling. On the 5th of December, toward three o'clock in the afternoon, one of its sides opened and there was an eruption of smoke such that all our old voyageurs have never seen anything equal to it. These eruptions of smoke took place for several days at intervals not far apart, after which eruptions of flame began. They take place almost continually, but with an intensity that varies greatly from time to time. I am led to believe that there are three craters at least, for I have observed several times three eruptions at once and at different places, although close to each other. Especially in the evening are these phenomena well observed, and they offer a magnificent sight to the spectator. There is at the foot of this mountain a little river whose waters empty into the Cowlitz. After the volcano manifested itself, almost all the fish that it used to feed died—which is attributed to the quantity of cinders with which the waters are affected.[47]

Father Bolduc does not mention the eruption of November 22, probably because he did not arrive at the Cowlitz Mission until the 30th of that month.

Three years later the Rt. Rev. Modeste Demers, also stationed at the Cowlitz Mission, wrote that St. Helens continued active and that "since the month of December 1842, the time when the mountain opened its sides from the drive of subterranean fires, the waters of this [the Toutle] river have carted cinders and scoria. After the first eruption the natives assured us that they had found dead fish."[48]

In October 1843, Overton Johnson and William H. Winter travelled to the Willamette valley. They noted at that time in a journal, which was published in 1846 as *Route Across the Rocky Mountains with a Description of Oregon and California 1843*, that St. Helens was then erupting: "Mt. St. Helens, a lofty snowcapped Volcano rises from the plain, and is now burning. Frequently the huge columns of black smoke may be seen, suddenly bursting from its crater, at the distance of thirty or forty miles. The crater is on the south side, below the summit."[49] On the following February 16, there was a particularly spectacular display. Peter H. Burnett, a lawyer who later became governor of California, observed it from a point near the confluence of the Willamette and Columbia rivers: "being a beautiful and clear day, the mountain burned magnificently. The dense masses of smoke rose up in one immense column, covering the whole crest of the mountain in clouds."[50] In what seems to be a slightly altered version of Burnett's description, Plummer adds that "in the evening its fires lit up the mountainside in a flood of soft yet brilliant radiance."[51] Burnett also indicated that lava, or at least hot mud, perhaps generated by hot ash falling on and melting snow fields, was being emitted:

> On the side of the mountain, near its top, is a large black object, amidst the pure white snow around it. This is supposed to be the mouth of a large cavern. From Indian accounts this mountain emitted a volume of burning lava about the time it first commenced burning [November, 1842?]. An Indian came to Vancouver with his foot and leg badly burnt, who stated that he was on the side of the mountain hunting deer, and he came to a stream of something running down the mountain, and when he attempted to jump across it, he fell with one foot into it; and that was the way in which he got his foot and leg burned. This Indian came to the fort to get Doctor Barclay to administer some remedy to cure his foot.[52]

The story of the Indian with the burned foot—one of the only two reported casualties caused by a volcanic eruption in the United States—with various embellishments, eventually became an established part of early Northwest lore. It may, however, be apocryphal. Napolean McGilvery, who represented himself as having been in charge of the Fort Vancouver commissary at the time, disclaimed any knowledge of the incident. In a late reminiscence published in 1899, McGilvery recalled his impression of the eruption as follows:

> The mountain was not visible from Vancouver at any time. The eruption probably occurred on one day, and was not discovered by us until the next, when, upon going out early in the morning, gray white ashes were found to cover the ground as a light fall of snow. Both days were beautiful and clear. There was no traveling at that time away from the water courses, except by

Indians, and very little by them. It has been published that during this eruption an Indian was caught in the hot lava, was badly burned and taken to Vancouver, where he was treated by Dr. McLaughlin. I had charge of the commissary, so that such an incident could not have happened without my knowledge, and I never heard of it until recently.[53]

In support of the original tale, it should be noted that Burnett's version states that the Indian was treated by Dr. Barclay, not the more famous Dr. McLaughlin, and that he is vague about the time, "about the time it [St. Helens] first commenced burning." It is possible that McGilvery was not present during the whole eruptive period.

Whatever the fate of Indians rash enough to approach the "fire-mountain," St. Helens "continued to burn" fitfully throughout the mid 1840s. On May 30, 1844, the Rev. George Gary, then on a ship off the Oregon coast, had "a very distant view of a volcano in action, throwing up clouds of smoke." At first Gary could not determine if the clouds were arising from the snowy peak of St. Helens or from a vent near it, but "on

Figure 14–4. Eruptions of ash and steam were seen daily, often several times a day, as Mt. St. Helens entered an active phase in late March, 1980 after being dormant since 1857. (Photo by Bob and Ira Spring.)

further inquiry I have learned that this volcano is in Mount Helen [sic] itself, and that either the snow is diminishing or the soot settling upon the white covering of the mountain presents the appearance of wasting snow. It is so cold near these snowy mountains and the snow is so deep I believe there has been no very thorough examination of them, and this volcano [active crater] is so high up the mountain as that the temperature at its base is but little, if any, affected by it. The falling ashes or soot have been seen and gathered from boards or anything of a smooth surface, say, fifty miles from the crater."[54]

The mountain was still in action on December 28, 1844, when Burnett noted that it continued "a burning volcano."[55] On February 15, 1845, Samuel B. Crockett wrote to his brother in Missouri that St. Helens, which is the highest peak that stands nearest the Columbia on the north side, sends forth columns of smoke from its frozen top."[56] These eruptions of the later 1840s do not appear to have been as violent as those of 1842-43 when large areas south and east of the peak were coated with sulphurous ash. They did, however, continue to attract attention.

By a stroke of good fortune one of those attracted by reports of St. Helens' fireworks was the Canadian painter Paul Kane. On a long cross-country tour from Toronto during which he collected material for paintings of Indians, wildlife and other natural phenomena, Kane arrived at the mouth of the Lewis River in late March, 1847. On the 26th of that month, from a point where he had a full and unobstructed view of the mountain, he made a preliminary drawing of the peak. As he noted in his journal, "There was not a cloud visible in the sky at the time I commenced my sketch, and not a breath of air was perceptible; suddenly a stream of white smoke shot up from the crater of the mountain, and hovered a short time over its summit; it then settled down like a cap. This shape it retained for about an hour and a half, and then gradually disappeared."[57] From this sketch Kane made the only well-known portrait of a Cascade volcano in eruption until Loomis took his celebrated photographs of Lassen Peak.

Kane's finished painting (Figure 14-3) is now housed in the Royal Ontario Museum of Archaeology in Toronto. It is a highly romanticized and dramatic work, showing a group of awed Indians watching a brilliant night eruption, the glare of which is reflected both on their upturned faces and on the river waters where their canoe is harbored. If it seems unlikely that the volcano would so obligingly put on a display for the artist who was to be its official portraitist, it must be remembered that Kane saw the volcano active on more than one occasion and that he depicted the position of the eruptive vent with great precision. Four days after making his sketch while at the Cowlitz outpost, he had another "fine view of Mount

St. Helen's [sic] throwing up a long column of dark smoke into the clear blue sky.'' He also painted the glowing eruption clouds emerging, not from the top of the mountain as popular taste might dictate, but from a vent about a third of the way down the north or northwest side. Only by having witnessed an actual eruption is Kane likely to have placed the crater so accurately.

It is undeniable, however, that Kane did represent the eruption as more of what he had heard of past activity than of what he personally saw. The conclusion to Kane's first journal entry on the subject indicates this: ''About three years before, this mountain was in a violent state of eruption for three or four days, and threw up burning stones and lava to an immense height, which ran in burning torrents down its snowclad sides.'' In the rhetorical tradition of the American West, Kane was apparently treated to some highly embellished versions of the 1842-43 eruptions, such as that published in 1848 by Dr. Elijah White, formerly a sub-agent for Indian Affairs. White described the volcano for his eastern readers as ''presenting a scene the most awful and sublime imaginable, scattering smoke and ashes several hundred miles distance; and in the meantime immense quantities of melted lava were rolling down its sides, and inundating the plain below.''[58] While ashes did fall at least 65 or more miles from the mountain in November, 1842, the ''immense quantities'' of melted lava White invokes are purely a figment of his Bunyanesque imagination. To his credit, Kane showed considerable artistic restraint and omitted the molten torrents from his painting. As an art historian as well as a recorder of how things actually looked, however, Kane was entitled to show St. Helens in her fiercest and most impressive guise.

That St. Helens was still lighting up the night skies a full year after Kane had so painted her is shown by Robert Caufield of Oregon City in a letter dated April 1, 1848:

> St. Helens which is still a volcano and continually covered with snow stands . . . about 70 miles north of this place. There has been two emptyings of this mountain since we came here. The report we could hear distinctly and the *reflections seen in the sky at night*.

Although references to ''flame'' and luminosity are frequent in descriptions of the volcano, Caufield is one of the very few who mentions hearing ''reports'' or explosive noises.

Further confirmation of Kane's general reliability both in his delineation of the mountain's form and the position of its crater is given by Charles Stevens, who viewed St. Helens from on board ship at the mouth of the Columbia. On April 10, 1853, Stevens wrote a letter which included a crude drawing of the mountain:

On the opposite side of this I have drawed a little sketch of Mount St. Helen, as it appears way down in the mouth of the Columbia River, it is not correct, but it will let you see how these mountains look. Where I drew the sketch is about two hundred miles from the mountains, and I suppose it might be seen one hundred miles at sea.

The little black spot near the top is a hole, where the fire and smoke comes out. It runs way up above the clouds, as you will see the spots near the bottom looks like black lava.[60]

Although Stevens considerably overestimated his distance from the mountain— it is a little less than 100 air-line miles trom the mouth of the Columbia—his rough drawing is important evidence. Unlike Kane he did not dramatize what he saw but apparently tried to reproduce the scene objectively.

By February of 1854 the volcano had notably increased its activity. On February 25 of that year the *Oregonian* reported that:

The Crater of Mt. St. Helens has been unusually active for several days past. Those who have been in a position so as to obtain a view of the mountain, represent clouds of smoke and ashes constantly rising from it. The smoke appears to come up in puffs, which was the case at the time we visited in August last. There is now more smoke issuing from it than there was then, which indicates that the volcanic fires are rapidly increasing within the bowels of this majestic mountain.[61]

The *Oregon Weekly Times* for the same date published a report from W. H. H. Halls, pilot of the Whitcomb, a Columbia River steamer, to the effect that "volumes of smoke... were thrown out at intervals."[62] Stevens also noted the activity in his diary, but added that he was not himself in a position to see it.

In his *Tremblements de Terre en 1854*, Perrey made several references to this eruption, including a notation that the volcano was active from February through April, an unusually long episode of volcanism.[63] It now seems impossible to verify or even guess at Perrey's sources, although he probably got his information from brief but relatively accurate items in eastern newspapers.

As in the case of Lassen Peak, several of St. Helens' historic eruptions may have gone unnoticed. Low-temperature night eruptions that produced no glow or flare, as well as outbursts during winter months when the mountain was veiled in thick clouds could not have been seen. How many of the milder expulsions of steam or ash mingled imperceptibly with the murk of night or storm will never be known.

After the prolonged activity of 1854, the mountain was apparently quiescent until April, 1857, a date which marks St. Helens' last recorded outburst. This time the eruption was publicized not by the Portland newspapers, which seem to have ignored the event, but by the far-removed Steilacoom, Washington, *Republican*. The issue of April 17 carried the following item:

> Mount St. Helens, or some other mount to the southward, is seen from the Nisqually plains in this county, to be in a state of eruption. It has for the last few days been emitting huge volumes of dense smoke and fire, presenting a grand and sublime spectacle."[64]

Again, the reference to "fire" may indicate either a high-temperature explosion of molten material or the electrical flashes common during such a disturbance. Since this final outburst seems to have produced no significant ash deposit nor to have been hot enough to initiate a recognized mudflow, it is probable that no more than billowing clouds of steam and dust were ejected. This, too, corresponds to the waning stages of Lassen Peak's 1917 eruptions, as well as to the last known activity of other Cascade volcanoes.

Position of the Crater

From the testimony of Frost, Parrish, Kane, Stevens and others, it seems certain that few, if any, of St. Helens' historic eruptions issued from the summit crater. From observations made "a year or two . . . after the [1842] eruption" Parrish concluded that the crater was "on the south side of the mountain about two-thirds of the distance from the bottom to the top."[65] Viewing the peak from the Columbia River, he "could still see distinctly the fire burning on the side of the mountain." Johnson and Winter also placed the active vent on the south side, as did Burnett and Stevens. To other eyewitnesses of the 1842-43 eruptions, however, the activity appeared to be centered on the north or northwest side of the mountain. The Rev. Hines, for instance, asserted that the ash was projected from "a chasm or crater on the north side of St. Helens, a little below the summit" and that this vent continued to "smoke" after the principal explosions were over.[66] Frost observed columns of smoke bursting from "the N.W. side of Mount St. Helens, toward the top."[67] At the Cowlitz Mission Father Bolduc, who saw "flame" and "smoke" issuing "from one of its sides," was convinced that "there are three craters at least, for [he] observed several times three eruptions at once and at different places, although close to each other."[68] Kane, of course, also depicted the volcano erupting from the north or northwest side about a third of the way down from the top. In 1849, when George Gibbs visited the region, he noted that "smoke was distinctly seen issuing from St. Helens during our journey" and that the crater was "on the northwest" side.[69]

When Thomas J. Dryer, the first editor of the Portland *Oregonian*, led the initial ascent of Mt. St. Helens in August, 1853, he apparently took pains to determine the precise location of the active vent. Remarking that "the crater has been represented to be on the southwest side of the mountain," he declared that this was "not the case."[70] Dryer's compass readings, he said, showed it "to be on northeast side. The smoke was continually issuing from its mouth, giving unmistakable evidence that the fire was not extinguished." Dryer's accuracy in locating the crater "on the northeast side" is supported by an earlier report of an eruption from that location. On March 21, 1850, the Oregon City *Spectator* carried a notice that both Mt. St. Helens and Mt. Baker were erupting. It added that St. Helens was emitting smoke from two craters "low down on the north and northeast sides." Activity at these sites was apparently of fairly long duration, for on May 10 the same newspaper reported that the volcano was continually "in a state of eruption."[71]

In his recent study of Mt. St. Helens' eruptive history, C. A. Hopson of the University of California found that the vulcanian eruption of 1800 occurred at a vent on the northwest flank of the volcano.[72] Although this vent was later filled by the growth of a dacitic dome, it is possible that some of the explosive eruptions that followed blasted new openings adjacent to the conduit filling. Some geologists believe that some 19th-century activity was centered at Goat Rocks, a shattered dacite dome which produced glowing avalanches on St. Helens' northwest slope (Figure 14-6). It is perhaps significant that the 1980 outbursts began at the northern corner of the summit dome.

Thermal Activity Prior to the 1980 Eruptions

Considering the relative frequency of St. Helens' eruptions, it is surprising that, for most of the 20th century, it emitted considerably less heat or steam than Baker, Rainier, or Hood. In the 1930s D.B. Lawrence learned from a mountaineer named Crum that there were then two concentrations of steam vents near the summit, one "on the southwest side of the peak, a short distance below the summit" and the other on the north side about "halfway up a lava outcrop called 'The Boot,' at its western edge."[73] Two years later a climbing party investigated both areas.[74] They could find no manifestations of internal heat southwest of the summit, but did discover "brilliantly colored" rocks that showed signs of severe hydrothermal alteration. On the north slope Phillips' group was more successful, for on The Boot, about 800 feet below the summit, they came upon active fumaroles. In his report of the expedition, Phillips stated that "tiny jets of steam issue quietly from crevices in the bedrock, and rather large areas of the rock are distinctly warm even where there is no apparent discharge. The largest fumarole has an opening no more than three inches in diameter." Phillips also remarked that the strong sulphur smell so noticeable on Hood and Adams was lacking there, although the gases escaping from Mt. St. Helens were "very nearly as hot" as those hissing from Crater Rock on Hood. The highest temperature recorded was 88°C (190.4°F) "not far below the boiling point at that altitude."

As part of a continuing effort to monitor potentially dangerous Cascade volcanoes, the U.S. Geological Survey recently conducted aerial surveys of several major peaks, including Mt. St. Helens.[75]

Infrared images made of the upper cone indicated no thermal abnormality on the southwest side but revealed the presence of several fumaroles on The Boot, much as Phillips had described them. Whether these "hot spots" marked the site of St. Helens' last 19th-century eruptions is uncertain, but they are not far from the presently active crater.

St. Helens Now and in the Future

Although only twelfth in height among the major Cascade volcanoes, St. Helens rises nearly 6500 feet above its base and dominates the skyline of southwestern Washington and the Columbia River basin. From Portland it rivals Mt. Hood as the most ethereal of the famed "Guardians of the Columbia." It stands virtually alone among its loftier Cascade fellows, however, in that the forces of volcanic construction still exceed those of erosive destruction. Still in the cone-building stage, St. Helens can be expected to pour out many more lava flows, add innumerable layers of tephra and glowing avalanche deposits to its slopes, and significantly increase its bulk and stature. If most of the modern cone is no more than 1000 years old, as geologists believe, then the passing of a few more millennia may see St. Helens transformed into one of the larger Cascade volcanoes. In time, St. Helens may rival Mt. Hood in size and volume.

Dangers from Future Eruptions

If Mt. St. Helens' present activity follows the pattern set by its past behavior, any one or several of a variety of volcanic events *may* occur. Since a volcano typically has many more minor eruptions than large ones, the most likely eventuality would be a repetition of the small-volume ejections of tephra that took place sporadically between 1831 and 1857 when ash fell for several tens of miles east and south of the volcano. Settling ash could clog machinery, reduce visibility during daylight hours, contaminate reservoirs and fish hatcheries, and cover nearby forests, towns, and farmlands with fine, gritty sand. The first stage of the 1980 outburst produced most of these effects.

If the much greater blow-out of pumice and lava fragments that characterized the 1800 eruption (which geologists believe to have produced a typically moderate-sized volume of tephra) were to be repeated, the immediate vicinity downwind from the mountain would be buried under several feet of volcanic debris. The subsequent lava flows and rise

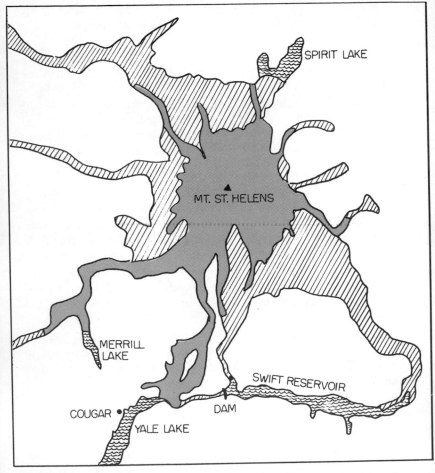

Figure 14–5. Extent of mudflows and pyroclastic flows (line pattern) and lava flows (shaded) from Mt. St. Helens during the last 4000 years. (After Crandell and others.)

of plug domes to fill the vents through which the tephra was ejected could melt large quantities of snow and ice, creating mudflows that could move at speeds of 25 to 50 miles an hour into stream valleys that head on the volcano.

During the 1800 activity the wind was blowing toward the north-northeast, thus carrying the ash away from the sites of most towns and cities near the mountain. The same winds prevailed during most of the large-scale pumice eruptions that occurred about 450 and 3000-4000 years ago. At least once during the eruptions that produced layer Y, however, northwest winds deposited ash southeast of the volcano. In 1842 ash fell in Vancouver, southwest of St. Helens. Northerly winds have also blown some 1980 ashclouds toward the Vancouver-Portland area.

More dangerous than ashfalls, despite the widespread pollution they cause, or lava flows, which have seldom traveled more than eight to nine miles down the volcano's flanks, are the mudflows generated by volcanic heat melting heavy snowpacks. Between 2500 and 3000 years ago a series of mudflows swept 40 miles down the Lewis River valley. Several hundred years later mudflows also descended the Toutle River valley, on the northwest, emptied into the Cowlitz River, and buried the site of Castle Rock. Today three large artificial lakes — hydro-electric reservoirs — occupy 25 linear miles of the Lewis River valley. Should a mudflow of extraordinarily large volume move rapidly into the upper reservoir, it could start a catastrophic chain reaction.[76] Water might spill over each successive dam, ultimately producing a flood of large proportions that could sweep away or bury the homes of more than 40,000 persons who live on the flood plain of the lower Columbia. Portland, Oregon's largest city, lies essentially at tidewater only 20 miles upstream from where the Lewis empties into the Columbia. The backwash from a series of flood waves and mudflows entering the Columbia from the Lewis River might cause considerable property damage and possible loss of life in the city's low-lying areas. Recognizing that Swift and Pine Creek valleys on the south side of the mountain are particularly susceptible to mudflows and flooding, during the 1980 activity authorities quickly lowered the water level of Swift Reservoir sufficiently to contain a mudflow of 125,000,000 cubic meters (equivalent to about 100,000 acre-feet), the largest scientists thought likely to occur.

In the meantime, the Mt. St. Helens area is threatened not only by natural but by manmade dangers. Giant logging companies, apparently more concerned with making a quick profit than with preserving the environment of America's most beautiful volcano, have already decimated forests encircling its southern and eastern flanks, and with the blessing of the Forest Service, are rapidly cutting toward the Spirit Lake environs. Greedy timber barons were thwarted in their rape of the Lassen Peak area in 1916 when Congress created Lassen Volcanic National Park; only similar action today can preserve St. Helens' numerous scenic and geologic attractions.

As mountaineer Harvey Manning wrote in *Trips and Trails, 2,* "Had a geologic miracle erupted Mt. St. Helens in New Jersey or Illinois, it would have become the first National Park, long before Yellowstone. In the volcano-overpopulated Cascades it offers a good (bad) example of the Forest Service mismanagement of scenery."[77]

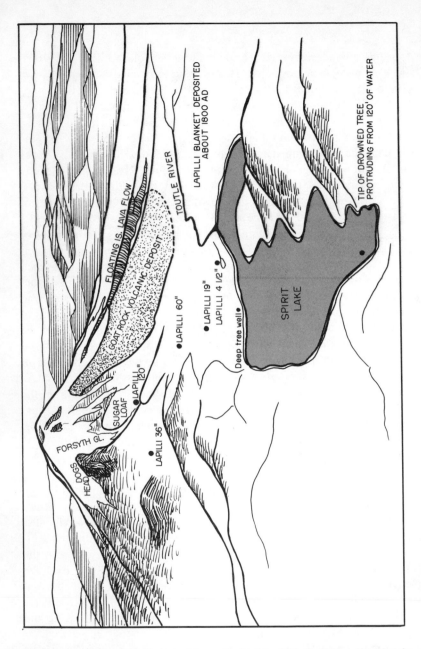

Figure 14–6. A diagrammatic map of the northeast side of Mt. St. Helens. Note that the depth of pyroclastic debris (lapilli) from the eruption of about 1800 A.D. varies from 120 inches at timberline to only four and half inches at the edge of Spirit Lake. The windblown ash blanket from this outburst extends for hundreds of miles north and east of the volcano. The crater at the summit was formed beginning with the March, 1980 period of renewed volcanic activity. (Based on a drawing by Lawrence, 1954.)

To prevent this depredation of the mountain, the Mt. St. Helens Protective Association (and earlier the Federation of Western Outdoor Clubs) has proposed the creation of an 80,000-acre National Monument, with the volcano as its center. If such a Monument is legislated and transferred to the jurisdiction of the National Park Service, the Forest Service could no longer create a public-relations smokescreen to mask the largely unregulated logging in the St. Helens vicinity. But unless the U.S. Congress, or renewed volcanic activity, intervene, the once green land surrounding Mt. St. Helens may become a very different kind of monument—still another ugly memorial to the timbermen's greed.

Chapter 14–References

1. Crandell, Mullineaux and Rubin, 1975, pp. 438-441; Mullineaux and Crandell, 1962; Crandell, written comm., 1974.
2. Lawrence, 1939, 1954.
3. Clark, 1966, pp. 20-22.
4. Hyde, 1973, p. 89.
5. Crandell, written comm., 1973.
6. Verhoogen, 1937.
7. Crandell and Mullineaux, 1973, p. A21.
8. Ibid., p. A8.
9. Mullineaux, 1964, p. 285.
10. Hyde, 1973, p. 86.
11. Borchardt and others, 1973, p. 3106.
12. Crandell and Mullineaux, 1973, p. A8.
13. Ibid., p. A20.
14. Hyde, 1973, pp. 90-96.
15. Crandell and Mullineaux, 1973, pp. A20-A21.
16. Mullineaux and Crandell, 1962; Hyde, 1970, p. 14.
17. Hyde, 1970, p. 14.
18. Greeley and Hyde, 1972.
19. Hyde, 1973,, p. 85.
20. Hopson, 1971.
21. Verhoogen, 1937.
22. Ibid.
23. Hopson, 1971.
24. Lawrence, 1939; 1954; Lawrence and Lawrence, 1959, pp. 15-16.
25. Hopson, 1971.
26. Okazaki and others, 1972.
27. Hopson, 1971.
28. Crandell, written comm., 1974.
29. Wilkes, 1845, pp. 439-440.
30. Holmes, 1955, pp. 198-201.
31. Gairdner, 1836, p. 206.
32. Holmes, 1955, p. 203.

33. *Thornton, 1855, pp. 256-57.*
34. *Lawrence, 1941.*
35. *Hopson, 1971.*
36. *Crandell, written comm., 1972-73.*
37. *Peterson and Groh, 1963, p. 35.*
38. *S. F. Emmons, 1877.*
39. *Thornton, 1855, p. 257.*
40. *Parrish, 1906, pp. 25-26.*
41. *Plummer, 1893.*
42. *Frémont, 1845, pp. 193-94.*
43. *Parrish, 1906, p. 25.*
44. *Anonymous, 1854.*
45. *Holmes, 1955, pp. 203-04.*
46. *Frost, 1934, pp. 373-74.*
47. *Landerholm, 1956, p. 148.*
48. *Ibid., p. 182.*
49. *Holmes, 1955, pp. 205-06.*
50. *Burnett, 1902, p. 424.*
51. *Plummer, 1893.*
52. *Burnett, 1902, p. 424.*
53. *Steel, 1899, p. 276.*
54. *Gary, 1923, pp. 76-77.*
55. *Burnett, 1902, p. 424.*
56. *Coombs, 1960, p. 13.*
57. *Kane, 1925, p. 136.*
58. *Allen, 1848, p. 200.*
59. *Holmes, 1955, p. 207.*
60. *Stevens, 1936, p. 251.*
61. *Dryer, 1854, p. 2.*
62. *Stevens, 1937, p. 73.*
63. *Holden, 1898, p. 42.*
64. *Holmes, 1955, p. 209.*
65. *Parrish, 1906, p. 26.*
66. *Plummer, 1893.*
67. *Frost, 1934, p. 373.*
68. *Landerholm, 1956, p. 148.*
69. *Gibbs, 1855.*
70. *Dryer, 1853, p. 2.*
71. *Holmes, 1955, pp. 207-08.*
72. *Hopson, 1971.*
73. *Lawrence, 1939, p. 54.*
74. *Phillips, 1941, pp. 37-42.*
75. *Moxham, 1970, pp. 100-101.*
76. *Crandell and Waldron, 1969, p. 16.*
77. *Sterling, 1968, p. viii.*
78. *Crandell, Mullineaux, and Rubin, 1975, p. 440.*

15
Mt. Rainier—The "Mountain That Was 'God'"

Built astride the Cascades of central Washington, Mt. Rainier towers 14,410 feet above the shores of Puget Sound, the inland sea which lies to the west. The highest peak in the range, Rainier's bulky mass is the most conspicuous landmark on the skyline of almost every major city in the area.

Mt. Rainier supports the single largest glacier system in the 48 contiguous states. Its 26 officially named glaciers are the sources of several major Northwest rivers—the Nisqually, Puyallup, Carbon, Cowlitz, and White Rivers—invaluable producers of hydroelectric power.

Thanks to its status as a national park, much of the mountain's base remains covered by stands of Douglas fir, cedar, alder and hemlock. The park-like areas between timberline and the permanent snowfields are carpeted in summer with wildflowers, mosses and heather. Rising from virgin forest, garlanded with alpine blossoms, and crowned with its great icecap, Rainier presents a superlative study in contrasting colors. Whether veiled in clouds or looming immense on a clear day, the volcano stands apart, an arctic island in a temperate zone.

Because of its exposed northern position and heavy load of glaciers, Mt. Rainier is not a smooth-sided symmetrical cone like Mt. St. Helens. Instead, each face of the mountain has been glacier-carved into a distinctive shape that bears little resemblance to the other sides. As the accompanying photographs demonstrate, the mountain reveals a totally different profile from various directions.

The most familiar view is probably that photographed from Paradise Valley, located a mile high on the south slope. From there, Rainier appears as a broad ice-covered dome with long rocky ribs standing black against surrounding snowfields. High on its east shoulder, the reddish-brown mass of Gibraltar Rock gives the mountain a bulky, elongated look. Farther to the east, Little Tahoma Peak, outcropping from the main cone, points a jagged triangle toward the sky .

From the west or southwest, Rainier presents an entirely different aspect. Here it shows something of the classic volcanic cone, albeit with irregular slopes and a truncated crest. From Olympia, it resembles Matthes' description of ''an enormous tree stump with spreading base and broken top.''[1] The western view also reveals the three separate peaks on Rainier's broad summit.

From the north Rainier is not recognizable as the same mountain familiar to tourists at the Paradise Visitor Center. The Carbon Glacier has dug deeply into the northwest flank of the cone, gouging out the largest natural amphitheatre on any single mountain in the Cascade Range. Curtis Ridge on the east and Ptarmigan Ridge on the west half enclose an enormous empty crescent—a cirque with headwalls rising almost vertically 3600 feet above the glacier to the summit icecap (Figure 15-1). These oversteepened north slopes form the precipitous Willis Wall, in which countless lava flows and breccia layers are exposed in cross-section. Avalanches of rock and ice often tumble from the overhanging edge of the 200- to 500-foot-thick summit glacier.

But Mt. Rainier is most impressive from the east side (Figure 15-3). Not only does the volcano look its grandest from the Sunrise Visitor Center located on the grassy tableland of Yakima Park, but it reveals many features which are geologically most interesting. The Emmons Glacier, the largest in the United States excepting Alaska, descends five miles from the summit to the depths of the White River Canyon 10,000 feet below. Broken and crevassed, the Emmons has ground deeply into Rainier's eastern flank. To the south rears the irregular, stepped-pyramid of Little Tahoma. This peak, the third highest in Washington state, appears to be a secondary cone which grew on Rainier's east side. Instead, it is a remnant of a once-continuous eastern slope, surviving to remind one how much Rainier's glaciers and other erosional processes have cost it in size and volume.

Emmons Glacier is bordered on the north by another conspicuous escarpment known as the Wedge or Steamboat Prow. Shaped like an inverted V, it, too, is an indicator of what the volcano has lost through a combination of glacial and volcanic action (cf. pages 202-210). Beyond it lie the Winthrop Glacier, Russell Cliff and the shadowed cirque of the Carbon Glacier.

From this brief round-the-mountain survey, it is apparent that Mt. Rainier— imposing as it is—is much diminished from its former self. Not a scrap of the volcano's original constructional surface remains anywhere to be seen; even highstanding features like Gibraltar Rock and

Figure 15–1. The Carbon Glacier (center) has not only bitten deeply into Mt. Rainier's north face, but descends to the lowest altitude (about 3000 feet) of any glacier in the conterminous United States. Winthrop Glacier (left center) flows from the youthful summit cone. Little Tahoma Peak appears at the extreme left. The dark outcroppings in the right center are Echo and Observation Rocks, remnants of two late (but pre-Fraser) satellite cones that formed on Rainier's north flank. (Photo by Austin Post, U.S. Geological Survey.)

Little Tahoma do not represent the mountain's former contours. An unknown number of lava flows once moved down a mountainslope which then lay *above* their present surfaces (Figure 15-5).

It is clear that Mt. Rainier has undergone tremendous changes during its long history. Many of these changes, particularly those which occurred during the last 10,000 years, can be described and even approximately dated by a careful examination of the geological record. For Mt. Rainier has left abundant evidence not only that it was once much larger and higher than it is now, but also that it experienced outbursts of cataclysmic proportions. Layers of ash, congealed streams of lava, and remnants of mudflows which once filled adjacent valleys to depths of

1000 feet indicate to the professional geologist some of the events which have shaped the modern cone.

Thanks to the combined research of several distinguished scientists, we can now almost "see" Mt. Rainier during its million-year development. In the reenactment of the mountain's early history which follows, I have liberally interpreted the work of Dwight R. Crandell (1963b), Richard S. Fishe, Clifford A. Hopson, and Aaron C. Waters (1963). Although details of prehistoric eruptions are necessarily invented, descriptions are based on the observed activity of volcanoes like Paricutin, which first appeared in 1943. Rainier's later history, that of the last 10,000 years, relies principally on the work of Dr. Crandell and Donal R. Mullineaux (1963a; 1965; 1967; 1969; 1971). Freely drawing on the discoveries of these, among other, geologists, we can enjoy a kind of "time-machine" adventure into the volcano's remote past.

The Setting

If one were transported more than 1,000,000 years back in time to the Pleistocene Eopch, just before the birth of Mt. Rainier, he would probably find the neighboring Cascade terrain—at least in general appearance—surprisingly recognizable. Then, as now, saw-toothed peaks and sharp ridges were intersected by deep canyons containing swift rivers. Some of the lower canyons were probably relatively narrow and V-shaped, while valleys higher in the mountains were broader, with rounded floors, the result of glacial action. The Tatoosh Range, which now borders Mt. Rainier's southern base, probably was nearly as craggy and picturesque as it is today.

Although Mt. Rainier began to erupt during the Ice Age, it probably appeared during an interglacial period as warm as that today. The few glaciers in what became Mt. Rainier National Park were then small and confined to the higher elevations. Dense coniferous forests, composed at least partly of familiar fir and hemlock, extended to a timberline of about 6000 feet. Animal life was relatively sparse but included some exotic specimens, such as the wooly mammoth, a few of which occasionally strayed upvalley from the neighboring lowlands.

The immediate scene of Rainier's birth was a rugged plateau more than a mile above sea level and surrounded by peaks from 2000 to 3500 feet higher. Several rivers, originating from alpine snow fields, flowed from this mountainous upland. The ancestral Carbon, White, Puyallup, and Mowich Rivers had already excavated large ravines extending north, northwest, and west to the Puget Sound lowland. In some places, it was a full 4000 feet from the loftiest peaks to the valley floors.

Mt. Rainier Is Born

The first warning that a new volcano was about to appear came in a series of earthquakes, which gradually increased in frequency. During the most severe of these shocks, the earth cracked in long fissures through which rose streamers of white vapor. Tremors continued until the ground vibrated almost incessantly and the wisps of vapor became surging columns of steam. Then, with an ear-splitting roar, an explosion ripped through one of the central fissures, tearing loose huge fragments of rock and hurling them high into the air. As each explosion was succeeded by another more violent, dust and volcanic ash billowed upward and spread out to darken the sky.

After nightfall, a glow vividly lit up the new vent. Pasty globs of molten rock soared through the air and showered down around the opening, piling up in sizzling heaps. Throughout the night, the eruptions continued unabated.

Daybreak revealed a scene of utter desolation. What only hours before had been a panorama of rock, snowfields, and clear alpine streams, was changed almost beyond recognition. It looked as if dirty gray snow had fallen over the entire landscape. Nearby creeks and streams carried heavy loads of ash, cinders, and floating pumice, and, to the northeast, trees were either defoliated or bent beneath a mantle of gritty volcanic dust.

The new volcano, which had overnight built a cinder cone 150 feet high, produced enormous quantities of pyroclastics, chiefly hypersthene — hornblende andesite pumice. At night, when the eruption cloud was not too dense, blazing sprays of red-hot particles shot skyward, while fountains of incandescent rock played against an inky curtain of falling ash. For years the magma from Rainier's subterranean reservoir was charged with too much gas pressure to allow the lava to escape quietly; it was blown out with pulverizing force.

After Rainier's pyroclastic cone reached a height of about 1000 feet, explosive activity temporarily declined. Following several years of quiet, the volcano introduced a variation in its eruptive pattern. Liquid rock rose into the summit crater, which for a moment appeared brim-full and ready to disgorge its first real lava flow. But the loosely consolidated fragmental structure could not bear the strain of so much lava within it. From the foot of the cone to the crater rim, the sides split into a network of fissures from which issued streams of fluid lava. The whole side of the cone was swept away by this irresistible torrent of molten rock.

Seeking the lowest channels in which to flow, the lava poured into a vacated riverbed near the base of the cone. Full of seething gases and registering temperatures of perhaps 1800 degrees Fahrenheit, the liquid

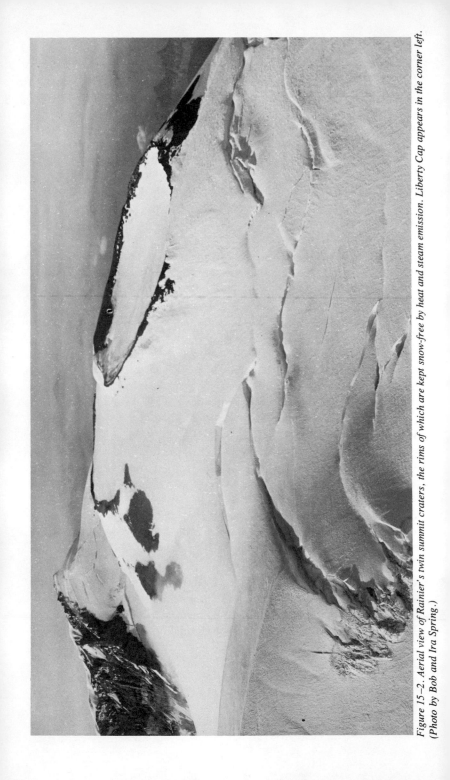

Figure 15–2. Aerial view of Rainier's twin summit craters, the rims of which are kept snow-free by heat and steam emission. Liberty Cap appears in the corner left. (Photo by Bob and Ira Spring.)

andesite moved swiftly downslope. A few miles from its source, however, the flow lost momentum. As its crust, exposed to the cooling air, hardened and thickened, the lava advanced only a few hundred yards per day. Where the old riverbed widened and deepened, the slowly-congealing lava accumulated to a depth of several hundred feet.

Eventually, gas pressure within the magma chamber was sufficiently relieved to allow the magma to sink back into its underground reservoir. Mt. Rainier's initial lava flow, the first of thousands, had ceased, but its slag-like surface remained hot for nearly a year, repelling the ensuing snows of winter.

Since the Rainier known to us in the 20th century is built almost exclusively of hypersthene-andesite flows, we might suppose that the new volcano grew chiefly by the quiet emission of lava. This, however, was not the case. For an unknown number of centuries the pyroclastic cone ancestral to the modern Rainier (and now concealed beneath its later lavas) erupted violently. The earliest evidence of this activity is not found on the mountain itself but in the Puget Sound lowland to the northwest. Deposits there include volcanic mudflows derived from an active volcano at the site of Mt. Rainier and are interbedded with glacial drift deposited by a lobe of the vast ice sheet which moved southward from Canada.

Some time about 700,000 years before the present, after the ancestral cone had been partly removed by erosion, Mt. Rainier began a series of voluminous lava flows. At this stage in its growth the volcano probably resembled a broad lava dome, with tentacles of black, red, and gray andesite extending from a large central crater (Figure 15-6A).

These prodigous flows probably issued from vents along the flanks of the volcano and some traveled many miles from their source. One flow entered the canyon of the Grand Park River (since vanished), which trended northeast from Mt. Rainier. Of extraordinary volume, this lava stream filled the valley wall-to-wall for a distance of more than 12 miles and to a depth of 2000 feet. (The remnants of the flow, since transformed into a free-standing ridge by erosion on either side, is now a mountain called Old Desolate and the flat bench underlying Grand Park.)

The deep gorges lying west of Mt. Rainier met a similar fate. Since the growing volcano sat atop a complex of ridges and ravines, its lavas did not pile up around the base of the cone. Instead they drained into nearby valleys, such as those occupied by the ancestral Puyallup and Mowich Rivers. One flow was scarcely cool before another spread over its surface. Overwhelmed by floods of molten rock, the rivers were crowded from their ancient beds and forced to cut new channels along the flow margins. As one eruption followed another, the old waterways of the Puyallup and Mowich Rivers were gradually buried beneath more than

2000 feet of solid andesite. On the east side of the volcano, another flow, 900 feet thick and several miles long, deflected the ancestral White River from its course. Another moved along the west face of Goat Mountain. (Today, after hundreds of thousands of years have passed, the cutting action of the dispossessed rivers has eroded most early intracanyon flows into isolated ridges which extend like spokes of a wheel away from the base of Mt. Rainier.)

The War of Fire and Ice

As Mt. Rainier grew, the climate gradually turned cooler. Winters were longer, snow fell to record depths, and the short summers brought insufficient warmth to melt the preceding winter's snowpack. The glaciers, which had retreated to cirques high on neighboring Cascade peaks shortly before Rainier was born, became weighted with compacted layers of unmelted snow, condensed under pressure to sharp granular crystals and began a new advance.

Canyons formerly occupied by streams were now filled to capacity with rivers of ice. V-shaped ravines were broadened as glaciers undermined canyon walls and scraped out valley floors in their progress toward the Cascade mountain front. Wrapped in an icy sheath, Mt. Rainier then lapsed into its longest period of inactivity to date. For years the ice scoured the mountain's flanks, hollowing out cirques and canyons. Streams of meltwater carried the resultant debris from Rainier's shrinking cone and deposited it far away on the Puget lowland. The mountain, so newly built, seemed doomed to piecemeal destruction. Only the thin column of vapor that drifted lazily from the summit crater indicated that the volcano merely slept.

When Rainier finally awoke, the effects were catastrophic. Explosions tore through the solidified plug in the volcano's conduit and sent fragments of old rock, mixed with fresh pumice and ash, thousands of feet into the air. Day was transformed into night as millions of tons of ash descended in a blinding curtain, sealing off light from the sun and blackening Rainier's snowy mantle.

Incandescent lava ejected onto glacial ice produced enormous mud flows. Steam, meltwater, chunks of molten rock, and shattered lava blocks were swept downslope in a chaotic mixture that moved at speeds up to 50 miles per hour. One remarkable lava flow poured down Mt. Rainier's north slope, where it consumed and replaced a glacier at least 1200 feet thick. (Now deeply eroded, it survives as Ptarmigan Ridge).

During the recurrent episodes of Pleistocene glaciation, fire and ice continued to shape the mountain. When the volcano was dormant, ice

Figure 15–3. Mount Rainier from the east. Looking from the south (left) to north (right) the principal features are: Little Tahoma Peak; above it is wedge-shaped Gibraltar Rock; descending from the summit is Emmons Glacier, the largest in the U.S. south of Alaska; dividing the Emmons from the Winthrop Glacier is the inverted-V of Steamboat Prow; above the Winthrop Glacier stands Russell Cliff; Curtis Ridge separates the Winthrop from the shadowed cirque of Carbon Glacier, the headwall of which appears in the extreme right. The road in the foreground leads to Yakima Park and Sunrise Visitor Center. (Photo courtesy of the Washington State Dept. of Commerce and Economic Development.)

carved new trenches in its slopes. When it erupted, these gullies were filled by fresh streams of lava. At the height of glacial expansion, Rainier's entire cone was encased in ice, which extended far westward to join the great ice sheet which smothered the Puget lowland.

After several cycles of glaciation, separated by periods of warm weather, Mt. Rainier further changed its eruptive habits. It no longer emitted canyon-filling lava flows, but produced thinner tongues of lava which piled up around the central crater. As a result, the volcano gained rapidly in height. While the earlier flows had constructed a broad foundation covering more than 100 square miles, the later lavas, rarely exceeding a thickness of 50 to 200 feet, erected a towering superstructure. The mountain began to assume the graceful shape characteristic of the world's great stratovolcanoes.

The Last 75,000 Years

About 75,000 years ago Mt. Rainier attained its maximum size. Although it then stood about 16,000 feet above sea level and was far more symmetrical than it is today, Rainier was never an absolutely perfect cone. Because of its great height, it undoubtedly supported glaciers even during the warmest Pleistocene interglaciations (Figure 15-6B).

New vents then opened on Mt. Rainier's northern flank and built two satellite cones, the eroded remains of which are known as Echo Rock and Observation Rock. Fluid streams of olivine andesite issued from these parasitic volcanoes and flooded the valleys and depressions at Rainier's northern foot to a maximum depth of 500 feet. Their northeastward extent was blocked by Old Desolate mountain, a remnant of the gigantic flow which had filled the Grand Park River canyon more than half a million years earlier.

Following the north side eruptions, Mt. Rainer's volcanic energies declined. Lava flows occasionally broke through the sides of the cone,

Figure 15–4. A rocky island in a sea of ice, Little Tahoma is a monument to the power of glacial erosion. The most conspicuous remnant of Rainier's once continuous eastern slope, Little Tahoma is rapidly crumbling, doomed to be leveled by the Emmons Glacier (foreground), the Ingraham Glacier (right), and the Fryingpan Glacier (top center). (Photo by Bob and Ira Spring.)

such as that which filled a meltwater trench along the margin of a glacier then occupying the Stevens River canyon, but activity at the summit was mainly restricted to the emission of corrosive, acidic gases.

At least three times during the last 65,000 years Mt. Rainier underwent extended periods of intense glacial erosion. During the first two glaciations, ice completely buried the mountain as well as the surrounding peaks, except for the very highest elevations. A glacier occupying the Cowlitz River valley reached a point 65 miles from the volcano.

During the last glacial episode, the Fraser Glaciation, Mt. Rainier was covered in sheets of ice which stripped away what remained of its original surface. Between approximately 25,000 and 10,000 years ago, about 2000 to 3000 feet of material were removed from all sides of the cone. By the time the Pleistocene glaciers had melted, a full one third of the mountain had disappeared.

Although Mt. Rainier erupted little fresh lava during the Fraser Glaciation, steam and other gases rising from magma deep inside the volcano gradually decayed the summit rocks and converted much of them into clay. While weakening the summit, this hydrothermal activity also prevented glaciers from forming inside the crater and significantly lowering the volcano's crest. At the beginning of the Holocene Epoch, Rainier still stood nearly 16,000 feet high (Figure 15-C).

Mt. Rainier in Post-Glacial Time

Most of Mt. Rainier's post-glacial eruptions have further diminished the peak rather than rebuilt it. Between 6600 and 5700 years before the present a particularly destructive cycle of activity took place.

Although drastically changed from the relative symmetry of its pre-Fraser appearance, Rainier at that time was still considerably different from what it is in our day. Not only was it nearly 2000 feet higher, but such prominent landmarks as Little Tahoma Peak and Steamboat Prow bore only a vague resemblance to their present forms. Both outcrops then extended much higher up the mountain and rose no more than a few hundred feet above the general level of the eastern slope. Instead of the gulf which presently separates them there was only a broad but relatively shallow basin, containing the ancestral Emmons Glacier.

A violent explosion brought swift changes, however. Loosened by blasts of steam, the glacier-worn eastern slope of the mountain collapsed and an enormous mass of shattered rock plunged into the canyon of the White River. Water from condensed steam within the rockfall transformed the mass into a mudflow hundreds of feet thick which streamed many miles down the White River valley. Carrying blocks of andesite as much as 30 feet in diameter, the mudflow also incorporated boulders of granodiorite which earthshocks sent tumbling from the walls of the White River canyon.*

The rockfall and mudflow stripped away another layer from Rainier's east side, exposing hydrothermally altered lavas that lay beneath the volcano's outer shell. Some of the newly-exposed lavas and breccias of Mt. Rainier's interior were tinted green, white, dull orange, or sulpur yellow, showing that hot water and chemicals in solution had decomposed once solid rock into soft permeable materials.

The steam explosions which showered rock fragments over a wide area east of the volcano and which triggered the east-side mudflow also initiated a massive avalanche which swept down the Nisqually Glacier on the south side of Mt. Rainier. Transformed into a mudflow, it rushed across Paradise Valley in a single wave 800 feet high.

The Destruction of the Summit

Mt. Rainier lost more than a fifth of a cubic mile in volume during the Paradise and Greenwater mudflows, but the loss was small compared to the destruction which followed. About 5700 years ago, after at least two more eruptive episodes during which hot bombs and ash were hurled out, the most cataclysmic of all Mt. Rainier's Holocene eruptions occurred.

To Indians camped on a hill near the present site of Enumclaw, about 25 miles northwest of the volcano, this eruption at first must have seemed little different from any other which they or their ancestors had witnessed. True, the mountain's summit was wrapped in an unusually large cloud of gray ash which prevented them from seeing exactly what was happening. It is also true that the roaring and thundering of Tahoma—the "mountain that was 'God' "—was more frightening than usual. But these cautious hunters were stationed on high ground, a good 35 miles down the wide, twisting valley which heads on the *east* side of the erupting volcano.

When they first noticed what was advancing toward them they must have dropped their stone implements in terror. Rushing across the prairie toward their camp was a wall of rock and mud nearly 100 feet high. The Indians ran toward a nearby ridge, but the wave of volcanic debris was moving at perhaps 40 miles per hour. They and their settlement were overwhelmed.

The unfortunate Indians never understood what hit them, but geologists have reconstructed the events which led to the formation of

_____
*Crandell has named this mudflow the Greenwater lahar.

this disastrous mudflow,* one of the largest known anywhere. It was caused by the sudden collapse of Mt. Rainier's former summit, which disintegrated like the dome of some great stone cathedral during an earthquake. Steam explosions directed a hurricane of shattered rock over the northeast side of the volcano. Simultaneously, the undermined summit toppled eastward, forming an avalanche of hydrothermally altered rock hundreds of feet high which easily overrode the apex of Steamboat Prow, momentarily submerging the entire structure.

One wave descended the Emmons Glacier between the Prow and Little Tahoma to flood the White River canyon; another sped down the Winthrop Glacier into the West Fork of the White River. Converging beyond the base of the mountain they extended 65 miles to inundate 125 square miles of the Puget lowland west of the Cascade mountain front. One lobe of the flow reached an arm of Puget Sound, burying the sites of Kent, Auburn, Sumner, and Puyallup. Within hours, rocks that had previously stood nearly 16,000 feet above sea level now lay beneath the waters of Puget Sound. Other parts of the former summit filled lowland valleys to create a level plain. Seldom in Holocene time has a volcanic mudflow affected an area so far from its source.

After this catastrophe, Mt. Rainier assumed a totally new appearance. The volcano's summit now housed a void, one and a half to two miles in diameter—a bowl-shaped caldera tipped toward the east (Figure 15-6D). The highest points (which remain today) on the caldera walls were, on the north, Liberty Cap (14,112 feet) and, on the southwest, Point Success (14,150 feet). The western caldera wall, relatively intact, stood somewhat higher, until about 2800 years ago, when another series of rockslides changed the volcano still further.

Originating high on the west face of Mt. Rainier, at a point below Liberty Cap, an avalanche of chemically altered rock was converted into a mudflow which temporarily filled the upper South Puyallup and Tahoma Creek valleys to a depth of at least 1000 feet. The western wall of the summit caldera also crumbled, leaving a wide gap through which icefalls of the Tahoma Glacier now descend. These rockfalls rendered the mountain even more vulnerable to erosion, for they uncovered the volcano's central plug, a yellowish unstratified mass so decayed by heat and chemical action that it offers little resistance to glacial cutting. As a result, the Puyallup and Tahoma Glaciers ate rapidly into the headwalls of this exposed area, creating the large western cirque known as the Sunset Amphitheatre.

---

*The Osceola mudflow, more than half a cubic mile in volume.

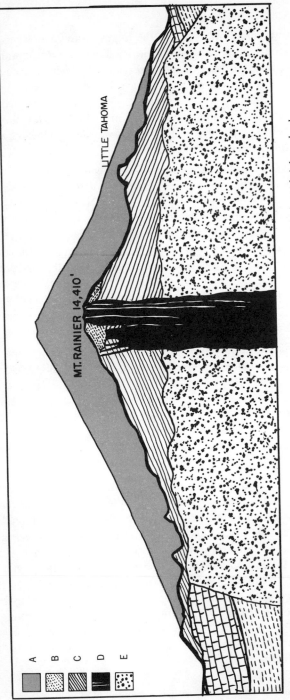

Figure 15–5. Simplified cross-section of Mt. Rainier. The present cone is marked in heavy outline; superimposed over it is the approximate profile of the volcano at the time of its maximum height and volume. (After Fiske, Hopson and Waters, 1963.)

A. Maximum height and volume.
B. Holocene summit cone.
C. Lava flows.
D. Lava conduits.
E. Granodiorite.

Building of the Present Summit Cone

About 2500 years ago Mt. Rainier introduced a welcome variation in its eruptive behavior. For the first time in perhaps 25,000 years a cycle of activity actually "repaired" some of the damage done by earlier outbursts.

Renewed construction began with a discharge of hot ash and molten breadcrust bombs. Blown from vents within the summit caldera, these accumulated around the mountaintop until repeated explosions sent them sliding down the west flank of the mountain. This hot avalanche, at least 200 feet high, traveled down the South Puyallup River valley and ignited groves of timber on the valley floor. Engulfed in a flowing mass with a temperature at least 600 degrees Fahrenheit, many tree trunks were reduced to charcoal. Carbon samples from this deposit enabled scientists to date the eruption which produced it.

In the next stage of activity, Mt. Rainier erupted large volumes of pumice which the winds carried northeast of the peak to blanket Yakima Park, where it lies a foot thick.

Following the pyroclastic eruptions, streams of liquid andesite poured from fissures in the caldera floor and spilled eastward through the low-lying eastern rim. These thin tongues of black, glassy lava did not travel far downslope, but they were sufficient to cause a sudden melting of the Emmons and Nisqually Glaciers. Again, volcanic mudflows poured into the White River and Nisqually valleys, raising canyon floors at least 80 feet above their present levels.

The lava flows quickly built a miniature new Mt. Rainier atop the old, shattered summit. As the cone grew, it eventually filled most of the summit depression left by the catastrophic avalanches of about 3700 years before (Figure 15-6E). This late and rare cone-building episode probably required no more than a few decades. When complete, the beautifully symmetrical young mountain sitting atop the ruins of its predecessor had a base a mile across and a crest that stood at least 1000 feet above the now-buried eastern lip of the old caldera.

A second, briefer, eruption of lava occurred some time after the first, forming a somewhat larger crater east of the older vent. Thirteen hundred feet across and perhaps 500 feet deep, this younger crater tilts noticeably toward the east. The point where the two recent craters overlap—now called Columbia Crest— marks the highest elevation of the volcano.

Despite its youth, the summit cone shows minor indications of glacial cutting— a few shallow depressions separated by low ridges preview future glacial trenches and basins. Were it not for constant heat and steam emission, glaciers might already have breached the crater rims. Occasional brief eruptions of steam and ash have originated at the summit vents during the past 2000 years, the last occurring within historic time. But, contrasted with the countless tons of material removed daily from the volcano by landslides, glaciers, and meltwater, the amount of new lava produced in recent centuries is negligible.

Our journey into Mt. Rainier's past has shown the volcano growing from a small cinder cone to an ice-covered giant; from a classic smooth-sided cone to its present craggy mass. Although its life-story has already spanned more than a million years, Mt. Rainier will be with us and our descendants for eons to come.

Mt. Rainier's Historic Eruptions

"Historic" time in the Pacific Northwest goes back scarcely a century and a half. Almost until the American Civil War the inhabitants of what is now western Washington were a mere handful of itinerant trappers, traders or employees of the Hudson's Bay Company. Tiny settlements at Olympia, Tacoma, and Seattle did not really take root until the 1850s. Despite the scanty population, however, casual observers logged no fewer than 16 apparent eruptions of Mt. Rainier between 1820 and 1894.[2]

The earliest historic activity supposedly occurred "about 1820." Years after the alleged event, an aged Indian named John Hiaton reported having seen "fire," heard "noises," and felt "an earthquake" emanating from Mt. Rainier.[3] He also said that his ancestors had witnessed many such disturbances in the past. The next printed reference to activity on Rainier appears in the bulletins of the noted Belgian seismologist, A. Perrey. For 1841 he recorded "violent" eruptions of Mt. Raynier [sic], Oregon."[4] Perrey also cited eruptions for 1842 and November 23, 1843. It is possible that he derived these dates from the published journal of Captain John Frémont who had written on November 13, 1843, that "at this time, two of the great snowy cones, Mount Regnier [sic] and St. Helens, were in action."[5] Frémont specified "the 23rd of the preceeding November (1842)" as the date when St. Helens scattered ashes as far as The Dalles, Oregon. It seems suspiciously coincidental that Perrey cites November 23 as also marking an eruption of Rainier.

An early Northwest missionary, Father De Smet, alluded to "signs of activity" at Mt. Rainier in 1846.[6] In his book on Mt. Rainier National Park, F. E. Matthes further asserts that "actual records exist of slight eruptions in 1843, 1854, 1858, and 1870."[7] Neither De Smet nor Matthes states his authority or gives any confirmatory details. As pointed out in Chapter 17, it seems strange that Matthes' dates correspond precisely to times when Mt. Baker is known to have erupted.

Because so many of these early accounts are brief to the point of obscurity, until recently most geologists dismissed them outright. After studying the historical records, Hopson, Waters, Bender, and Rubin (1962) concluded that unusual cloud formations, dust from rock-falls, and other non-volcanic phenomena had been mistaken for eruptions. In 1967, however, Donal R. Mullineaux discovered a previously unrecognized deposit of fresh, light brown pumice from Mt. Rainier. By dating newly formed glacial moraines on which the thin sprinkling of pumice occurred, Mullineaux determined that at least once between 1820 and 1854 the volcano had indeed been active.[8]

Indirect confirmation of unusual thermal conditions in the crater during the mid-19th century comes from the account of a Yakima Indian named Saluskin. According to his testimony, given when he was a very old man, he had, in June, 1855, guided two "King George men"—the Indians' term for Caucasians—to the east flank of Mt. Rainier. Climbing via the Emmons Glacier route, these early mountaineers apparently reached the summit.[9] After their safe return they told Saluskin, who had waited at base camp, that there was "ice all over top, lake in center and smoke or steam coming out all around like sweat-house."[10] One is inclined to credit the authenticity of this early ascent, if only because there is no other way for the men to have observed these summit features than by reaching the crater rim.

Today the eastern crater contains snow and ice equivalent to one billion gallons of water,[11] quite enough to form a small lake. If volcanic heat in 1854 was sufficient to melt the crater icepack and create a body of standing water, this is a strong indication that there was more thermal activity at Rainier then than at present. The alleged "eruption" of 1854 may have been a column of water vapor rising from fumaroles surrounding the crater lake.

When the first "official" climb of Mt. Rainier was made by Hazard Stevens and Philemon Van Trump in August, 1870, quantities of steam and sulphur fumes were noted in both summit craters, but there was no sign of a lake.[12] Thermal activity at the summit had by then evidently decreased to the relatively mild but constant state it maintains to this day. The 1870 party took refuge overnight in the steam caves of the west crater. Nauseated by hydrogen sulphide and alternately scalded by steam jets or frozen by icy gusts, Stevens and Van Trump spent a miserable night.

No evidence of newly erupted material was noticed in August, 1870, which casts doubt on the authenticity of an eruption which Matthes (1914) reported for that year. However, a violent earthquake the following September triggered a large rockfall from Liberty Cap, the mountain's northern peak. According to Plummer (1893), about 80 acres of material cascaded downslope, leaving a nearly perpendicular face on the southern side of Liberty Cap. Very likely the dustcloud from this avalanche was mistaken for a volcanic explosion.

Several other signs of activity were reported in the 1870s and 1880s. Nearly all of these reputed outbursts were viewed from a considerable distance, so many of them may have been little more than trailing streamers of fog, or dust kicked up by landslides. A few, however, may have been actual expulsions of steam, gas, and small amounts of volcanic ash. These eruptions, if genuine, were too feeble to leave any recognizable deposit.

Frederick G. Plummer, an early Northwest scientist, cites activity beginning at 4 p.m. on October 19, 1873, and lasting for a full week.[13] The *Washington Standard*, an Olympia newspaper, reported on October 25, 1873, that the previous Sunday afternoon "clouds of smoke were seen pouring from the highest peak of Mount Rainier. The smoke was seen until nearly dark when clouds shut down upon the mountain hiding it from view."[14] The following November 29 the same paper again noted that "smoke has been ascending from the highest peak of Mount Rainier, within the past few days."

Len Longmire, a pioneer settler after whose family the community at Mt. Rainier's southwestern base was named, recalled sightings of "a series of brown, billowy clouds issuing from the crater in 1879 and again in 1882."[15] In his authoritative textbook, *Volcanoes*, Gordon A. Macdonald accepts Longmire's date of 1882 as marking the last activity on Rainier.[16] Plummer (1893), recorded a later disturbance: "On June 16, 1884, at about 7 p.m., jets of steam were seen shooting upward from the summit of Mount Tacoma to a considerable height. This phenomena [sic.] was repeated at short intervals until darkness cut off the view. There was no fire, and no earth tremors were reported."

The last 19th century report of an "eruption" was highly publicized by the Seattle *Post Intelligencer* and the *Tacoma Daily Ledger* in November-December, 1894. Although the stories run by these enterprising dailies are by far the most specific and detailed of any accounts, it seems doubtful that anything more than journalistic imagination was active.

In his newspaper essay of 1893, Plummer had eagerly looked forward to future volcanic upheavals, but denied that Mt. Rainier was active in 1894. In a preface to his compilation of historic eruptions in Oregon, Washington, and Alaska, he wrote: "There can be no doubt that many eruptions are reported which might be contradicted if examination were possible. For example, the reports of the eruption and change in the summit of Mount Tacoma [Rainier] from November 21 to December 25, 1894, filled many columns of press dispatches, and possibly were intended for that purpose. December 25th was the most perfect day for observation, and, with my 6½-inch refractor, the crater-peak and its surroundings were carefully examined, and no change could be seen. No eruption was noted, other than the usual emission of steam, which varies with the barometer.

"However, reports came in later from a press party* [of the Seattle P-I] which claimed to have reached the slope of the mountain and witnessed an eruption of smoke. The party was about five miles from the summit, and my telescope, with low power, brought the summit within half a mile. Although this was the clearest and most definite report of an eruption, yet it is so flatly contradicted by the continuous telescopic observations and the later examinations of climbers, that it is omitted from the table (of reported eruptions)."[17]

Recent Thermal Activity

Although Mt. Rainier has not had a *bona fide* eruption in nearly a century, neither has the mountain remained entirely at rest. In addition to areas of hot rock and fumaroles on the summit cone, the volcano still produces occasional steam explosions on its flanks. Reports of these phenomena seem to have increased in frequency during the past decade. Beginning in the early 1960s summer climbers were sometimes startled by hearing loud reports and seeing columns of vapor pour from crevices in the rocks. In 1961 steam blasted a hole near Gibraltar Rock, sending a column of pressurized vapor 200 feet into the air and scattering debris over the nearby Cowlitz Glacier.[19] This vent remained active throughout the summer, though with diminishing energy.[20] In March, 1965, skiers were amazed to observe clouds of steam spouting from a ridge above the Kautz Glacier and setting off an "avalanche."[21]

A much greater avalanche—the largest in historic time—may have been initiated by a steam explosion on December 14, 1963. About noon on that date, forest rangers about 12 miles northeast of the mountain

---

*In its issue of December 29, 1894, the Seattle *Post Intelligencer* reported that the climbing party, headed by Major Ingraham "noticed smoke and steam rising from the mountain. . . . Shooting upward with nothing to intercept the view except the clear blue sky, were jets of steam like immense geysers, while from another place rose slowly and in a perpendicular line a column of dense black smoke. . . . The party . . . was only turned back by the firm conviction that to push on would be certain death."[18] The *Tacoma Daily Ledger* even published a front-page drawing of Mt. Rainier in eruption, based on the climbers' description.

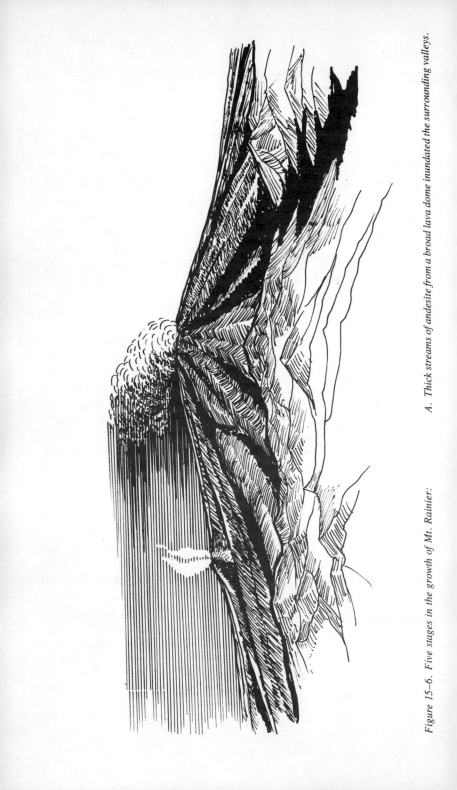

Figure 15–6. *Five stages in the growth of Mt. Rainier:*

A. *Thick streams of andesite from a broad lava dome inundated the surrounding valleys.*

B. At the zenith of its conical perfection, about 75,000 years ago, Mt. Rainier towered 16,000 feet above the Puget Lowland.

C. After repeated glaciations, the cone was reduced to an irregular mass of steep cliffs and cirques. Seen from the east, the emerging forms of Little Tahoma, Steamboat Prow and Russell Cliff began to appear.

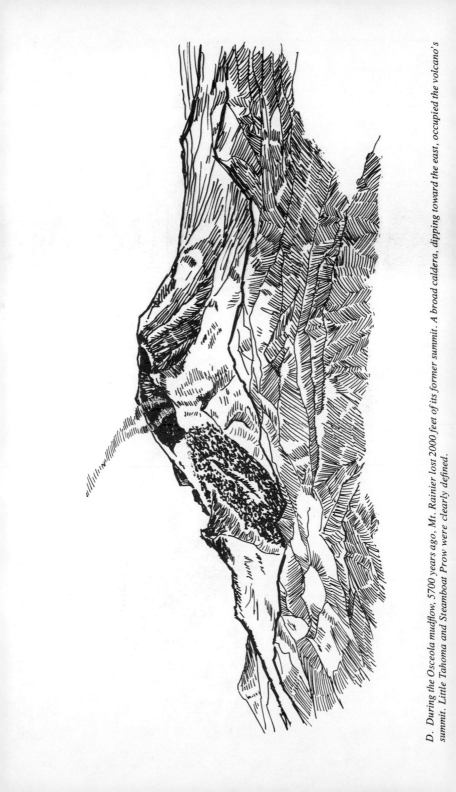

D. During the Osceola mudflow, 5700 years ago. Mt. Rainier lost 2000 feet of its former summit. A broad caldera, dipping toward the east, occupied the volcano's summit. Little Tahoma and Steamboat Prow were clearly defined.

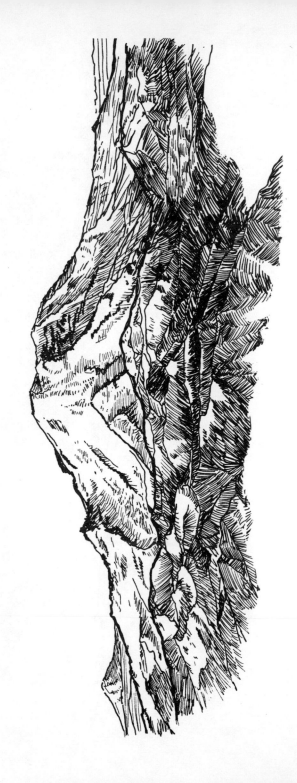

E. About 2000 years ago renewed activity built the present summit cone.

heard "a very loud, sharp boom in the direction of Mount Rainier."[22] When clouds and falling snow cleared enough for the rangers to observe the eastern slope through field glasses, they could see a large amount of rock debris covering the lower Emmons Glacier.

What the rangers could not perceive from their location was that approximately 14 million cubic yards of lavas and breccias had fallen from the north face of Little Tahoma Peak. Plummeting straight downward for 1700 feet onto the glacier's surface the avalanche struck with tremendous force. Because of its large mass and the steepness of its landing site, the avalanche shot across the Emmons' surface buoyed up by a cushion of compressed air, at speeds up to 100 miles per hour.[23] When it reached the glacier's snout it simply soared into space. A stream-gauging station, six feet high, was untouched as millions of tons of rock hurtled overhead. Where the upper White River valley curves or is constricted, the flowing mass of rock fragments and trapped air surged up canyon walls as high as 300 feet. When it finally came to rest, a scant half mile from the White River Campground, it had traveled about four miles from its source while dropping some 6200 feet in altitude. Some of the boulders transported are as large as buildings. One measures 60 by 130 by 160 feet and weighs approximately 50,000 tons!

Later studies revealed that at least seven separate rockfalls and avalanches had taken place in quick succession.[24] The plywood gauge house, undisturbed by one avalanche, was later carried several hundred feet by a blast of air escaping from the margin of another avalanche which stopped a short distance away. At least two square miles of the Emmons Glacier and upper White River valley were covered by the rockfalls. Had the event occurred in summer, a number of hikers might have been killed.

More recent steam explosions have been observed on the west side of the mountain. In August and September, 1967, clouds of water vapor and "steam" were seen billowing from cliffs above the South Tahoma Glacier. During the same period, floods and mudflows repeatedly descended the Tahoma Creek valley. Described as causing a deep rumbling noise and vibrations of the ground, these small lahars swept large boulders downstream and generated waves of mud up to 15 feet high.[25] Further sightings of "steam and smoke" rising from the west face of the volcano were reported in August, 1968, and February, 1969.[26] These rockfalls and slurry floods may have been initiated by a steam vent located beneath the South Tahoma Glacier.[27]

A more threatening manifestation of Mt. Rainier's internal heat occurred high on the Emmons Glacier during the summer of 1969. Between an elevation of 10,000 and 13,000 feet the normally intact ice surface broke into a network of potholes and crevasses. In some places, gaps in the ice opened wide enough to reveal bare rock beneath the glacier. This melting by subsurface heating was brief, however, and by the summer of 1970 new ice and snow had filled in most of the caved-in area. Nonetheless, such melt-depressions on glaciers—unrelated to weather conditions—are the kind of warning to be expected when a dormant volcano is preparing to erupt.

The "Volcano Watch"

Because of these—and other—signs of geologic restlessness, scientists at the University of Washington and the United States Geological Survey keep a "volcano watch" on Mt. Rainier.

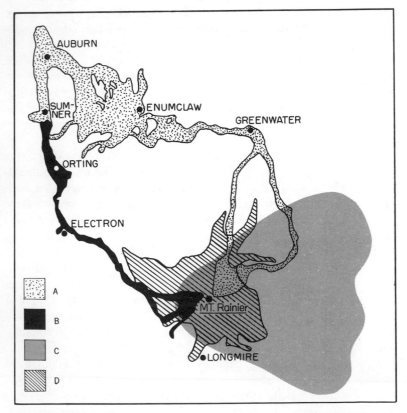

A. *Osceola mudflow*   C. *Extent of airborne pyroclastic deposits*

B. *Electron mudflow*   D. *Lava flows*

Figure 15–7. Map of the area covered by lavas, mudflows, and pyroclastics from Mt. Rainier. Note that the Osceola (about 5700 years ago) and the Electron (about 600 years ago) mudflows overwhelmed the sites of several towns and cities in western Washington. (Based on Crandell, 1973.)

In the 1960s, the U.S.G.S. began taking aerial photographs and infrared images of the summit craters, Little Tahoma Peak, and the Emmons and South Tahoma Glaciers. In addition, seismographs were placed at various locations on the mountain, one as high as Camp Muir at the 10,000-foot level. These quake-monitoring stations record swarms of microearthquakes centered beneath the peak, which should they significantly increase in number and intensity, may mean that magma is rising through the volcano's conduit toward the surface. The tremors thus far recorded demonstrate that some activity continues in Mt. Rainier's subterranean magma chamber.[28]

The infrared surveys have officially confirmed what climbers have always known—Mt. Rainier's summit craters are definitely hot.[29] The zones of most intense volcanic heat were found along the northwestern rim of the east crater, the north side of the west crater, and along a pattern of concentric arcs on the western flank of the summit cone. A later survey indicated a possible increase of thermal anomalies along the southern rim of the west crater, but that may have resulted from imperfections inherent in the infrared techniques.[30] In general, the hottest areas correspond to swaths of exposed rock, which stand out as black patches amid the summit icefields.

When geologist and mountaineer Dee Molenaar measured the heat generated at fumaroles in both summit craters, he found that the steam issues at temperatures of about 186 degrees Fahrenheit (the boiling point of water at 14,000 feet).[31] In the summer of 1970, Robert Moxham of the U.S. Geological Survey installed inside the west crater an instrument which was programmed to take the volcano's daily temperature and relay it via space satellite to a ground station for interpretation.[32] This sophisticated device operated for only five weeks before the sub-zero weather and howling gales of the fiercest autumn storms in a decade destroyed key units of the equipment. Even so, the heat sensing and relaying instruments functioned long enough to demonstrate the feasibility of utilizing space satellites in monitoring volcanic temperatures.[33]

The Summit Steam Caves

Weary climbers who reach 14,410-foot Columbia Crest seldom have either the desire or time to explore one of Mt. Rainier's most interesting features. These are the "steam caves," a 1½ mile-long maze of twisting corridors and high-ceilinged caverns melted beneath the snow which almost fills the twin summit craters. So far as is now known, Mt. Rainier, Mt. Baker, and Mt. Wrangell in Alaska have the only volcanic craters on earth containing such a labyrinth of ice tunnels.

Snow fills the east crater to an estimated depth of 360 feet, but steam jets and fumaroles along the inner crater walls have melted out a system of passageways having a cumulative length of at least a mile. These tunnels, which are actually spaces between the inside slope of the crater and the overlying icecap, are extremely steep and littered with blocks of andesite, mud, and pumice. The lowest point to which scientists have thus far descended is about 540 feet below the highest elevation of the crater rim,[34] or 340 feet beneath the surface of the crater snowpack. The crater floor, sloping downward at an angle of 32 degrees, here touches the ice ceiling and prevents further exploration.[35]

The western crater—only about 1000 feet across—has a smaller cave system. But it does contain an accessible pool of meltwater which, in August, 1972, measured about 120 by 40 feet and was 18 feet deep.[36] Mt. Rainier thus boasts another unique feature—a crater lake located 14,000 feet above sea level and under an arching canopy of pure ice. This unnamed lake may, however, vanish as the delicate balance between steam-melt and annual snowfall inevitably undergoes change.

The Future

What will happen when Mt. Rainier erupts again? Geologists of the U.S. Geological Survey have recently made extensive studies of probable dangers to be expected from a future outburst.[37] As is the case with other glacier-bearing Cascade volcanoes, the chief hazard stems from volcanic mudflows created when hot lava or ash suddenly melts large quantities of ice and snow. The resulting floods and debris flows are especially dangerous because they move downslope at high speeds and can extend to low-lying areas many miles beyond their point of origin. From our review of the volcano's past history, we recall the immense impact of the Osceola Mudflow.

If renewed activity centers in the summit craters, the chemically altered rocks along the northern crater rims could easily give way, releasing perhaps a billion or more gallons of water derived from the snow now contained in these vents. Should fresh lava rise into the eastern crater, steam explosions caused by hot magma in contact with meltwater might also rupture the crater walls, causing another Osceola-type mudflow.

Judging by the effects which volcanic eruptions during the last 7000 years have had on nearby valleys, Crandell lists the Puyallup, Tahoma, Nisqually, and White River valleys as among the zones of highest risk.[38] The Cowlitz and Carbon River valleys seem to have been seldom affected by mudflows during the past several thousand years.

Since prevailing winds from the Pacific would probably carry the eruption clouds eastward from the volcano, it seems unlikely that Seattle, Tacoma, Olympia, or other Puget Sound cities would suffer a heavy ash-fall. Towns downwind such as Ellensburg or Yakima, might find their air polluted, water supplies muddied, and machinery clogged by ash. Only if Mt. Rainier exploded on a scale comparable to the catastrophic eruption of Mt. Mazama 6600 years ago would there be a serious threat to population centers to the west.

With pyroclastic eruptions restricted to the size of those which preceded the building of the present summit cone 2000 years ago, appreciable damage would probably be confined to a radius of 10 to 15 miles downwind from the crater. Curious persons standing on ridges at a closer range, even though they would be safe from mudflows in the canyons below, might easily be struck by flying chunks of rock or by falling pumice. It is well to remember that previous Holocene eruptions have thrown rocks up to four feet long as far as eight miles from the summit.

Of course there is always the possibility that Mt. Rainier might produce an eruption of much greater magnitude than any it has known in the past 7000 years. In that event, no one can really predict what would happen. If such a paroxysm should seem imminent, a speedy removal to high ground as far upwind from the volcano as possible would be highly recommended.

Visiting Mt. Rainier

As a major national park visited by hundreds of thousands of persons each year, Mt. Rainier Park is accessible from almost every side by paved roads. In addition, hundreds of miles of dirt logging roads and hiking trails of varying difficulty criss-cross the park from heavily forested valley floors to wind-swept meadows at timberline and above.

The most popular automobile route is that from Longmire at the mountain's southwestern base, to Paradise Valley, a mile high, where an inn, restaurant, observation tower and museum, information center, and other tourist facilities cater to the public.

The Nisqually Glacier Vista trail provides memorable views of the three-mile-long river of ice. An undemanding one-mile round-trip through flowering meadows and across clear rivulets, the trail runs uphill to the left of the Visitor Center.

For a panorama of the Cascades south of Rainier, including the snowy cones of Adams, St. Helens, and Hood (102 miles distant), hike 2.5 miles from the Visitor Center to a meadow at 7000 feet.

Early morning and after five in the evening, when summer haze is at a minimum, are the best times.

Sunrise Visitor Center at Yakima Park, on the volcano's east side, offers a close-up view of Emmons Glacier, the largest in the conterminous United States. Follow the Stevens Canyon road (with its spectacular bluffs and water falls) around Rainier's southern base, and, following directional markers, drive up to the 6000-foot level. Sunrise offers no overnight accommodations, but the White River Campground, a short distance downriver from the snout of the Emmons Glacier, has excellent campsites with water.

Climbing Rainier, at any season, should be attempted only with experienced guides and proper equipment, including ice ax, rope, crampons, overnight supplies, warm clothing and other indispensables. Rainier is so high that it makes its own highly changeable weather; sudden storms may rage around the summit while valleys below bask in sunlight. For an authoritative discussion of the numerous climbing routes, consult Fred Beckey's *Cascade Alpine Guide:Climbing and High Routes*, The Mountaineers, Seattle, 1973, pp. 85-128.

The Skyline Trail, intersecting the park, is part of the Pacific Crest Trail which follows the Cascades' north-south axis throughout their length. The Wonderland Trail encircles the mountain itself.

Chapter 15 – References

1. Matthes, 1914, p. 7.
2. Hopson, Waters, Bender, and Rubin, 1962; Holden, 1898.
3. Plummer, 1893.
4. Holden, 1898.
5. Frémont, 1845, pp. 193-94.
6. Plummer, 1893.
7. Matthes, 1914, p. 9.
8. Mullineaux and others, 1969.
9. Haines, 1962, pp. 15-17; Kirk, 1968, pp. 47-48.
10. Ibid., p. 48.
11. Kiver and Mumma, 1971.
12. Stevens, 1876.
13. Holden, 1898.
14. Hopson, et al., 1962, p. 637.
15. Coombs, 1960.
16. Macdonald, 1972, p. 441.
17. Holden, 1898, pp. 24-25.
18. Hopson, et al., 1962, pp. 637-38.
19. Schear, 1965, p. 33.
20. Crandell and Fahnestock, 1965, pp. A27-29.
21. Schear, 1965, p. 30.
22. Crandell and Fahnestock, 1965.
23. Ibid., p. A20.
24. Crandell, 1969, pp. 35-36.
25. Crandell, 1971, pp. 58-62.
26. Ibid.
27. Crandell, written comm., 1974.
28. Unger and Decker, 1970.
29. Moxham, 1970.
30. Ibid.
31. Molenaar, 1971, p. 176.
32. Ibid., p. 177.
33. Moxham and others, 1972, pp. 198-99.
34. Kiver and Mumma, 1971.
35. Kiver, written comm., 1975.
36. Tacoma News Tribune, August 29, 1972, p. A3.
37. Crandell and Mullineaux, 1967; Crandell, 1973.
38. Crandell, 1973.

16
Glacier Peak—White Goddess of the North Cascades

According to Greek mythology, Mt. Olympus was the home of the 12 major Hellenic gods. If the dozen greatest Cascade peaks were to be identified with the ruling deities of classical antiquity, lonely Glacier Peak would undoubtedly be the mountain to typify Artemis. Known to the Romans as Diana, this virgin goddess shunned civilized life and withdrew into the wilderness to roam with the wild creatures who inhabit it. Given her choice of a Cascade dwelling place today, she would find Glacier Peak ideal, for it is the most remote and inaccessible volcano in the range.

Although at 10,451 feet only about 300 feet lower than Mt. Baker, this solitary peak is unfamiliar even to many alpine enthusiasts. No roads approach the mountain, and one must hike many miles through extremely rough terrain to reach its base. Surrounded by deep valleys, cliffs, and forbidding ramparts of ice, Glacier Peak bestows familiarity only to those willing to strive for it.

Named for the many glaciers visible from her summit, Glacier Peak and the surrounding mountains seem to be in the midst of a contemporary Ice Age. Although existing glaciers are smaller than those which buried the region during the Pleistocene Epoch, aerial views of the area resemble Arctic landscapes—a sea of ice through which loom isolated peaks and ridges.

Not only are the Cascades broadest in this northern stretch, summits are consistently higher—many exceed 8000 feet. Glacier Peak sits on top of a long ridge of this elevation, immediately west of the Cascade divide. Hikers can reach the volcano from the west via the White Chuck Valley, or the Suiattle River valley; from the east, it may be approached from the western tip of fjord-like Lake Chelan, which extends from the eastern border of the Cascades deep into their interior.

The Geology of Glacier Peak

Although Glacier Peak's chief distinction among geologists is the widespread layer of pumiceous ash it erupted about 12,000 years ago, most of its cone was built by relatively quiet flows of dacite lava. The earliest flows, unusually fluid for dacites, issued from a vent on the east slope of Lime Ridge, a northwest trending spur on the Cascade crest. The earlier lavas poured eastward into valleys tributary to the Suiattle River.[1] They were blocked on the west by the high mass of Lime Ridge until after the volcano had grown to a height of perhaps 2000 feet above its surroundings; then lavas were able to spill westward into the ancestral White Chuck River and related stream valleys (Figure 16-2).

Because all recognized Glacier Peak lavas exhibit normal magnetic polarity,[3] the cone was presumably built during the last 770,000 years. Its activity continued until at least 12,000 years ago, but there is no way to date the first eruptions.

The Latest Eruptions

As is the case with most Cascade volcanoes, the Glacier Peak eruptions which occurred after the melting of canyon-filling Pleistocene glaciers are the best known. Lava flows and pyroclastics extruded upon ice-free surfaces have a much better chance of remaining in place long enough for geologists to study them. Although material erupted into the valleys is almost always reworked and redistributed by streams, extremely large valley fills and pumicefalls lying on flat ridge tops are often well preserved.

Glacier Peak's final activity seems to have occurred during a period from 13,500 to 12,000 years ago.[3] Perhaps among the first of these Holocene eruptions was the extrusion of two dacite domes high on the south and east flanks of the volcano. Outcrops of the southern dome, which now forms Disappointment Peak, appear between altitudes of 8755 feet to as low as 7200 feet.[4] Intersecting earlier lavas of the summit cone, the dome forms a bulbous protrusion on the otherwise smooth southern slope.

A second dacite dome, roughly contemporaneous with the first, rose on the east side of the mountain. Similar to Crater Rock on the south side of Mt. Hood, this dacite mass oozed upward above a vent located 2000 to 3000 feet below the summit. Extremely viscous and brittle, it rapidly crumbled sending avalanches and mudflows into the Suiattle River valley below. These recurrent slides and mudflows, alternating with meltwater floods, overwhelmed the Suiattle River valley, and pushed the river against bedrock slopes on the east, radically changing the drainage pattern at Glacier Peak's eastern base.[5]

Figure 16–1. Heavily glaciated, Glacier Peak surmounts a labyrinth of sharp ridges and twisting valleys. This volcano has been quiet for nearly 12,000 years, but it produced one of the most violently explosive eruptions in the history of the Pacific Northwest. (Photo by Bob and Ira Spring.)

As with Crater Rock, the eastern dome seems to have developed in several stages. After the first eruptive episode, streams cut V-shaped gullies in the valley fill; then, when volcanic activity resumed, a fresh wave of shattered rock and sand poured into the newly cut stream beds. Since several lava flows lie over the debris fan— and are also found on the flanks of the main cone—it seems that fluid eruptions accompanied or followed the growth of the domes. Altogether, at least a full cubic mile of new material moved into the Suiattle River valley during these eruptions.[6]

The Final Explosions

After quietly pouring out lava for most of its history, about 12,000 years ago Glacier Peak burst into violent activity, expelling immense quantities of light gray pumice, which prevailing winds carried hundreds of miles to the east. According to Dr. Stephen C. Porter, a University of Washington geologist, a series of at least nine eruptions, closely spaced in time, laid down a layer of dacite pumice up to 12 feet thick as far as 12 miles downwind from the volcano.[7] A blanket of ash was deposited over most of eastern Washington, northeastern Oregon, the Idaho panhandle, western Montana, and parts of southern Canada. In the postglacial period in the United States, only the ashfall from Mt. Mazama covered a larger territory. Because these two geologically recent eruptions left distinctive ash layers of such vast dimensions, scientists use the two deposits to help date other geological formations or archaeological remains that are found associated with them. Glacier Peak, in its last significant eruptions, thus produced a time marker which makes an extremely useful scientific tool.

During or shortly after these outbursts, large quantities of pumice, a third of a cubic mile in volume, slid or were washed down the west side of the volcano into the White Chuck valley. This White Chuck fill resembles the Suiattle debris fan in having been deposited in a series of avalanches and mudflows. Normal stream sediments seem to have added to the accumulation, which extends for several miles down the White Chuck valley.[8]

In spite of the large volumes of pumice discharged, Glacier Peak did not collapse like ancient Mt. Mazama. Instead, it produced yet another violent summit eruption. This time a glowing avalanche raced down the west slope of the volcano, carrying chunks of dense dacite lava, pumice bombs, and other fragmental debris. This hot avalanche blanketed the older pumice deposits with 15 to 50 feet of compacted, glassy ash far down the White Chuck valley. Creeks and rivers have since excavated deep ravines in the volcanic deposits of both the Suiattle and White Chuck valleys.[9]

Several other thin layers of pumice and ash have been recognized at Glacier Peak, but it is not certain whether these came from the volcano itself or from other vents nearby. Near the west base of Lime Ridge, for example, stands the White Chuck Cinder Cone, which erupted pyroclastics as well as several basalt lava flows. Its eroded remnants are overlain by a thin white ash which may represent a fallout from the Mt. Mazama eruption of 6600 years ago. The age of the cone is unknown, but it is definitely post-glacial and antedates a Neoglaciaton of 3500 to 2000 years ago.[10]

Since these last eruptions, glaciers have continued to modify Glacier Peak's cone. Lava ribs stand hundreds of feet above the icefields that surround them, indicating that much, if not all, of the volcano's original surface has been removed. Glacier Peak's earliest lava flows, which filled narrow gorges to the east, now underlie ridge tops or appear as isolated fragments, their connection to the main cone severed by ice and stream cutting. Only the outlines of a summit crater remain, breached at both the eastern and western crater walls, from which, respectively, flow the Chocolate and Scimitar Glaciers. The north crater wall is highly

Figure 16-2. The growth of Glacier Peak volcano:

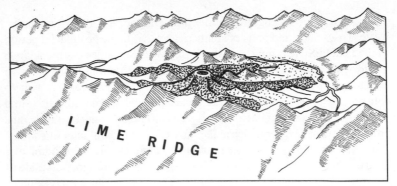

A. *In Pleistocene time, the earliest Glacier Peak lavas erupted east of Lime Ridge and flowed into valleys tributary to the Suiattle River.*

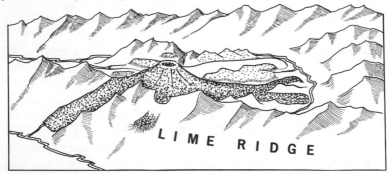

B. *Glacier Peak overtopped Lime Ridge and sent streams of lava westward into tributaries of the White Chuck valley; some of these flows are dissected by erosion. On the east, erosional remnants of the oldest flows, which filled valleys, are now perched on top of ridges. Younger flows descended ancestral Vista Creek and Chocolate Dusty Creek.*

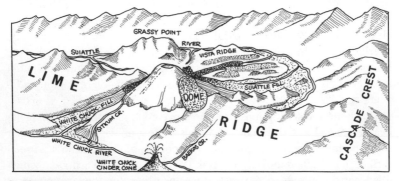

C. *The present valleys were glaciated in Holocene time. The oldest flows were eroded into isolated ridge caps, and the younger ones into remnants clinging to valley sides. Valley bottom flows have descended Vista Creek and Kennedy Creek. Disappointment Peak Dome issued from the south side of Glacier Peak and the Suiattle fill was discharged from a dome on the east side. An explosive eruption has mantled the area with pumice. On the west the pumice has washed down to form the White Chuck fill, which was overlain shortly thereafter by a thin layer of glowing avalanche deposits. (After Tabor and Crowder, 1969.)*

oxidized, with some of its rocks stained a blotchy yellow, suggesting that they have been attacked by steam and acid fumes.[11]

Although there are no fumaroles at the summit, the presence of three hot springs on the flanks of the cone—the Gamma, Kennedy, and Sulphur Hot Springs—suggests that magma still exists at depth. But Glacier Peak has probably had fewer Holocene eruptions than any of the other four major volcanoes in Washington state. Even so, the 1973 outbreak of the Helgafell volcano in Iceland, thought to have been dead at least 5000 years, may indicate that announcements of Glacier Peak's demise, like Mark Twain's, may someday prove greatly exaggerated.

To see Glacier Peak

Viewing Glacier Peak in its entirety requires a substantial amount of physical effort. Probably the easiest route to views of the volcano is the White Chuck River road. Take Exit 194 east from Interstate 5, then follow signs to Granite Falls. From Granite Falls follow the Mountain Loop Highway to the White Chuck River Road, No. 314. Follow the road about 7 miles to a marked viewpoint where Glacier Peak looms at the head of the valley. To get a closer view of the mountain requires hiking. (See Meadow Mountain, hike number 45, in *101 Hikes in the North Cascades*, by the Mountaineers.) At mile 5½ on the White Chuck River road, turn

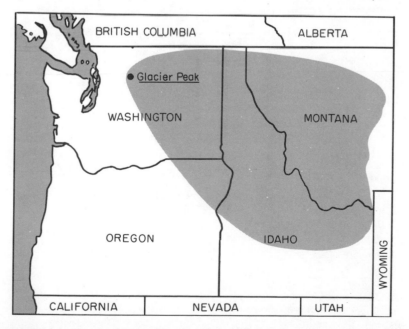

Figure 16–3. Map showing the area covered by ashfalls from the eruptions of Glacier Peak (about 12,000 years ago).

232 Fire and Ice

left onto Straight Creek Road shortly after crossing the White Chuck River. Climb and switchback, following "Meadow Mountain" signs at junctions, to the road end at 5 miles, elevation 3400 feet. Climb a steep trail for 1¼ miles to a meadow. Cross a small brook, and for the best views, hike the main trail eastward for 2 miles to a 5800 foot spur ridge of Meadow Mountain.

The above views are of the west side of the mountain. To see the eastern side of Glacier requires time, stamina, a certain amount of hiking expertise, and route information beyond the scope of this book.

Chapter 16 – References

1. *Ford, 1959; Tabor and Crowder, 1969, p. 24.*
2. *Tabor and Crowder, 1969, pp. 25-27, 57.*
3. *Ibid., p. 27.*
4. *Ibid.*
5. *Ibid., p. 45.*
6. *Ibid., p. 24-25, 27.*
7. *Williams, 1975, p. 133.*
8. *Tabor and Crowder, 1969, pp. 41-43.*
9. *Ibid., pp. 43-44.*
10. *Ibid., pp. 44-47.*
11. *Ibid., p. 24.*

17
Mt. Baker—
The "Great White Watcher"

When Captain Vancouver sailed into Puget Sound in April, 1792, his third lieutenant, Joseph Baker, sighted "a very high, conspicuous, craggy mountain . . . towering above the clouds; as low down as it was visible it was covered with snow; and south of it was a long ridge of very rugged snowy mountains, much less elevated, which seemed to stretch to a considerable distance." Two years earlier the Spanish explorer Manuel Quimper had also seen the peak and had christened it *La Montana del Carmelo* — loosely translated as the "Great White Watcher." [1]

Northernmost of the American Cascade volcanoes, Mt. Baker receives an extremely heavy annual snowfall and supports 20 square miles of active glaciers. Since it is almost entirely sheathed in ice and, in clear weather, visible throughout northwestern Washington and southwestern British Columbia, the Nooksack Indians' name for it, *Koma Kulshan* ("white steep mountain") seems more appropriate than that which Vancouver assigned the peak.

To the Lummi tribe, Mt. Baker was known simply as *Kulshan*, which reportedly means "shot at the point," [2] an apparent reference to a prehistoric eruption that shattered the former symmetry of the summit. Geologically speaking, the Lummi title is suggestive, for Baker's principal crater, now located several hundred feet below the summit, was blasted open late in the volcano's history, probably in postglacial time. The formation of this vent undoubtedly reshaped Baker's summit area. Today this crater is the most thermally active in the Cascade Range. Recently renamed the Sherman Crater to distinguish it from the ice-filled summit vent, it has almost continuously discharged varying amounts of steam and hydrogen sulphide gas since the mid-19th century.

On March 10, 1975, a dramatic increase in fumarolic activity took place. In the late afternoon on that date, Roy Ashe, operator of the Upper

Figure 17–1. This east-side view of Mt. Baker shows both the lower Sherman Peak (left), and the main summit (10,778 feet). The thermally active Sherman Crater lies between the two Peaks. (Photo by Bob and Ira Spring.)

Baker Dam at the Baker Lake hydroelectric reservoir, reported that an unusually large dark gray plume of vapor was rising above the crater rim. Aerial photographs taken the next day revealed striking changes in the snow-covered crater: large new steam vents, melt pits, semicircular crevasses, and ponded meltwater had appeared; in addition, a thin dusting of what seemed to be gray ash extended approximately 300 to 1000 feet outside the crater.[3]

Since March 10 several more layers of dust or ash (derived principally from thermally altered rock in the active vents and containing only minor amounts of old lithic and glassy particles) have been deposited over most of the crater and eastward down the surface of Boulder Glacier. Most of the ash issued from a large new fumarole located at the base of Lahar Lookout, a crumbling mass of heat decayed rock which borders a large gap in the crater's eastern rim. In April, the central ice depression developed into a 130-foot-deep ice pit in which a 164 by 230 foot shallow, acidic lake formed. Registering 94 degrees Fahrenheit and with a Ph. content of 2.5 on July 11, the lake drained through the eastern cleft in the crater wall into a stream that runs beneath or inside the Boulder Glacier.[4]

The most impressive change in the Sherman Crater, as of August, 1975, has been the break up and melt of the crater icepack. Vents have not only opened in the glacier descending from the northern summit into Sherman Crater, but as the normal summer melting season progressed, the exposure of snow-free ground revealed the presence of many previously unobserved fumaroles. Whether the thermal *area* has grown since March 10 or formerly had been hidden by snow is not certain, but many new fumaroles around the central lake and main steam vent have appeared.

Steam emission has varied in power and intensity. At their most active the vents have spewed dark clouds an estimated 2000 feet above the crater rim. Climbers have reported that the vapor was released "under pressure" and that the jets "pulsated" violently. The amount of hydrogen sulphide being released has greatly increased: in March a University of Washington study found that 2,800 pounds of sulphur were being ejected hourly; by July the discharge rate had grown to more than 21,000 pounds of sulphur per hour, making Mt. Baker one of the worst air polluters in the Pacific Northwest, second only to the notorious copper smelter in Tacoma.

Because the sudden acceleration of thermal activity might indicate an impending eruption, scientists quickly began to monitor Mt. Baker. The present monitoring system set up by the U.S. Geological Survey, the University of Washington, and others includes making frequent aerial photographs of the crater, establishing seismic sensors to register earth movements which might indicate rising magma, and visitations to the crater to detect changes in gas emission and temperature. Although Baker continues to emit large volumes of steam, hydrogen, carbon monoxide, and other acidic gases, seismographs have not thus far registered any significant earthquake activity.

Mt. Baker's Geologic History

Mt. Baker is a relatively young stratovolcano which was built atop the rugged and deeply eroded western edge of the North Cascades, fifteen and a half miles south of the Canadian boundary. According to a reconnaissance study published in 1939 by H. A. Coombs, professor of geology at the University of Washington, the rocks underlying Baker are Paleozoic and Mesozoic in age and thus much older than those below Mt. Rainier or Mt. St. Helens. In the Pleistocene Epoch, when Mt. Baker first erupted, these metamorphic and sedimentary rocks had already been carved into deep valleys and serrated ridges, forming a terrain similar to that of the present. Consequently, when the earliest lavas appeared they drained into spacious glacier-scoured canyons and typically ponded to depths of several hundred feet. Like the early intracanyon flows from

Figure 17-2. Aerial view of the Sherman Crater. Note the steam rising from active fumaroles near the eastern gap in the crater rim (foreground), and along the western and southern walls. Layers of hydrothermally altered lava visible in the western wall slant upward toward the snow-filled crater on the highest (northern) summit. (Bob and Ira Spring photo.)

Mts. Rainier and Hood, some of Baker's first lavas have been eroded into high-standing ridges that now radiate from the base of the cone.

Mt. Baker's first eruptive center is marked by the Black Buttes, which lie about two miles west of the main peak. This ancestral volcano erupted thick viscous andesites that traveled only a few miles from their source. After building a dark lava mass approximately 3000 feet high (or about 8000 feet above sea level), activity shifted two miles east to the site of Baker's present cone. Glaciation then transformed the Buttes into irregular crags and cliffs that, too steep to hold snow or ice during summer months, stand out bleakly against the smooth snowfields of the present Mt. Baker.

Because of their advanced state of disintegration, compared with that of Mt. Baker itself, it is probable that the Buttes were formed much earlier in Pleistocene time. Two very old flows thought to belong to the Black Buttes eruptive period, recently dated by the potassium-argon method, yielded an age of 400,000 years, plus or minus 100,000 years.[5]

Eruptions at Baker's new central vent produced a series of relatively thin, fluid lavas, which spread out to form an 80 square mile base upon which the modern cone stands. Coombs estimates that lava flows comprise 95 per cent of Mt. Baker's volume, indicating that pyroclastic eruptions were few and intermittent.[6] Some tuff and pumice are present, but the most common airborne deposit is a dark crystalline ash.

The presence of several large cirques on Baker's north side indicates that the main cone was erected before the last Pleistocene glaciation. Baker is, however, much less eroded than many of its southern counterparts, such as Rainier, Adams, or Hood. Whereas Rainier has lost thousands of feet from its original surface through glacial erosion, Baker has lost only a few hundred.[7] Existing glaciers may account for much of the moderate dissection of the cone that has thus far occurred.

As its excellent state of preservation suggests, Mt. Baker remained active well into the Holocene Epoch. One post-glacial lava flow, which emerged from a cinder cone at the south base of the mountain, is the longest Baker flow known. It poured down the Sulphur Creek valley for 12 miles, displacing a stream issuing from the Easton Glacier. The pre-flow stream has been replaced by two rivulets, Sulphur Creek and Rocky Creek, which now pursue new courses marginal to the lava.[8] The Sulphur Creek andesite is obviously older than the 500-year-old trees growing on it, but younger than the latest advance of the Easton Glacier which scoured the valley in which the lava occurs.[9] Small remnants of much older flows, separated from the volcano by erosion, are common north of

Mt. Baker. However, "an extremely fresh flow of andesite" covers the valley floor in which Mt. Baker Lodge stands.[10]

Jack Hyde of the Tacoma Community College and Dwight Crandell of the U.S. Geological Survey recently studied post-glacial deposits at Mt. Baker to appraise the potential volcanic hazards. They found that during the last 10,000 years Mt. Baker has erupted airborne pyroclastics at least four times, lava flows twice, and one pyroclastic avalanche, as well as numerous mudflows, some of which may have accompanied eruptions. The most recent ashfall on the east side of the volcano received a radiocarbon date of 390 years, plus or minus 200 years.[11] Baker's 19th century eruptions, although well authenticated, apparently did not leave recognizable deposits.

The Summit Area and Recent Fumarolic Activity

Mt. Baker's summit area consists of two peaks, separated by the Sherman Crater. The higher, northern peak terminates in a flat, ice-covered plateau about the length of a football field. The lower, southern horn is called Sherman Peak and forms the southern rim of the crater. Aerial photographs taken in the summer of 1940, when snow accumulation was unusually low, reveal what seems to be part of a crater rim on the actual summit. Photographs of the northwest walls of Sherman Crater show layers of lava slanting upward toward their source near the northern crest.

An ice stream descending from the north peak partly fills Sherman Crater. Prior to 1975 two major clusters of steaming fumaroles perforated the crater icepack, one on the southwest side and the other on the east side, perhaps through glacial ice. Thermal action was also intense along the western rim where swarms of hissing jets sent up impressive columns of vapor. Before the large new vent opened at the base of Lahar Lookout, the noisiest fumaroles were within the eastern perforation, just inside the deep cleft in the eastern crater rim. Acidic snow melt from Sherman Crater was channeled into a single stream which flowed through the east gap in the crater wall and disappeared in or under Boulder Glacier. A roaring fumarole on the stream bank forcefully ejected vapor and water from sulphur-encrusted crevices in a rock outcrop. Typical temperatures were about 180 degrees Fahrenheit, approximately the boiling point of water at that altitude.[12]

Because of long-continued exposure to heat and acidic gases, much rock in the Sherman Crater has been converted to soft, clayey material which is extremely susceptible to sliding. At least six times between 1958 and 1973 avalanches of snow, ice, and hydrothermally altered rock and mud have fallen from Sherman Peak, which borders the breach in the crater rim. All six avalanches traveled nearly identical paths down the Boulder Glacier but none reached the glacier's terminus. Lahar Lookout, at the northern edge of the breach, is a similar mass of unstable, heat-altered rock and clay. The threat of a major avalanche from this area now poses the principal volcanic hazard at Mt. Baker. Because of potential danger from slides and mudflows, in the summer of 1975 the Forest Service closed a large area downstream from Boulder Glacier, barring the public from Baker Lake and adjoining campgrounds.

The Steam Caves

Although the 1975 thermal changes have already altered their size and extent, the Mt. Baker steam caves, approximately ¾ of a mile in total length, remain one of the most interesting features of Sherman Crater. Baker and Rainier have two of the only three crater ice cave systems known in the world. Like those in Rainier's summit craters, the Baker caves were formed by heat emission and warm air currents which melted a series of passageways and chambers between the crater floor and the overlying snowpack, which largely fills the bowl-shaped vent.

Although a few climbers may have observed their entrances before, it was not until August, 1974, that the caves' existence and extent were

Figure 17-3. Increased heat emission in Sherman Crater melted the base of the 150 foot thick ice mass in the background and caused a chaotic jumble of ice blocks. The steaming middle ground was covered by thick ice before March, 1975. (Photo courtesy of Fred Munich.)

officially established. Dr. Eugene Kiver, professor of geology at Eastern Washington State College, led an expedition (of which the author was a member) to explore and map the caves. Even before the recent thermal increase, air inside the caves was so murky that flashlight beams could not penetrate more than a few feet. The stench of hydrogen sulphide— the "rotten egg" odor produced by active volcanoes—was overpowering, but it was the presence of other gases, carbon dioxide and carbon monoxide, that made wearing gas masks a necessity. The 1974 party discovered that an opening in the snowcover near the northwest crater wall led into a long passage that apparently extended across the crater and connected with the large ice perforation near the gap in the eastern crater wall. Unfortunately, the passage floor was so water saturated near its terminus that quicksand or quickclay made it impossible to exit from the eastern end. Kiver's group noted several small pools of standing water, but no lake of any consequence. Dr. Kiver's second exploration, in August, 1975, revealed that the passage from the western rim now ends at the lake of hot meltwater which has since formed in the central ice pit.

Baker's Historic Eruptions

Because no complete analysis of Mt. Baker's eruptive phases had yet been made, it is impossible to determine precisely when its last significant activity took place. The volcano seems to have been quiet when Quimper and Vancouver first sighted it, although Indian lore embodies accounts of past cataclysmic eruptions. When George Gibbs[13] made his reconnaissance of the "physical geography" of the region, he referred to Mt. Baker as an active volcano. Gibbs noted that

> . . . it would seem to have only recently resumed its activity; as I am informed, both on the authority of officers of the Hudson Bay Company, and also of Indians, that the eruption of 1843 was the first known. It broke out simultaneously with St. Helen's and covered the whole country with ashes.

Gibbs also spoke of Indian reports that the ". . . Skagit River was obstructed in its course, and all the fish died. This was, in substance, what they assured me on my visit to the river, adding that the country was on fire for miles round." Although this last phenomenon may be explained by a forest fire of non-volcanic origin, Gibbs was certain that the fish ". . . were destroyed by the quantity of cinders and ashes brought down by the Hukullum [now Baker River]. Since the above date, smoke is frequently seen issuing from the mountain."

Although 1843 is the date usually accepted as that of Mt. Baker's first recorded activity, there are one or two intimations that the volcano was active a few years earlier. Plummer[14] cites the testimony of John Hiaton, an aged Pacific Northwest Indian then still living, who claimed to have witnessed eruptions of both Mt. Rainier and Mt. Baker "about the year 1820." According to Plummer, Hiaton had "...seen fires from Mount Baker, and a tradition of his race is to the effect that this mountain was formerly much higher and that a tremendous explosion threw down the entire south side." Plummer also quoted a Father De Smet that "...in the year 1846 Mounts Saint Helens and Baker became volcanoes, the latter immediately preceding the time of writing had undergone considerable changes on the south side where the crater was formed." These are the first known allusions to radical changes taking place in the configuration of Baker's summit, which became a recurring theme in newspaper accounts of eruptions in the 1860s. While outbursts in the Sherman Crater, which is located on the south flank of the highest peak, may have blackened snowfields on that side of the mountain, there is no recognized evidence of any major summit collapse dating from the 19th century.

Significantly, in 1896 when Plummer compiled a catalogue of reported eruptions in Alaska and the Pacific Northwest,[15] he did not include the reputed 1820 activity of either Baker or Rainier on his list. He did, however, note 1842 and 1846 as marking eruptions on Baker, strangely omitting reference to the well-authenticated outburst of 1843. In faraway Belgium, Perrey recorded eruptions on Baker for both 1842 and 1843.[16] As in the case of Mt. St. Helens, both eyewitness and second-hand accounts seem almost hopelessly contradictory about dates.

In his catalogue of the active volcanoes in the United States, Coombs[17] accepts 1843, 1854, 1858, 1859, and 1870 as reasonably well confirmed dates of eruptions. But Mt. Baker seems to have been at least mildly active on other occasions not recognized by Coombs. The *Oregon Spectator* of March 21, 1850, announced that both Mt. St. Helens and Mt. Baker were then "...in a state of eruption." Plummer's detailed description of an event three years later seems reliable, though he may have mistaken an avalanche or rockslide for a lava flow: "In January, 1853, persons living down [Puget] Sound could distinctly see a long black streak on the southwest slope of Mount Baker, which was variously estimated at from 1,000 to 2,000 feet in width. It was several months before the mass of lava (as it undoubtedly was) had cooled so as to receive the falling snow." Since debris avalanches from the eastern wall of Sherman Crater are even now a common occurrence, it may be that a temporarily active fumarole melted snow on the west side as long ago as 1853. Such a slide or mudflow, however, is entirely hypothetical. It is perhaps significant that Plummer's sources fail to mention an eruption cloud or any other indication of volcanic activity accompanying the supposed "lava flow."

By far the most authoritative and convincing account of Mt. Baker's historic eruptions is that of George Davidson, a scientist from San Francisco's Davidson Observatory. In a long letter to *Science* he wrote:

> In 1854 I was one day observing at the trigonometrical station on Obstruction Island in the Rosario Strait, Washington Sound: I had finished the measure for horizontal direction of the summit of Mount Baker, and was commencing a series of measures of the vertical angles for elevation, when I found the whole summit of the mountain suddenly obscured by vast rolling masses of dense smoke, which in a few minutes reached an estimated height of two thousand feet above the mountain, and soon enveloped the higher parts. Baker was distant thirty-nine geographical miles from my station.... The weather was fine, and we hoped to see a brilliant display at night; but unfortunately the sky clouded, and we could not see the light at night, nor the mountain next day: when the weather cleared, the eruption had ceased; and instead of the white mountain mass, we discovered that the snow covering it was apparently melted away for two or three thousand feet below the two heads. Of course the snow may not have been melted, but only covered with ashes and scoriae; and we had not the means of deciding the question at that distance.[18]

The fact that Davidson was actually taking scientific measurements of Mt. Baker with his whole attention focused on the mountain when without warning he saw the summit enveloped in "rolling masses of dense smoke" heightens his credibility. These observations, the suddenness of the outburst, the thick column of dark vapor, the relatively brief duration of the explosion, and the subsequent covering of the snow mantle by a dark ashfall all correspond to Parrish's description of the eruption of Mt. St. Helens on November 22, 1842. The general features of the activity seem remarkably similar.

Davidson also noted that "... the crater was not on the summit, or on the secondary peak to the south-eastward, but on the flank of the higher peak, and opening towards the south or southwest. In subsequent years we occasionally saw small volumes of smoke issuing from this crater" (possibly the present gap in the southwest wall of the Sherman Crater.) Again, Baker's activity resembled that of St. Helens in that the erupting vent was located below the summit.

Four years later observers were treated to a night display that bad weather had denied to Davidson in 1854. Friends in Victoria, British Columbia, informed the scientist that "... night clouds over Mount Baker were brilliantly illuminated by the light from an eruption." This radiance was not necessarily produced by molten matter within the crater; it may have been electrical flashes that typically accompany an eruption.

During November and December of 1859 a similarly "brilliant" eruption occurred. According to the *Pioneer and Democrat* of November

Figure 17-4. Described as resembling "an ice floe on a frying pan," Sherman Crater's ice pack melts and breaks up as thermal activity continues. In late 1975 one of the fumaroles registered 267 degrees Fahrenheit. Steam in left background issues from a newly-formed vent 15 feet in diameter – the largest active one in the Cascades. This fumarole produced the 1000 foot steam plume on March 10, 1975 that heralded Mt. Baker's present thermal increase. (Photo courtesy of Fred Munich.)

25, published in Olympia, Washington, "two large bright jets of flame were seen having the appearance as if issuing from separate fissures or openings. It was seen but a few days and not accompanied by quantities of dark smoke." The newspaper commented that such eruptions were not unusual.

The following December 3 brought another show, this time with both sound and light effects. "Bright flashes as of lightning with report like heavy thunder proceed from Mount Baker, which was in a state of eruption. On December 4 the volcano has shown a dense cloud of smoke all day."[19] While such natural fireworks may have been the result of genuinely molten fragments being ejected from the crater, it seems more likely that the "flashes as of lightning" were simply electrical displays which typically occur during volcanic eruptions.

Mt. Baker seems to have remained spasmodically active throughout the first half of the following decade. Perrey[20] recorded an eruption of April 26, 1860, which was probably a continuation of the 1859 activity. As usual, Perrey gave no details or even his source, but he is likely to have received his information from items reproduced in eastern newspapers or journals. On December 28, 1860, for example, the *Pioneer and Democrat* of Olympia reported that "Mt. Baker is in a state of eruption, throwing off clouds of steam and smoke." A similar item appeared in the Washington *Sentinel* of August 18, 1863: "Mt. Baker is reported in a state of eruption." Except for noting the bare fact that Mt. Baker was allegedly erupting these frontier papers manifest a dearth of scientific curiosity. Had early accounts been more informative, Mt. Baker's reputation as an active Pacific Northwest volcano might well rival that of Mt. St. Helens.

In any event, Mt. Baker's 19th century activity was sufficiently intense to inspire wildly exaggerated tales about the destruction of its summit. A correspondent for the *Scientific American*[21] reprinted an *Oregonian* story of the previous April: " 'Mt. Baker, it is said, is rapidly sinking in. It is asserted that the mountain has fallen 1000 or 1500 feet, and that its summit, which was formerly a sharp point, is now much flattened. This peak has been for some time in a state of active eruption. Dense clouds of smoke have of late issued from it.' Correspondents of the California papers speak of the same phenomenon, one of whom asserts that the emission of steam is immense, and that 1200 feet of the summit has fallen in."

In this context, it is reassuring to return to Davidson's article in *Science*. He states that he made an exact drawing of the volcano's profile, "... the more particularly because rumors had found their way into the newspapers, asserting that the summit of Mount Baker had fallen in. On the contrary, I was perfectly satisfied, from my years of familiarity with its features, that no such catastrophe had taken place between 1852 and 1870; nor was I able to detect any changes in 1877, when I was daily in sight of Mount Baker for some time."[22]

Davidson's conscientious observations are confirmed by the climbing party of E. T. Coleman, which in 1868 made the first successful ascent of Mt. Baker. On September 1 of that year the *Oregonian* carried an interview with members of the group which established the fact that the familiar two peaks of the mountain remained in place as before. In a mountaineering article for *Harper's* published the following year Coleman described the "summit plateau" of the higher peak as about a "quarter of a mile in diameter ... the white surface of the snow was unrelieved by a single rock".[23]

One of the climbers, David Ogilvey, explored the crater (presumably the Sherman Crater) and concluded that "... the existence of a volcano is established beyond a doubt, the crater being about 300 feet wide, and at least 600 feet deep, from which puffs of sulphurous vapor are being emitted. The crater lies between two high peaks of the mountain, where the summits form a plateau quite bare and free from snow''.[24] Thomas Stratton, a mining geologist and member of the party, discovered ''three extinct craters,'' which may have been subsidiary vents responsible for some of the historic eruptions. Coleman later stated that the main crater was not 300 feet but ''...about three hundred yards wide'' with walls ''...of black rock, streaked with sulphur yellow, red, and green. On the Baker River side, 300 feet of the lip had been torn away where successive layers of lava had flowed out and cooled.''[25] (Coleman may here be referring to a breach in the eastern crater rim near which numerous debris avalanches have originated, the latest in 1973.) He also commented that ''...no traces of fire were visible by daylight but smoke was plainly observed. Fire must be slumbering beneath as there is no snow on the lava.''[26]

Two years after the first ascent, Davidson witnessed another apparent eruption of the volcano. In 1870, when he was about 60 miles distant from the mountain, he ''...beheld great volumes of smoke projected from the higher peak''.[27] If this was a genuine outburst, it seems to have been the only historic one to have issued ''from the highest peak,'' which is now completely buried in ice and manifests none of the thermal anomalies so abundant in the Sherman Crater. Because of his great distance from Mt. Baker, it is possible that Davidson mislocated the active vent. When J. S. Diller,[28] an eminently reliable authority, referred to the fact of authenticated eruptions in 1854, 1858, and 1870, he undoubtedly had Davidson's published observations in mind.

Plummer's catalogue[29] lists two more eruptions, in December, 1880, and the autumn of 1891, but, again, no details are available. It is likely that these ''eruptions'' were merely intensified exhalations of vapor, rather than expulsions of new material. Indeed, Mt. Baker has been reported ''smoking'' well into the 20th century. When C. E. Rusk was climbing the east side in 1903, his party ''saw large volumes of smoke rolling from between the two peaks'' (presumably from vents in the Sherman Crater). Arriving at the crater rim, Rusk found it ''the most thrillingly weird spectacle (he) had ever seen.''

> In the bowl-like depression immediately between the two peaks was a great orifice in the snow. It was perhaps fifty feet across, although the western side was partly blocked with snow so that the opening had somewhat the shape of a half-moon. At a distance of possibly two hundred feet a semicircular crevasse swept halfway around it. From the unknown depths of this abyss the black smoke rolled. It drifted away, shifting with the wind, until it was finally dissipated in the rarefied air. The wild, unearthly loneliness of the scene impressed us profoundly, for its counterpart perhaps does not exist on earth.[30]

Event	Approximate age, or limiting dates (years ago)
Increased fumarolic activity at Sherman Center	Present (1975)
Several small avalanches and mudflows extended down Boulder Glacier	Recent past to present
Eruption of tephra consisting of hydrothermally altered rock debris from Sherman Crater	Within the last few centuries
Two or more mudflows extended short distances down Sulphur Creek valley	Do.
At least two mudflows extended 11 km down Boulder Creek valley	Do.
Avalanche extended at least 9 km down Rainbow Creek valley	Do.
A mudflow extended 14 km down Park Creek valley	500
A mudflow (or avalanche) extended about 3 km down Middle Fork Nooksack River valley	Between 6,000 and 300

Eruption of tephra	Between 6,600 and 500
A mudflow extended more than 10 km down Sulphur Creek valley	Between 6,600 and 300
A mudflow extended at least 29 km down Middle Fork Nooksack River valley	6,000
A mudflow extended 14 km down Park Creek valley	6,650
Eruption of tephra	Between 10,000 and 6,600
A mudflow extended at least 8 km down Sulphur Creek valley	Do.
A lava flow extended 12 km down Sulphur Creek valley	Do.
Eruption of scoria at vent in Sulphur Creek valley	Do.
Pyroclastic flows, mudflows, and two lava flows moved down Boulder Creek valley, some of which reached Baker River valley	About 8,700(?)
A mudflow extended at least 6 km down Sulphur Creek valley	10,340

From Hyde and Crandell, 1975

Figure 17-5. Chart of postglacial events at Mt. Baker

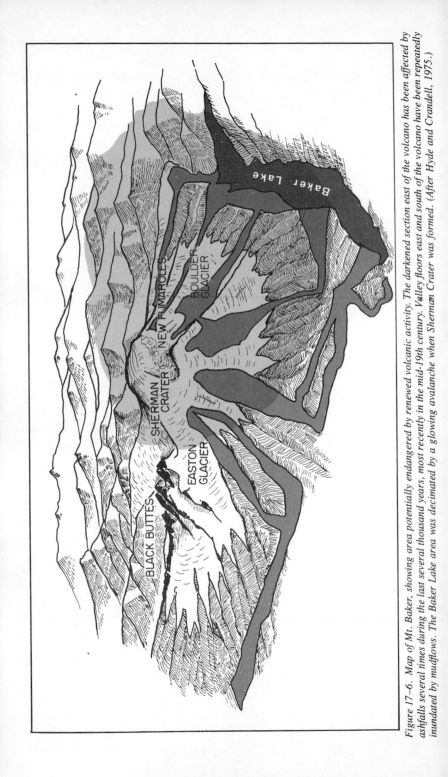

Figure 17–6. Map of Mt. Baker, showing area potentially endangered by renewed volcanic activity. The darkened section east of the volcano has been affected by ashfalls several times during the last several thousand years, most recently in the mid-19th century. Valley floors east and south of the volcano have been repeatedly inundated by mudflows. The Baker Lake area was decimated by a glowing avalanche when Sherman Crater was formed. (After Hyde and Crandell, 1975.)

A photograph taken "about 1900" shows the crater "in practically the same condition" as it was when Rusk visited it. But by August, 1906, thermal activity had apparently declined for there was then "no sign either of orifice in the snow or smoke".[31] Apparently heat and vapor emission in the Sherman Crater has varied considerably during the 20th century. Writing for the *National Geographic*, Leo A. Borah noted that "the Great White Watcher" ". . .still occasionally breathes smokily from several craters near its summit."[32] Aerial photographs taken in 1940 reveal that there was then significantly less fumarole activity than there is at present.[33]

Present and Future Hazards

Although the quantity of gas and ash being discharged from Sherman Crater did not increase appreciably between the time measurements were taken in mid-July and again in September, 1975, there was an apparent rise in fumarole temperatures. A U.S. Geological Survey sampling made in September revealed that the principal vent on Lahar Lookout was expelling superheated gas registering 218 degrees Fahrenheit.[34] It is still too early to determine whether Mt. Baker is about to have its first 20th century eruption or whether the present thermal activity merely reflects a change in the volcano's internal plumbing.

In case Mt. Baker does erupt, however, authorities are chiefly concerned about the danger from mudflows triggered by avalanches of hydrothermally altered rock from Sherman Peak, Lahar Lookout and other nearby formations. Even a relatively small rockfall could dam the eastern outlet from Sherman Crater and permit a lake of considerable size to form. A sudden failure of the debris-fill dam could release large volumes of water which might pour down Boulder Glacier, gather additional stored water within the crater ice and the glacier, and possibly create an outburst flood in upper Boulder Valley.

A really large mudflow could sweep down Boulder Glacier and threaten two large artificial lakes downstream. The dams impounding the two reservoirs, Baker Lake and Lake Shannon, which have a combined length of 18 miles, are not expected to fail, but a spillover caused by large volumes of mud flowing into the lakes could mean serious difficulties for persons living in valleys at the southeast base of the mountain.[35]

Since andesite lava flows are slow-moving, no danger to life is expected from them directly. But lava erupted onto glacial ice could cause sudden melting and consequent flooding of valleys below. If a lava flow does occur it will probably emerge somewhere on the flanks of the mountain. If erupted below the snowline, hot lava might start a forest fire among the thick stands of fir, cedar, and hemlock that carpet the volcano's base. Because of prevailing westerly winds, ashclouds would probably be carried into unpopulated areas east of the volcano. No post glacial ash deposit thicker than four inches a few miles east of the crater has yet been recognized. Even a temporary reversal of the usual wind patterns would produce only a dense haze and light dusting of ash near Bellingham, the largest city in the area. But a sudden darkening of the sun and falling ash could cause poor visibility, panic, and traffic congestion. The handling of crowds of sightseers would also present local authorities with a vexatious problem.

Should Mt. Baker explode a glowing avalanche of superheated gas and rock fragments, as it has done before in post-glacial time, a thorough incineration of the affected area could be expected. One such Holocene pyroclastic flow descended the east side of the cone and traveled at least as far as Baker Lake.[86]

Mt. Baker's main danger zones are the fishing resorts, lakes, lodges, campgrounds, trails, and summer homes located on valley floors near the southeast flank of the mountain. Since the Forest Service has already closed many of these areas to the public, a future eruption is not likely to affect many people.

To See Mt. Baker

From an automobile, Mt. Baker is best viewed without obstruction from the Glacier Creek Road. From Interstate 5 in Bellingham, take Exit 255 onto Highway 542 (watch for the Mt. Baker exit sign). Drive about ½ mile beyond the Glacier Ranger Station and turn south onto Glacier Creek Road No. 3904. Drive 8 miles over easy switchbacks to a turnaround viewpoint at about 4000 feet. The view eastward to Mt. Baker takes in the Black Buttes as well as the Roosevelt and Coleman Glaciers.

A 6-mile round trip hike brings tremendous views of the north side of Mt. Baker. About 100 yards after turning onto the Glacier Creek Road, turn left onto the Dead Horse Road No. 3907. At 12 miles is a parking area and the trailhead. The trail ascends fairly steeply to a large meadow. Continue on the trail for another ¾ mile around the right side of a knoll that partly blocks the view of Baker. Once around it, walk up the easy slope of the knoll to the top for an unobstructed view.

Views of the south side of Baker are best had from the Shuksan Creek Road No. 394. From the town of Concrete on Highway 20 (the North Cascades Highway), drive the Baker Lake Highway to about 3 miles beyond Baker Lake Resort. Turn left onto Shuksan Creek Road No. 394 and follow it to its end with views of Mt. Baker most of the way.

The Boulder Ridge Trail, hike #17 in *101 Hikes in the North Cas-*

cades, affords the best view of Boulder Glacier, directly below Sherman Crater, and probably the best vantage without climbing the mountain, from which to view the current activity, if it is visible at all. However, it is a round trip hike of 8 strenuous miles. At the time of this printing, the campgrounds are closed because of danger from the activity in Sherman Crater. It would be best to inquire about road closures before planning this trip.

Chapter 17 –References
1. *Phillips, 1971.*
2. *Ibid.*
3. *Malone and Frank, 1975.*
4. *Ibid.*
5. *Easterbrook and Rahm, 1970, p. 20.*
6. *Coombs, 1939, p. 1499.*
7. *Ibid.*
8. *Easterbrook and Rahm, 1970. pp. 20-22.*
9. *Ibid.*
10. *Coombs, 1939.*
11. *Hyde and Crandell, 1975, p. 7.*
12. *Frank, Post, and Friedman, 1975; Malone and Frank, 1975.*
13. *George Gibbs, 1870.*
14. *Plummer, 1893.*
15. *Published in Holden, 1898.*
16. *Ibid.*
17. *Coombs, 1960.*
18. *Davidson, 1885.*
19. *Coombs, 1960, p. 3.*
20. *Holden, 1898.*
21. *Anonymous, 1865.*
22. *Davidson, 1885.*
23. *Quoted in Edson, 1968, pp. 155-156.*
24. *Steel, 1906, p. 28.*
25. *Edson, 1968, p. 156.*
26. *Ibid.*
27. *Davidson, 1885.*
28. *Diller, 1915, p. 56.*
29. *In Holden, 1898.*
30. *Rusk, 1924, p. 127.*
31. *Ibid., pp. 130-134.*
32. *Borah, 1933, p. 144.*
33. *David Frank, U.S.G.S., oral comm., 1974.*
34. *Frank, oral comm., 1975.*
35. *Crandell and Waldron, 1969, p. 13.*
36. *Hyde and Crandell, 1975, pp. 8-10, 16, 18.*

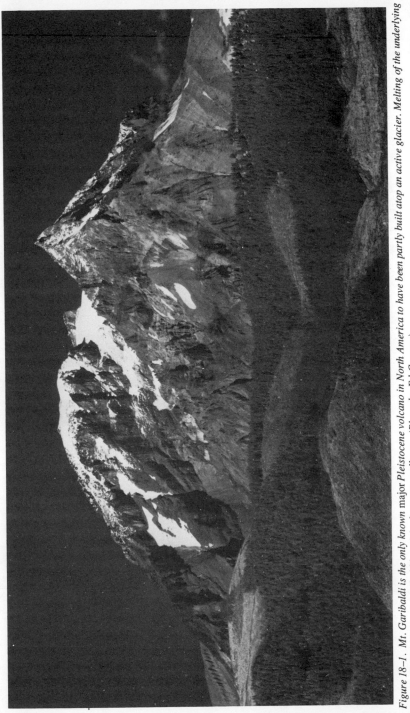

Figure 18–1. Mt. Garibaldi is the only known major Pleistocene volcano in North America to have been partly built atop an active glacier. Melting of the underlying glacier caused much of Garibaldi's original cone to collapse. (Photo by Ed Cooper.)

18
Mt. Garibaldi—
The Volcano which
Overlapped a Glacier

Although most discussions of the Cascades view the range as terminating near the Canadian border, several volcanoes found in the Coast Mountains of southern British Columbia may be structurally related and represent a northern extension of the same geologic system.[1] Perhaps the most "Cascade-like" of these volcanic centers is the group located in or near Garibaldi Provincial Park.

Compared with Cascade giants like Hood, Shasta, or Rainier, the volcanic cones of southwest Canada are unimpressive. Few reach or exceed 8800 feet in height and thus do not tower above the surrounding peaks of crystalline rock. Like their United States counterparts, most Coast volcanoes were built principally of andesite and/or basalt.

The exception is Mt. Garibaldi (8787 feet), the central topographical feature of Garibaldi Provincial Park (Figure 18-1). Located 40 miles north of Vancouver, Garibaldi is not only popular with the general public—thousands of whom visit it yearly—but its twin-peaked, half-destroyed cone also attracts the professional geologist.

First, Mt. Garibaldi is unusual in being composed almost exclusively of fragmental material, so loosely compacted that large boulders and other debris dislodged from its slopes are constantly tumbling downward into the adjacent valleys. Secondly, Garibaldi's core, which protrudes upward to form the southern peak of the mountain, is a solid column of banded dacite lava. Along with Glacier Peak, Garibaldi is one of only two major stratovolcanoes in western North America to be formed entirely of dacite.

Finally—and this renders Garibaldi unique among Cascade volcanoes —it was partly built atop a large ice sheet, so that the western base of its growing cone was supported by an active glacier. Metaphorically raised by fire on top of flowing ice, Garibaldi is the only known *major* supraglacial Pleistocene volcano in North America.[2]

Judging by the available evidence, Garibaldi was a relatively late arrival. It began to erupt only after the last Pleistocene ice sheet had reached its maximum thickness and had apparently begun to decline. Even so, the lowland glacier which Garibaldi partly overlapped still rose to the 4400-foot-level on the neighboring mountains. In its climactic phase, this Cordilleran ice sheet had previously attained an altitude of 6400 feet in the Garibaldi area.[3]

The Birth and Growth of Mt. Garibaldi

Mt. Garibaldi began life as a viscous spire of dacite lava which emerged through a ridge completely surrounded by ice several thousand feet thick. Like that of Lassen Peak, Garibaldi's growth was accompanied by the crumbling and avalanching of the rising lava mass. Large banks of talus were thus formed around a stiff, pasty core.

More spectacular were the glowing avalanches of incandescent lava fragments and the accompanying clouds of hot ash which repeatedly swept down the flanks of the volcano. Apparently laid down in quick succession, the voluminous deposits of fine ash and shattered rocks soon erected a fragmental cone ultimately 1.5 cubic miles in volume.[4] Although constructed mainly of pyroclastics, Garibaldi's slopes were extremely gentle, averaging only 12 or 15 degrees. (Subsequent erosion has made the mountain much steeper.) Where the cone rested on the ice occupying pre-existing valleys or on ice-free ridges standing only slightly above the general ice-level, the glowing avalanche deposits extend at least three miles away from their source. But where the cone banked against higher ground, the volcano's slopes are correspondingly shorter and more abrupt. On the west, and, to a lesser degree, the south, the volcano significantly overlapped the edge of the Cordilleran glacier.

After the main explosive eruptions had ceased, the surrounding ice surface rose to a height of 5500 feet. Whether this glacial resurgence was merely a return to pre-eruption levels after the thawing effects of the glowing avalanches had abated or a result of general climatic cooling is not known.[5] In any event, the Cordilleran ice sheet subsequently began its final diminution. The melting of the ice tongue which had supported the western foot of the volcano was disastrous to Garibaldi's unstable cone. As the glacier shrank and wasted, Garibaldi's western flank began to slump and slide out in a series of avalanches and mudflows.

Where the layer of ice between the glowing avalanche deposits and bedrock was thin, the melting of the ice produced only minor breaks in the surface of the cone. In this way the steep scarp at Cheekye Ridge was probably formed. However, where the volcano overlay ice hundreds or thousands of feet thick, as in the Cheekye Basin, radical disruption of the cone occurred. By the time all the underlying ice had disappeared, Garibaldi's western flank, broken and over-steepened, was ready to produce the rock slides which carried nearly half the original cone into the adjacent Squamish Valley.

Today a large amount of debris derived from Mt. Garibaldi occupies much of the Squamish Valley, an extensive depression at the head of Howe Sound. Mathews estimated that 10 square miles of the valley floor are underlain by an average thickness of about 300 feet of dacite blocks and rubble that once composed the western slope of Mt. Garibaldi.[6] Not all of this material (approximately 0.6 cubic miles) poured into the Squamish Valley at once. Several fans of debris now form terraces up-valley toward the ruined volcano, indicating that a series of several slides or avalanches occurred as the glacier wasted away.

After most, or all, of the ice sheet had thawed, Mt. Garibaldi again became active. But instead of exploding incandescent avalanches and hot dust clouds as it had done repeatedly in the past, Garibaldi this time erupted more quietly. Streams of liquid dacite issued from a crater north of the central plug and flowed down the north and northeastern flanks of the mountain. One dacite stream extended several thousand feet west-ward over the landslide scar on the volcano's western face. This late flow traveled down a slope of 30 to 35 degrees, a grade far steeper than the original 12 to 15 degree angle of the hot avalanche deposits.

While Garibaldi's southern peak is formed by the intrusive dacite plug, the slightly higher northern summit is composed of several super-posed dacite lava flows, which slant northeastward at an angle of 30 to 35 degrees. Other lava flows from the same early post-glacial period cover the lower northern and eastern flanks of the cone. These may have issued from the same or nearby vents, but glaciers on that part of the mountain now obscure the source and relationship of the flows.[7] In all, approxi-mately 0.15 of a cubic mile of dacite lava mantles the northern face of Mt. Garibaldi, covering that side of the volcano with a thin veneer of solid rock.[8]

At present slightly more than half—about 0.8 of a cubic mile—of the original pyroclastic cone remains in place; an almost equal amount of ma-terial now lies in the Squamish Valley.

The dune-like drifts of volcanic dust shrouding Brohm Ridge have also attracted scientific attention. These interesting dunes, up to about 15 feet high, rest on bedrock and glacial till. Although they may be wind deposits of dust from eroded tuff, geologists think it more likely that they are instead the remains of unusually dense ash clouds which were laterally directed by explosions during an eruption of Mt. Garibaldi.

Other Volcanoes in the Garibaldi Area

Although the highest, Mt. Garibaldi is by no means the only intriguing volcano in the area. Three and a half miles north of Mt. Garibaldi stands The Table, one of the most unusual volcanic structures to be found anywhere. This conspicuous, flat-topped, steep-walled pile of andesitic dacite rises several hundred feet above the immediate terrain. From a distance it resembles a mesa similar to those found in the southwestern United States; from other angles it resembles the famous Devil's Tower in Wyoming, a volcanic neck exposed by erosion. Closer inspection, however, reveals that it is not the remains of a lava plug that had filled the throat of a vanished cone. Its mass is horizontally layered by numerous round lava sheets that apparently spread one atop the other like a stack of poker chips. In addition, a few streams of congealed lava cling to the almost vertical sides of the pile.

As in the case of Mt. Garibaldi, this picturesque landform was created by the interaction of volcanic "fire" and glacial ice. According to Mathews, The Table was built by the repeated flooding of lava into a more or less cylindrical vent thawed through the Cordilleran ice sheet which, in late Pleistocene time, mantled the entire region. The lava flows which plaster the nearly vertical sides of The Table like frosting on a cake are thought to have formed where molten rock flowed down into the gap, thawed between the dacite mass and the encircling walls of glacial ice.[9]

The Garibaldi area abounds in uncommon formations; explaining them challenges the ingenuity of the professional geologist. The Black Tusk, for instance, a massive spire of dark lava shaped rather like a walrus tusk, seems to defy classification. From certain angles it resembles the monolithic plug of Oregon's Mt. Washington. Because it is so extensively eroded, its origin and nature are not clear. It may have been an intra-glacial vent like The Table, although the flows composing its summit are not horizontal. The Black Tusk's north-south elongation, parallel to the local direction of ice movement as at The Table, may possibly be the result of its originally being erupted along a northward-trending fissure, by ice movement at the time of eruption, or simply by later glacial erosion.[10]

A series of sheer pinnacles on the west side of the Squamish Valley, opposite the town of Squamish, also have puzzling features. The highest of these, known locally as The Castle, terminates in an impressive spire.

It is also distinguished by a semicylindrical groove extending up its southern end "like a flue up some huge split smokestack."[11] Mathews suggests that this spire, which does not seem to conform to any known geological category, may in fact be a lava spine, much as those extruded by Mont Pelée in the West Indies.

Other formations worth a visit include the slumped and asymmetrical Cinder Cone, a 500-foot-high mound of pyroclastics which stands between two arms of Helmet Glacier on the flanks of Mt. Garibaldi. This cone, topped by a crater which contains an ice-melt lake much of the summer, as well as numerous other vents and associated lava flows, attest to the wealth of volcanic activity in this region during early post-glacial time.

Why Is Mt. Garibaldi Now Quiet?

In 1952, when Mathews made the most comprehensive study of Mt. Garibaldi's volcanic and glacial history to date, he apparently found no evidence of activity later than that of the early Holocene lava flows. In a later report (1958) he offered an interesting hypothesis to explain the coincidence between the final disappearance of the last Pleistocene ice sheet and the almost simultaneous cessation of volcanism in the Garibaldi area. The facts are these: near the end of the last glaciation, a relatively large volume of lava, roughly four cubic miles, was extruded; since the ice sheet melted little or no lava has been erupted. While the Pleistocene glaciers were melting, the coastal region rose isostatically about 1000 feet; since the ice vanished it has remained stable. Mathews suggests that the Garibaldi eruptions may have been genetically related to the uplift and that since isostatic equilibrium has been achieved magmatic activity, if any persists, has been confined to locations far beneath the earth's surface.[12] Whatever the cause, Garibaldi lacks any sign of internal heat and may well be extinct.

To See Mt. Garibaldi

Drive Highway 99 northward from Vancouver, B.C., past the town of Squamish. The turn-off to Diamond Head in Garibaldi Park is sign-posted; watch along the east side of the highway between Squamish and Brackendale for the sign. Drive to Diamond Head base camp and hike the jeep trail 6 miles to Diamond Head Lodge. There is no automobile travel from the base camp to the lodge. From Diamond Head Lodge to the Gargoyles is about 2 more miles. The elevation gain from the parking lot to the Gargoyles is 2000 feet. From the base of the Gargoyles the view of Garibaldi's south side is unobstructed.

Chapter 18 – References

1. *Crickmay, 1930; McBirney, 1967.*
2. *Mathews, 1952.*
3. *Ibid., p. 97.*
4. *Ibid., p. 102.*
5. *Ibid.*
6. *Ibid., p. 100.*
7. *Ibid., pp. 91, 92, 102.*
8. *Mathews, 1958, p. 194.*
9. *Mathews, 1951; 1958, p. 190.*
10. *Mathews, 1958, p. 190.*
11. *Ibid., pp. 190-191.*
12. *Ibid., pp. 195-196.*

Cascade Ice and Fire—
Now and in the Future

Our peak-by-peak survey of the principal Cascade volcanoes has told us much of their past, but what of the future? What, for example, are the chances that the now banked volcanic "fires" which built these great mountains will break out during our lifetime? May we expect an eruption in the Cascades before the year 2000? And what of the glaciers? Are these rivers of ice now in retreat and destined to shrink until they disappear altogether? Or are the Cascade glaciers now advancing—the harbingers of a new Ice Age?

While final answers to these questions are not yet possible, geologists have made some educated guesses about the future behavior of both the volcanic "fire" and glacial ice which fashioned the Cascade Range we know today. Since glacial fluctuations have been more consistently observed and precisely recorded for longer periods of time, let us examine them first.

The Glaciers

To most tourists and other visitors to the Pacific Far West the shimmering ice which encases the high peaks of Rainier, Shasta, Hood, St. Helens, or Baker is the mountains' most delightful feature. But besides their beauty, and their practical value as a year-round source of water and hydroelectric power, these frozen reservoirs also serve as a reminder of a time not long past when vastly larger glaciers covered not only most of the mountains, but some of the adjacent lowlands as well. When glaciers advance, as some are now doing, it is easy to believe that another Ice Age might be on the way.

In reviewing the current activity of the Cascade glaciers we might first briefly summarize their behavior during the last few thousand years. After the Pleistocene Epoch ended, 10,000-12,000 years ago, there followed an unusually warm period ("Hipsithermal") which lasted until about 3000 years ago. It is thought that, except for those on the highest peaks, few of the Cascade glaciers survived this warm interval. But renewed glacial vitality then resulted in a "Little Ice Age." Dating of terminal moraines indicates that major advances also took place approximately 600 years ago; some of these culminated as late as the mid-18th or 19th centuries.[1] Not all the Cascade glaciers reached their Neoglacial zenith at the same time. On Mt. Rainier various glaciers attained their maximum size between approximately 1350 and 1850.[2] Following this period of growth, glaciers throughout the Cascade Range began a recession which made their ultimate disappearance seem possible. Rapid melting was particularly evidence in the decades following 1900.

Twentieth-century glacial activity at Mt. Rainier provides a fair example of glacial trends in other parts of the Washington Cascades. It must be emphasized, however, that there is no precise consistency or simultaneity of glacial events throughout the range as a whole. The recent behavior of Rainier's glacier system, which is better studied than that of most other Cascade peaks, demonstrates this. During the mid-1800s, the ice on Mt. Rainier covered an estimated 45 to 55 square miles.[3] By 1913 the area had shrunk to about 40 square miles, leaving sections of bare rock exposed for the first time in many hundreds of years. By 1950 glacial ice mantled no more than 39 square miles of the volcano's surface.[4] Since 1950, however, Mt. Rainier's glaciers have visibly responded to the cycle of cooler, wetter weather which began in the mid-1940s.

Emmons Glacier, the largest in the conterminous United States, is now advancing about 98 feet per year and has advanced 601 feet between September 18, 1967 and September 24, 1973.[5] On other sides of the mountain, the Cowlitz-Ingraham Glacier is presently growing at the rate of about 57 feet per year, while the Carbon Glacier is advancing about 53 feet annually. Other glaciers record a slower growth: the Tahoma Glacier, which streams down the west face of Mt. Rainier in a spectacular ice-fall, is advancing about 16 feet annually along one of its two terminal lobes and about 8 feet per year at the other.

Other Rainier glaciers, however, are definitely retreating. Nisqually Glacier— the magnificent ice stream which sweeps down the south slope of the volcano and skirts the Paradise Visitor Center—advanced 131 feet from 1964 to 1968, but then withdrew 178 feet from 1968 to 1973. The Kautz Glacier, the lower portion of which was destroyed in an outburst flood in 1947, is also retreating slightly. South Tahoma Glacier advanced strongly prior to 1967, then experienced outburst floods which were released from the center of the glacier at the 7400 foot level, possibly because of active steam vents located beneath the glacier. Since the floods, more than a mile of glacier below the flood release point has stagnated and has been melting *in situ*.[6]

Since 1945 the Cascades have experienced several winters of abnormally high snowfall. Records indicate that the average snowpack in the North Cascades, for instance, is about 50 per cent greater in the last decade than during the period of low precipitation which characterized the 1920s and 1930s. Since the winter of 1969-1970 snow depths have set new records. Because abnormally high snowfalls have persisted into the 1970s, we may predict that more Cascade glaciers will soon be advancing, at least temporarily. A change toward drier winters and warmer summers would quickly reverse the present trend.

Still other glaciers—the Fryingpan, Winthrop, and Puyallup—show little or no change. What prompts Rainier's glaciers to behave so differently? Why such uneven patterns of growth and wastage of ice on the same mountain? The cause apparently involves several complex factors. First of all, each glacier has its own peculiar position on the mountain. Different combinations of steepness, ice thickness, and the shape of the bedrock channel through which it flows all affect the glacier's behavior. In addition, glaciers take a varying length of time to react to changes in climate. During the past several decades there have been episodes of high snowfall and low melting, as well as years of little snow and high melting. Since the region of heaviest precipitation may lie several thousand feet higher than the glacier's terminus, it can take many years for the upper part of the glacier which received the high snow intake to move down to the terminal area and cause the glacier's front to advance. For example, although the Nisqually Glacier is now retreating at its terminus, a "bulge" of thicker ice is flowing down; when the new "ice wave" reaches the glacier's snout it will cause the glacier front to move forward.

Glacier Activity at Other Cascade Peaks

While statistics are not so complete for other major Cascade volcanoes as they are for Mt. Rainier, a similar non-synchronous pattern of growth, stabilization, and shrinkage is now taking place elsewhere in the range. In the North Cascades, noted for their unseasonal storms and obstinately cloudy weather, several glaciers are advancing steadily while others nearby are stagnant or retreating. Again, no single factor such as climatic warming or cooling, or increase or decrease in precipitation is entirely responsible. As at Mt. Rainier, such elements as steepness and configuration of the bedrock surface influence the individual glacier's behavior. Nevertheless, some general conclusions can be drawn: most of the expanding ice streams face north or northeast, where they are shadowed much of the day by their host mountain. Most of the advancing glaciers have higher mean altitudes than other glaciers in the immediate vicinity which are not growing. All dwindling glaciers have lower mean altitudes than nearby glaciers which have presently attained a state of equilibrium.

The recent severity of winter snowstorms has sufficiently lowered the annual snowline to rejuvenate all but those glaciers with low average elevations.[7] In short, the higher a glacier heads on its host peak, the more likely it is to grow under favorable climatic conditions.

U.S. Geological Survey reports show that at least six glaciers on Mt. Baker were definitely growing at the close of the 1960s. Between 1953 and 1969 the Boulder Glacier, on Baker's east side, advanced 2135 feet. Between 1949 and 1968 the Coleman and Roosevelt Glaciers, on the volcano's northwest slope, moved ahead more than 1300 feet. During roughly the same period the Park, Deming, and Easton Glaciers also recorded impressive gains of well over 1000 feet. On the other hand, the Sholes Glacier, located low on Baker's north flank, notably declined.[8]

Glacier Peak supports at least eight glaciers which have advanced significantly since 1949. Between 1949 and 1956 the Chocolate Glacier advanced 1100 feet, while the Cool, Kennedy, Scimitar, North Guardian, Vista, Dusty and Ermine Glaciers all pushed ahead several hundred feet. However, two large ice streams in the area, the White Chuck southwest of the volcano and the Honeycomb to the southeast, have continued retreats which began in 1906 or earlier.[9]

The Oregon and California Glaciers

Thanks to the Mazamas, the prestigious mountaineering organization based in Portland, several of the Oregon Cascade glaciers have been carefully monitored during the past few decades. The Eliot Glacier, on the north side of Mt. Hood, is the most fully studied. Like many other Pacific Northwest glaciers, the Eliot declined in thickness and length after 1900. Shrinkage was so nearly continuous that Hood's extensive glacier system seemed in danger of vanishing altogether. In 1958, however, the Eliot was rejuvenated when an "ice wave" from the upper glacier—the result of increased snowfall in the late 1940s and after —reached the terminus. Since that date the annual increase in glacial thickness has, with some variation, been fairly constant. Between September 1970 and September 1971, the Eliot Glacier gained a volume of ice equivalent to about 147 acre feet of water.[10] This is good news to the farmers and fruit growers in the Hood River valley, who depend upon Mt. Hood's ice fields for their water supply.

Perhaps in response to the past decade's heavier snowfalls and shorter melting periods, two tiny glaciers may have reportedly formed on the shaded north flank of Mt. Thielsen. This sharp pinnacle was almost destroyed by glacial erosion during the Pleistocene Epoch, but apparently became entirely free of glacial ice after the 19th century. In 1965, two small unconnected tongues of ice were observed in a cirque previously believed to be ice free. According to a 1971 report the eastern ice arm measured about 400 feet long and 50 feet wide, while the western ice stream was approximately 300 feet long and 100 feet wide.[11] A few crevasses breaking the steep ice surface indicate that these are true glaciers and not merely stagnant ice fields. Some 35 or 40 miles farther south, Mt. McLoughlin's northeastern cirque remains empty of crevassed ice—where a glacier of considerable size existed as late as about 1900.

Southernmost of the glacier-bearing Cascade peaks, Mt. Shasta has lately received record-breaking snowfalls. The winter of 1973–1974, for example, deposited more than 40 feet of new snow on the volcano's slopes. According to Austin Post, rejuvenation of the larger glaciers on Shasta's northern and northeastern flanks is already under way. If northern California winters continue to be as prodigal in their supply of snow and ice and if a sufficiently large amount of the snow manages to survive the hot summer months, Shasta's glaciers may expand significantly. The largest ice stream, Whitney Glacier, has already advanced slightly in recent years.[12]

Volcanic Hazards in the Cascade Range

The more exciting speculation about the future of the Cascade Range concerns the prospect of renewed volcanism. Earlier in this century many geologists believed that the Cascade volcanoes were probably a dying species, if not already extinct. But thanks to more thorough field research in the past few decades, it appears that the present quiet period is no indication of approaching extinction. Instead, evidence is accumulating that there have been as many eruptions in the Cascades during the most recent 10,000 years as there were during previous periods of comparable duration.[13] In short, geologic evidence shows that the Cascade volcanoes as a group are far from dead, but are in the middle years of a long life which stretches back tens to hundreds of thousands of years into the past and which may extend equally into the future.

Survey of Present Hazards

Potential loss of life and property from future eruptions has increased markedly during this century. Recreational, industrial, and economic use of the Cascade Range continues to grow at an accelerating rate. Pressure from a rapidly expanding population ensures that more people than ever before will occupy the Cascades. From California to Canada there are thousands of new summer homes, scores of lumber camps, hydroelectric projects, ski resorts, dams large and small, artificial lakes, and reservoirs tens of miles long. In addition to residents of the mountain areas, millions of fishermen, hikers, campers, and other tourists visit Cascade parks and other recreation spots yearly. Absorbed in the beauty or economic potential of the mountains, most businessmen, engineers, and vacationers alike are unaware of the menace. For many of the vacation homes, resorts, campgrounds, dam sites, and lumbering communities lie directly downstream from the great snow-capped volcanoes which provide both an incentive to tourism as well as the resources for commercial development.

It may be helpful to begin a review of volcanic hazards in the Cascades by dispelling some popular misconceptions about the latent danger. Local newspapers, as well as the national press, have sometimes suggested that Pacific Northwest cities like Seattle, Tacoma, and Portland are doomed to become modern Pompeiis, buried beneath layers of ash and pumice. Citizens of these cities may wonder if this is a strong possibility. Travelers to the Far West might similarly ask if the danger is so imminent that one should cancel a planned visit to Mt. Rainier, Crater Lake, or Lassen Volcanic National Park. Are these apparently benign peaks likely to explode suddenly and kill everyone for miles around?

We may safely dispel a few of these media-inspired fears. First of all, neither Seattle, Tacoma, Portland, Olympia, Bellingham, nor any other major city lying west of the range is expected to suffer the fate of Pompeii. This assurance rests on the simple meteorological fact that winds blowing in from the Pacific Ocean would almost certainly carry erupted clouds of ash eastward—away from the most populous townsites. Only a highly unusual reversal of the normal wind patterns would alter this situation. (Favorable wind conditions, however, do not ensure that floods, mudflows, or other indirect consequences of volcanic eruptions would not endanger population centers along Puget Sound or the lower Columbia River area.) Towns located east of the range—such as Yakima and Ellensburg in Washington, The Dalles, Redmond, Madras, Bend, and Klamath Falls in Oregon— could receive damaging fallout from eruption clouds. Other communities built at or near the base of volcanoes, such as the northern California towns of Mt. Shasta, Dunsmuir, Weed, and McCloud, might be in grave danger from both ashfall and mudflows. Many more communities lie downstream from large dammed reservoirs which, if overtopped by a large-volume increase via mudflow or flood, could cause disaster in the lowlands below. Towns that possibly could be affected by mudflows include dozens of settlements downvalley from Mt. Rainier, including the homes of 50,000 people.[14]

A few towns, such as Bend, Mt. Shasta and Weed, are vulnerable to being hit by what is probably the most frightful of all volcanic phenomena—glowing avalanches. These swift-moving "firestorms" can sweep through and incinerate large areas in only a few minutes' time.

A second mitigating factor in evaluating a volcano's lethal potential is that volcanoes usually give ample warning of eruption. Most eruptions, moreover, begin on a small, harmless scale. For this reason no one need omit a Cascade national park from his vacation itinerary. Before a catastrophic outburst were to occur, unmistakable warning signs would almost certainly persuade government authorities to order mass evacuation of the endangered area. What are the signs to look for? Increased steam emission; swarms of microearthquakes recorded on seismographs, even if not felt by human beings; the appearance and/or proliferation of "hot spots" detectable on infrared images; even "swelling" of the volcano as noted by a tiltmeter—all would give clear indication that an eruption was imminent. As pointed out in Chapter 1, the U.S. Geological Survey, as well as several universities and scientific foundations, are presently using sophisticated instruments to monitor several Cascade peaks.

It is always *possible*, of course, that a volcano might explode violently before there was time to evacuate the surrounding areas. Or, contrary to its normal behavior pattern, one might erupt on a scale vastly greater than any it had known in the past. It is even conceivable that Rainier, Adams, Hood or some other could be the source of a cataclysm which, in power and destructiveness, would exceed that of Mt. Mazama 6600 years ago.

In addition, there are a few places in the Cascades, such as Mt. Rainier and the valley floors immediately adjacent, where massive avalanches of rock occur without warning. A sudden thaw, an earthquake, or an unheralded steam explosion could at any time send millions of tons of rock crashing down, as happened at Little Tahoma Peak in 1963.

Chaos Crags, near the north base of Lassen Peak, pose a comparable avalanche threat. The danger is considered so real that in 1974 the National Park Service moved the entire Lassen visitor center, public campgrounds, museum, and hotel and dining accommodations from their location near Manzanita Lake to a new site. Since each summer thousands of persons daily used these facilities—which were built atop volcanic avalanche debris formed as recently as 300 years ago—the move was a wise precaution. As other high risk zones throughout the Cascade Range are identified, many other resorts, homes, and businesses may have to be relocated.

A Summary of Volcanic Hazards

To estimate the damage a Cascade volcano might do if it erupted, it is necessary to know as much as possible about its past conduct. Unfortunately, the life histories of only a very few of the Cascade firepeaks have been analyzed with the required thoroughness. In most cases, only a general idea of the volcano's behavior during the last 10,000 to 12,000 years is known. With the exception of Lassen Peak, no Cascade volcano has erupted since about the middle of the 19th century. As a result, geologists have had to depend upon study and interpretation of the recognized deposits left by post-glacial eruptions.[15]

Assuming that in future activity a volcano will adhere to its former eruptive habits—a questionable assumption at best—we can make a brief survey of what might be expected from the following Cascade volcanoes:

*Lassen Peak, Chaos Crags: Almost any part of Lassen National Park is susceptible to renewed volcanic activity. High risk areas lie north and east of Lassen and within four to five miles of Chaos Crags, with danger from hot blasts, mudflows, glowing avalanches, pyroclastic explosions, and short lava flows.

*Mt. Shasta: There would be serious danger to communities near the base of the volcano from flooding, lava flows, ashfall, and glowing avalanches; Shasta Lake and communities along the upper Sacramento River would be threatened if an eruption occurred in winter or spring and generated a major mudflow. (See Chapter 20).

Mt. McLoughlin: Lava flows might occur near the base of the cone; a small pyroclastic eruption in northeast cirque is possible; there would be little danger from mudflows except during winter and spring when the mountain is snow-covered.

Crater Lake (Mt. Mazama): Eruptions would probably be confined to the lake caldera or the immediate flanks of the volcano; ashfalls could disrupt traffic along Highway 97 to the east; no large communities would be endangered.

Mt. Thielsen: Probably extinct.

Newberry Volcano: Eruptions would probably be limited to the caldera or outer slopes of the shield; it is not likely that any settlements would be affected by an eruption.

Three Sisters group: Winds could blow ash over Sisters, Bend, Redmond, and resorts like Sunriver; glowing avalanches from vents near Broken Top could incinerate sites of Sisters and Bend; a sudden eruption during climbing season could injure many campers and hikers.

Three Fingered Jack and *Mt. Washington:* Probably extinct.

Mt. Jefferson: Not noted for extensive pyroclastic eruptions; its lava flows would be confined to near the base of the cone; although it is located in an unpopulated area, ashfalls could inconvenience communities along Highway 97 in north-central Oregon.

*Mt. Hood: Ashfall could blight ranches and orchards in Hood River

Valley, The Dalles, and other communities north, northeast, and east of the mountain; mudflows could flood reservoirs downstream from the volcano and contaminate water supplies at Bonneville Dam; McNary and Dalles reservoirs could also be affected by ashfall; lava flows would probably be confined to the immediate vicinity of the cone; growth of a new dome could send avalanches of rock debris into adjacent valleys.

Mt. Adams: Its eruptive history is little known, but ashfalls could blanket Yakima and nearby communities; floods and mudflows from melting glacial ice could descend adjacent valleys and flow as far as the Columbia River; lava flows on the flanks of the cone could ignite forest fires.

*Mt. St. Helens: This most explosive of Cascade fire-mountains has seriously affected 10,000 square kilometers with ashfalls; lavas might flow 8 to 10 miles from the base of the cone; glowing avalanches could descend many miles from their source; mudflows could affect existing or future dams or reservoirs on the Lewis and Kalama Rivers; Kelso, Longview, and Castle Rock could be damaged by long-distance lahars; falling ash could inconvenience Vancouver, Portland, White Salmon, The Dalles, and other communities.

*Mt. Rainier: There would be high danger from mudflows, which have repeatedly swept many miles down adjacent valleys. Lava flows would be short; ashfalls would extend a few tens of miles east, southeast and/or northeast of the peak. Principal danger would be to towns— Orting, Sumner, Auburn, Puyallup, Enumclaw, etc.—which lie on deposits from major mudflows (See Chaper 15 and Figure 15-7).

Glacier Peak: Relatively short lava flows, glowing avalanches, pumice falls and mudflows would affect adjacent canyons. Winds could carry violently ejected ash hundreds of miles to the northeast. Because of the volcano's remote position in the range, it is unlikely to endanger population centers.

*Mt. Baker: Lava flows from the flanks of the cone could travel 8 to 12 miles from their source; pyroclastics could erupt explosively from the Sherman crater; block-and-ash flows could descend the east side of the cone; mudflows, particularly along Boulder Glacier and the valleys below would endanger reservoirs and towns located down-valley.

Mt. Garibaldi: Glowing avalanches would be limited to three or four miles of the peak; short lava flows and some flooding of nearby valleys from melted ice and snow could occur.

The above evaluation of the threats represented by selected volcanic

---

*Volcanoes marked by an asterisk (*) have been active within historic time, roughly the last 150 years.

centers does not take into account the (probable) future birth of entirely new volcanoes or the reactivation of the hundreds of cinder cones and smaller volcanic mountains which characterize almost the entire Cascade Range. It is, consequently, tentative and merely suggests the possible dangers attending future outbursts of existing volcanoes.

What can be done to minimize injury and loss of life to persons living near the Cascade fire-mountains? Observing the four simple procedures described below would certainly help.

1. The more recently-active peaks should be regularly monitored by the installation of seismographs to detect underground movement of magma when it rises toward the surface and/or by periodic aerial infrared surveys to register increased heat emission. This is now being done, unsystematically, at a few of the major Cascade volcanoes.

2. Allocation of federal and/or state funds so that geologists can study the past conduct of volcanoes located near populated areas. Knowing what a volcano has done previously—and what areas it has affected—forewarns us about its probable future activity.

3. Local, state, and federal officials should formulate plans of action for warning and evacuating people in endangered areas.

4. Future land use around volcanoes, particularly valley floors, should be carefully planned with the probable effects of future eruptions in mind. Persons living in high risk areas should be so informed and prepared for emergencies created by an eruption.

Of the majestic peaks that tower above the general Cascade skyline, probably only a few are actually extinct. Most of the others are surely part of Vulcan's unfinished business.

Chapter 19—References

1. *Austin Post, written comm., 1974.*
2. *Crandell, 1969, pp. 32-33.*
3. *Molenaar, 1972, p. 19; Austin Post, written comm., 1974.*
4. *Post, written comm., 1974.*
5. *Ibid.*
6. *Ibid.*
7. *Ibid.*
8. *Ibid.*
9. *Ibid.*
10. *Dodge, 1964; 1971, p. 26.*
11. *Nafzinger, 1971, p. 31.*
12. *Post, written comm., 1974.*
13. *Crandell, written comm., 1973.*
14. *Crandell and Mullineaux, in press.*
15. *Ibid.*

When Mt. Shasta Erupts

(The following account is a fictional scenario for "What might happen" should Mt. Shasta become the second Cascade volcano to erupt during the 20th century. The events described below are not a prediction of how Shasta will erupt, but are based on the volcano's known behavior during the recent geologic past. Without trying to forecast their exact nature, the narrative presents the *kinds of dangerous activity* we can expect when Shasta awakes from its present sleep.)

Mt. Shasta, the enormous multiple-cone that visually dominates much of northern California, shows signs of geologic restlessness. On August 2, 19 ___ , climbers reported that they had seen "wisps of steam" issuing from the crater of Shastina, the large satellite volcano on Shasta's western flank. Forest Service Rangers who climbed Shastina to investigate the mountaineers' story could find no new steam vents, but noted a strong sulphurous odor typical of volcanic gas. Informed of this discovery, the United States Geological Survey will make a reconnaissance flight over the dormant volcano to take infrared impressions which might reveal new "hot spots" on Shastina.

In a report dated August 6, the U.S. Geological Survey states that its initial flight over Mt. Shasta detected no increase in heat emission, although a plume of "water vapor" was seen drifting eastward from Shastina. Plans are underway for another aerial survey within the week.

At 5:13 a.m., August 7, a sharp earthquake jolts the northern California towns of Dunsmuir, McCloud, Weed, and Mt. Shasta. Seismologists place the epicenter of the shock two or three miles east of Mt. Shasta at a depth of 16 miles beneath the earth's surface. Although felt in Yreka, the temblor, which registered about 3.2 on the Richter Scale, was much milder there.

A second perceptible earthquake, scoring nearly 4.0 on the Richter Scale, rolls through parts of Siskiyou County the night of August 7–8. That morning two lighter shocks, with epicenters between 10 and 11 miles underground, are recorded on the newly-installed seismograph at the College of the Siskiyous in Weed. A more severe jolt follows at 11:15

a.m., August 8, which causes mild alarm as far south as Redding and as far north as Klamath Falls in southern Oregon. Registering 4.6 on the Richter Scale, this quake is centered at a depth of only six miles. The increasing shallowness of the epicenters may indicate that magma is rising toward the surface, possibly heralding an eruption of the long-dormant volcano.

During the next 24 hours, the Weed seismograph records at least 120 microearthquakes, only two of which are strong enough to be felt by human beings. A second U.S. Geological Survey flight discovers two large "hot spots" on Shastina, both inside the summit crater. The larger of the two is located close to the V-shaped gash which heads Diller Canyon, the deep ravine which cuts through the volcano's western slope.

By 6:00 p.m., August 9, residents of Weed, Mt. Shasta, and McCloud report an almost constant rattling of windows and dishes in cupboards. Timbers in old frame houses creak eerily as the earth shifts beneath them.

On several occasions a thin white streamer is seen wafting eastward from the crest of Shastina, but it remains uncertain whether this is volcanic steam or merely one of the odd-shaped clouds that typically hover over the mountain. More ominous than vapor emission, is the swarm of microearthquakes which now register at the rate of 25 to 40 per hour on the Weed seismograph.

After consulting with representatives from the U.S. Geological Survey who have flown to Mt. Shasta from the Denver Federal Center, the California State Board of Emergency Preparedness alerts the local police and Forest Service to a possible mass evacuation of the area if Mt. Shasta actually begins to erupt. The Governor of California has already placed the State Police on alert and requested help from the National Guard if the removal of several thousand people from their homes becomes necessary.

Another swarm of mild earthquakes, which strikes the Mt. Shasta region just before dawn, August 10, has an epicenter of less than a mile beneath the surface. The U.S.G.S. aerial survey of Shastina, conducted before daybreak, finds that the two previously recognized thermal areas have expanded significantly, forming an arc of hot rock around the crater rim. Conspicuous melt pits have developed within the crater snowfield and several pools of standing water have formed near the blocky lava domes inside the old vent. A third "hot spot" has appeared high on Shastina's north face, on cliffs above Whitney Glacier, the large ice stream which occupies the saddle between Shastina and Shasta.

At approximately 10:00 a.m., August 10, a giant column of dark ash suddenly bursts from the top of Shastina and rises an estimated 10,000 feet skyward. The eruption cloud is an awesome sight: huge masses of gray and black "smoke" surge upward with tremendous force. A low rumbling, reminiscent of distant thunder, accompanies the cloud, which rises and unfurls outward like a huge black umbrella. Fortunately, prevailing winds direct the cloud to the sparsely inhabited country east of the volcano, where ash begins to cover the Medicine Lake Highland, 35 miles distant.

A U.S. Army research airplane radios that Mt. Shasta's snowfields are blackened by the ashfall. Large fragments of solid rock litter the Whitney, Bolam, Hotlum, and Konwakiton Glaciers, as well as the summit icefields. The material thrown out thus far seems to have been cold, for it lies on snowdrifts without having melted the underlying ice. Most of the ejecta, a Geological Survey spokesman explained, is probably derived from the solid lava plug which blocked the volcano's "throat." This is no guarantee, he cautioned, that future outbursts won't bring molten rock to the surface.

Moderate explosions occur spasmodically for more than a week, while the microearthquakes beneath the peak increase in number and frequency. By order of the California State Police, the general public is barred from the mountain's vicinity. Citizens of Weed, Mt. Shasta, McCloud, and Dunsmuir, as well as ranchers and summer residents near the base of the volcano are warned to leave immediately if the eruptions grow more violent. The Yakahovians and Seekers of Light, two of the many local religious sects, formally protest this restriction, which they claim infringes upon their constitutional freedom. The prohibition against climbing the mountain, they argue, will interfere with the international brotherhood festival which they planned to celebrate on Shasta's heights.

Shortly before the dinner hour, August 17, local conjecture about Shasta's intentions is answered by a roar heard for a hundred miles in every direction. As a column of jet-black ash soars 50,000 feet above Shastina, boulders large enough to be seen miles away by the naked eye are tossed high into the air and crash downslope. The whole mountain trembles with these detonations, triggering avalanches of freshly erupted material and dislodging old rock formations.

By evening the eruption grows more violent. A ruddy glare shows amid the inky billows towering above Shastina's crest. Unseasonal northerly winds now bear the ash cloud over the head of the Sacramento Valley. A steady rain of ash falls at Shasta Dam, 45 miles south of the volcano. Radio stations in Redding, nine miles farther south, report that fine dust has begun to drift through the sultry air, compounding the usual "smaze" which pervades the atmosphere of this agricultural region.

Roused from his bed in Sacramento, the Governor of California issues a state-of-emergency proclamation. The curtain of warm ash spreading over the Shasta Reservoir, which holds an estimated 4.5 million acre feet of water, has alarmed Forest Service and U.S. Geological Survey officials, who have been up all night debating measures to ensure the safety of persons living within the endangered area. In spite of protests from owners of large ranches in the Sacramento Valley, the governor orders that the sluices of Shasta Dam be opened to permit a large outflow of water down the Sacramento River. Because of the increasing temperature of the eruptions, authorities fear that quantities of the snow and glacial ice mantling Mt. Shasta may be melted and generate catastrophic mudflows. If a mudflow large enough to reach Shasta Lake were to occur, it could displace millions of acre feet of water, which would spill over the dam crest and inundate the upper Sacramento Valley. Tens of thousands of persons may be in peril.

By late evening of August 18, the towns of Weed, McCloud, Mt.Shasta, and Dunsmuir are evacuated. Approximately 7500 to 8000 people, in some cases forcibly, are removed from their homes and transported to sites upwind from the erupting volcano. Hundreds of private cars, vans, trucks, and busses are commandeered for the rescue operations, which are greatly hindered by falling ash.

Ash now blankets the abandoned towns at Shasta's western foot to a depth of eight inches, while McCloud is completely cut off from all automobile traffic from the west. Telephone and telegraph contact with all these emptied communities was severed several hours before their final evacuation.

State authorities have barricaded Route 97 at Doris, a tiny hamlet just south of the California-Oregon border. Interstate 5 was closed last evening between Yreka in the north and Redding in the south. Meanwhile, northern California has become a land of perpetual twilight; the sun can not penetrate the enormous canopy of ash which arches across the sky.

By August 19 the ash cloud attains a height of nearly 100,000 feet above Mt. Shasta. The McCloud and Sacramento Rivers flowing into Shasta Lake are as turgid as Mississippi flood waters, permeated with countless tons of ash. Authorities fear that sediments will accumulate on the lake floor and eventually, if the eruption continues at its present intensity, cause the stored water to overtax the Shasta Dam spillway. Already the ash has affected the Dam's giant turbines, which may be ruined if enough volcanic grit settles into the machinery. Run-off from the dam is now at maximum capacity; the reservoir water level is lowered by nearly five feet, but much more will have to be drained if a large mudflow from Mt. Shasta moves into the reservoir. Residents of the upper Sacramento Valley towns of Redding, Red Bluff, and Chico are warned of the possible danger should Shasta Dam overflow.

The one fortunate aspect of this catastrophe is that it has happened during late summer when a minimum of snow and ice remain on Mt. Shasta. If it had occurred in mid-winter or spring when the mountain supports a heavy snowpack, the heat would have created devastating mudflows by now.

A pre-dawn survey flight by the U.S.G.S. on August 20 reveals that explosive action has diminished. The wind has altered its direction and is now blowing the eruption cloud almost directly east so that the fall of ash into Shasta Lake has ceased. The hot spot on Shastina's northern face, however, presently registers the highest temperature on the volcano. Either a second explosion vent is about to open there or a lava flow is pending.

While the eruption cloud declines to about 25,000 feet above the mountaintop, new danger threatens from a massive lava stream which has emerged through fissures near Shastina's northern summit and is flowing down the escarpment above Whitney Glacier. If it melts the ice sheet, a disastrous mudflow may result.

A reconnaissance flight made about noon, August 20, radios that a lava flow, perhaps 150-200 feet thick, is cascading onto the surface of Whitney Glacier. Forewarned, California Highway Department work-men abandon an attempt to clear ash from Highway 97 which skirts the northwestern foot of the volcano. Citizen volunteers relay emergency warnings to all farms and ranches along Whitney Creek, Juniper Flat, and adjoining areas north of Mt. Shasta.

Helicopters carrying a television crew to photograph the advancing lava stream radio that the Whitney Glacier is largely destroyed. The lower two-thirds of the glacier disintegrated on contact with the incan-descent lava, which shattered into fragments as the ice beneath it ex-ploded into steam. Enormous slabs of ash-blackened ice and chunks of molten rock are swept down the north slope of the cone at tremendous speeds. Near the mountain's base floodwaters from the melted glacier, mixed with hundreds of thousands of tons of hot ash and angular boul-ders, are transformed into a yellow-brown mudflow. The helicopter crew reports that the mudflow quickly overflowed the banks of Whitney Creek and spread over surrounding timberland, crushing broad stands of pine. As it sweeps across the Southern Pacific Railroad tracks and onto the relatively level area traversed by Highway 97, thousands of acres of pine forest, sagebrush, and manzanita disappear beneath the churning mass. Portions of the cliffs on upper Whitney Creek collapse, adding to the volume of material avalanching downslope.

Advancing at about 25 miles an hour, the mudflow obliterates Juniper Flat. From the air not a single familiar landmark can be seen still

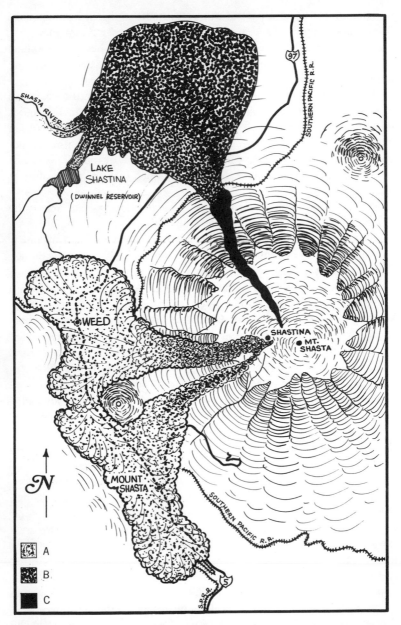

Figure 20–1. Map showing area affected by Mt. Shasta's theoretical eruption. A. Glowing avalanche that destroyed Weed and Mt. Shasta. B. Mudflow. C. Lava flow.

standing. What were ranchlands, summer homes, and pine groves only an hour before, are now a wasteland of streaming mud and boulders. Much of the debris flow comes to rest on this broad plain, but several arms of the flow continue moving along adjacent gullies and creek beds. One lobe reaches Lake Shastina, a large reservoir located a short distance west of Juniper Flat. A tangle of broken trees, snags, and debris from bridges, fences, and farms stretches across the mudflow's front, somewhat slowing its progress.

At 4:30 p.m., August 20, a wall of mud nearly 18 feet high enters Lake Shastina, sending waves of water rushing before it. Luckily, the water level was lowered several feet below its normal state in anticipation of this event. Even so, the influx of debris from Mt. Shasta seems likely to overwhelm the lake bed, causing severe damage to the resorts and summer homes located along its shores.

Miraculously no lives are lost, but property damage is already estimated in the tens of millions of dollars. The economic losses from the millions of board feet of timber destroyed by ashfalls east of the mountain are yet to be calculated.

As another summer night closes over northern California, two separate flares glow in the dust-charged darkness. One burns at the summit of Shastina, where sporadic explosions spray molten fragments over the cone. The second, much larger, glow radiates from the stream of lava coursing down the northern slopes of the volcano. Its surface broken and cracked by the steepness and irregularity of its descent, this molten river follows the same pathway as the mudflow it had generated earlier in the day.

By 7:00 a.m., August 22, the lava occupies the full length of Whitney Creek gulch and has crossed Highway 97, blocking that route to Oregon with a barricade two and a half miles wide and 200 feet high. Resembling an enormous pile of coal, the lava crust occasionally breaks open to reveal a gleaming interior, but the flow's appearance in daylight is disappointing to the newsmen and photographers who have flown in to view it from the air. Vehicular travel to the affected area remains impossible; the chaotic mixture of boulders and rubble which covers this section of Highway 97, as well as the county road connecting with it, denies access even by foot.

Thousands of tourists and sensation-seekers flocking to witness the spectacle have seriously impeded the removal of persons living immediately downstream from Mt. Shasta. The enforced closure of Interstate 5, Highway 97, 99 West, and all other thoroughfares between Chico, Redding and the California-Oregon boundary continues, but rash persons with four-wheel drive vehicles or snowmobiles which can negotiate the ash drifts continue to circumvent the barricades.

By August 23 the eruption seems to be dying; the lava flow has slackened and only puffs of white steam issue from Shastina. The displaced residents of Dunsmuir, Weed, McCloud and Mt. Shasta clamor to return to their homes. Scientists are reluctant to give their approval even for clean-up crews to enter the devastated area, however, because seismographs have begun to record another cycle of microearthquakes. Although these mini-quakes became fewer immediately following the recent eruptive climax, they have steadily increased in number during the past two days. Geologists suspect that Mt. Shasta is ready for another eruptive episode.

Since Shastina is now only mildly steaming, most state and federal officials are agreed that it is probably safe for those who so wish to return home and begin digging out from the layers of ash and mud. A research geologist with the U.S. Geological Survey, however, emphasized that the microearthquakes similar to those which preceeded the first outburst have not stopped, but, instead, have accelerated in frequency and intensity. "If the civil authorities give the word that people should go back." he said, "I will ask the national news media to broadcast that it is *not* safe to return until the earthquake activity is clearly declining."

"An alarmist," declared Mr. James Fitz-Brown in a televised interview regarding the geologist's warning. "Naturally," added Mr. Fitz-Brown, president of the Mt. Shasta Summer Development Association, "we understand the excessive concern which the recent little blow-off can inspire in someone whose job is related to geologic hazards, but we who have lived and worked near this wonderful mountain know that it is fundamentally a recreational attraction, not a menace. It will do no good to scare people away. We've got to keep our heads, not get hysterical."

As the debate to reopen the Mt. Shasta area continues, aerial surveys of the peak show that a large dark mass has risen into Shastina's crater, almost filling the western half of the vent. One prominent local businessman argues that this phenomenon proves that the volcano's throat is now plugged, preventing any further eruptions. Scientists who viewed the latest development are sceptical of that conclusion.

Pre-dawn flights over the mountain, made on August 24, find that heat emission has increased tremendously. The newly upheaved lava spires have been split and fractured by wide fissures, so that they are crumbling rapidly, undermined by steam explosions proliferating around their bases.

For the next five days Shastina rumbles ominously, throwing out black, angry-looking puffs of smoke and projecting showers of rock down its steep slopes. Refugees from the earlier eruption, unimpressed by this relatively mild activity, are eager to get back to house and job, but the U.S. Geological Survey adamantly refuses to sound an "all clear." Several engineering geologists, brought in by real estate brokers headquartered in Los Angeles, have announced to the media that it *is* perfectly safe to reoccupy Weed, McCloud, and Mt. Shasta. Understandably, people are confused. (Residents have already gone back to Dunsmuir on the assurance that there is not enough snow remaining on the southwest side of the mountain to form a mudflow large enough to reach the townsite.)

A U.S. Geological Survey team, which established a volcano watch at a Forest Service lookout a safe distance west of Shasta Valley, maintains radio communication with a temporary U.S.G.S. monitoring station in Yreka. A member of the team states that he feels as if "we are living in the eye of a hurricane, a moment of calm between two catastrophes." The Governor of California, however, following advice given by geologists representing corporate interests in the Mt. Shasta vicinity, issues a statement permitting all residents of McCloud, Mt. Shasta, and Weed to reoccupy their towns within two days. The continuing microearthquakes picked up on the Yreka seismograph, these scientists explain, are "simply the result of the earth's crust settling back into place after the disturbance occasioned by Shastina's recent eruption." According to this view, the current activity on Shastina is only the release of the slight pressure remaining after the outburst of two weeks ago.

Near midnight, August 28, the U.S.G.S. group in the fire lookout west of the volcano reports that a towering column of incandescent matter is now spiraling upward from Shastina and is brilliantly visible far down the Sacramento Valley. The roaring of this "fire storm" and the accompanying earthshocks indicate that something momentous is about to happen.

The Climax

At exactly 7:32 the morning of August 29, 19—, an immense "burning cloud" sweeps down the west slope of Shastina and totally consumes the towns of Mt. Shasta and Weed. The entire area simultaneously bursts into flames, with temperatures in the center of the holocaust approaching 2000 degrees Fahrenheit. Iron roofs, steel frame buildings, and glass windows melt into unrecognizable heaps; most wooden structures are simply vaporized. Smoke from burning forest and buildings intensifies a dense haze of ash settling from the incandescent cloud, rendering visibility almost nil.

From their vantagepoint on a massif west of Mt. Shasta, the U.S.G.S. geologists have a complete view of the phenomenon. The intensely convoluted cloud, impressively rent by lightning flashes, rolls and boils upward like the cloud from an atomic blast. Perhaps the most awesome aspect of the eruption is the near silence with which the cloud moves. It sounds like wind rushing through treetops of a dense forest.

The source of this disaster is an avalanche of seething gas and lava fragments which exploded from near the head of Diller Canyon, rushed westward down that declivity and then expanded north and southward as it reached the base of Shastina. After incinerating Weed and Mt.Shasta, it continued westward for a short distance past Interstate Highway 5. The lethal cloud of hot ash which rose thousands of feet above the avalanche spread over wide areas on both sides of it.

By September 3, five more glowing avalanches have issued from Shastina. At least two of these are of the same magnitude as the first. To the small towns in their path the subsequent eruptions mattered little, for not a wall or other man-made structure remained standing in either Weed or Mt. Shasta after the first. In an incredibly brief space of time—no more than three or four minutes—the entire area was reduced to smoking rubble as though it had been the target of a nuclear attack.

Two days after the initial avalanche, a spine of pasty lava began to rise in Shastina's shattered crater. According to scientists who observed it, this is a column or dome of viscous andesite being pushed upward by pressure from below. Such elevating domes and glowing avalanches are typically related, the geologists report. This was the case when Mont Pelée destroyed St. Pierre in 1902 and it seems to have been true during postglacial eruptions of Shastina. Both the decimated towns, Weed and Mt. Shasta, were built atop glowing avalanche deposits erupted within the last few thousand years. The latest eruptions are simply the recurrence of a pattern.

When the first heavy winter snowfall blankets the Siskiyou and southern Cascade mountains in early November, Mt. Shasta does not become the crystal tower it normally is at this time of year. On its north flank, jagged masses of lava, steaming in the wintery cold, stand out blackly amid the snowy mountainscape. The west face of Shastina is almost devoid of its customary white mantle. Residual heat from the "fire storm" which burst from the now quiescent satellite keeps the volcano's west side free from snow and ice. Gray vapor still ascends from Shastina's crater, which has been largely filled by a jumbled heap of boulders, broken from the top of a lava column which is gradually congealing there.

Scientists tell us that earthquake activity beneath the mountain has virtually ceased. What continues derives from the settling and cooling of magma in Shasta's underground feeding chamber. As the great peak settles into post-eruptive serenity, the reinhabited areas surrounding the volcano undergo similar readjustment. Snowplows have long ago cleared the thick layer of ash and pumice-stones from the main highways and most byroads which almost encircle the western foot of the mountain. But the scene, although approaching a kind of normality, will never be the same as it was before that fateful morning last August. The towns of Mt. Shasta and Weed have vanished; not a scrap of them remains. The formerly green country around Mt. Shasta is also changed: eastward, in a swath 100 miles across, stretch miles of gray ashen desert; westward lies the path of the fiery hurricane which carbonized the two doomed towns. North-northwestward extends the channel of destruction laid down by the lava-triggered mudflow which buried a four-mile-long section of Highway 97, as well as Juniper Flat and adjacent land beyond. Lake Shastina, which absorbed one arm of the mudstream, now contains as much mud as water.

This display of volcanic power vividly reminds us that the Cascade volcanoes can be the sources of real danger to populations located downwind or downstream from them, but it has also taught us that prompt and well organized action by municipal, state, and federal agencies can prevent loss of life. Nothing can spare property that lies within reach of ashfall, lava, mudflow, or glowing avalanche, but it is to the enduring credit of all official groups involved that in California's worst natural disaster since the 1906 San Francisco earthquake, not a single person was killed.

Surveying the aftermath of this cataclysm, one is moved to speculate which of the peaks that surmount the Cascade Range will next erupt. Will it be ice-laden Rainier, youthful St. Helens, or ethereal Mt. Hood? The citizens of many west-coast cities and towns might well wonder if it will be *their* mountain.

APPENDIX A

CATALOGUE OF CASCADE VOLCANOES ACTIVE IN HISTORIC TIME OR NOW MANIFESTING THERMAL ANOMALIES

NAME OF PEAK	DATES OF ERUPTIONS	NATURE AND/OR PRODUCTS OF ERUPTIONS	PRESENT THERMAL ACTIVITY
1. Brokeoff Mountain (Mt. Tehama), Calif.	—	—	Intense solfataric activity: hot springs, fumaroles, steam jets, sulphur pots, mud volcanoes, etc.
2. Lassen Peak, Calif.	1914-1921	Violent explosions; pyroclastics; lava flow, with attendant mud-flows; steam.	Small steaming crevices in summit craters; hot spots on north flank.
3. Chaos Crags, Calif.	1854-1857	Steam	None.
4. Cinder Cone, Calif.	1850-1851	Lava flow (?); pyroclastics (?);	None.
5. Mt. Shasta, Calif.	1786 (?); 1855 (?)	Pumice fragments; steam.	Hot sulphur spring at summit.
6. Mt. Bailey, Oregon	—	—	Fumaroles; no visible steam.

7. Newberry Crater, Oregon (lies 30 miles east of Cascade Range)	—	—	Hot springs in East Lake.
8. Bachelor Butte, Oregon	—	—	Fumaroles on north slope; no visible steam.
9. Mt. Hood, Oregon	c. 1800; 1846 (?); 1854 (?); 1859; 1865; 1907.	Steam; pyroclastics.	Numerous steam vents & hot spots surrounding Crater Rock; emission of hydrogen sulphide.
10. Mt. Saint Helens, Washington	c. 1800; 1831; 1835; 1842-1857, inclusive.	Strong explosions; pyroclastics; lava flows (?); steam.	Small steam fumaroles on north slope, near summit.
11. Mt. Adams, Wash.	—	—	Hydrogen sulphide gas & small amounts of steam escaping from vents near western summit.
12. Mt. Rainier, Wash.	c. 1820 (?); 1841-1843 (?); 1854 (?); 1879; 1882.	Light pumice fall between 1820 and 1854; steam thereafter.	Intermittent steam explosions on upper slopes; numerous steam vents and hot rocks in summit craters.
13. Mt. Baker, Wash.	c. 1820 (?); 1843; 1846; 1853-54; 1858; 1859-60; 1863; 1870.	Steam; pyroclastics.	Intense thermal activity in crater, greatly increased after March, 1975; intermittent steam explosions; minor mudflows on east slope.

APPENDIX B

Bibliography

1: Introduction

Anonymous, 1971, The Volcano Watchers: *Newsweek*, vol. 78, no. B, p. 123.

Atkeson, Ray, 1969, *Northwest Heritage: The Cascade Range*, Charles H. Belding, Portland, Oregon, 181 p.

Baldwin, Edward M., 1964, *Geology of Oregon*, 2nd ed, J. W. Edwards, Publisher, Inc., Ann Arbor, Michigan.

Crandell, D. R., and Waldron, H. H., 1969, Volcanic Hazards in the Cascade Range: In Olson, R. A., and Wallace, M. M., eds., *Geologic Hazards and Public Problems*, Office of Emergency Preparedness, Region Seven, Federal Regional Center, Santa Rosa, California, pp. 5-18.

Diller, J. S., 1915, The Relief of Our Pacific Coast: *Science*, vol. 41, pp. 48-57.

Easterbrook, Don J., and Rahm, David A., 1970, *Landforms of Washington*, Western Washington State College, Bellingham.

Ekman, Leonard C., 1962, *Scenic Geology of the Pacific Northwest*, Binfords and Mort, Publishers, Portland, Oregon.

Emmons, S. F., 1877, The Volcanoes of the Pacific Coast of the United States: *Journal of the American Geographical Society*, vol. 9, pp. 45-65.

Griggs, A. B., 1969, Geology of the Cascade Range: In U.S. Geological Survey, *Mineral and Water Resources of Oregon, Oregon Dept. of Geology and Mineral Industries Bulletin 64*, pp. 53-59.

Hague, Arnold and Iddings, Joseph P., 1883, Notes on the Volcanoes of North California, Oregon, and Washington Territory: *American Journal of Science*, 3rd. series, vol. 26, no. 153, pp. 222-235.

Macdonald, G. A., 1966, Geology of the Cascade Range and Modoc Plateau: In *Geology of Northern California*, California Division of Mines and Geology, Bulletin 190, pp. 65-95.

McKee, Bates, 1972, *Cascadia: The Geologic Evolution of the Pacific Northwest*, McGraw-Hill, New York.

Manning, Harvey, 1965, *The Wild Cascades, Forgotten Parkland*, Sierra Club, San Francisco, 128 p.

Manning, Harvey, and Miller, Tom, 1964, *The North Cascades*, The Mountaineers, Seattle, 95 p.

Matthews, William H., 1968, *Guide to the National Parks, Their Landscape and Geology, Vol. I, Western Parks,* Natural History Press, New York.

Moxham, R. M., 1970, Thermal Features at Volcanoes in the Cascade Range, as Observed by Aerial Infrared Surveys: *Bulletin Volcanologique*, vol. 34, no. 1, pp. 77-106.

Peattie, Roderick, ed., 1949, *The Cascades*, The Vanguard Press, New York.

Russell, Israel C., 1897, *Volcanoes of North America*, Macmillan, New York.

Weissenborn, A., ed., and Cater, F. W., 1966, The Cascade Mountains, In U.S. Geological Survey, *Mineral and Water Resources of Washington*, Washington Division of Mines and Geology Reprint 9, pp. 27-37.

Williams, Howel, 1962, *Ancient Volcanoes of Oregon*, 3rd edition, Condon Lectures, University of Oregon Press, Eugene, Oregon.

Williams, John, 1912, *The Guardians of the Columbia*, John H. Williams, Tacoma.

2: How a Volcano Works

Bullard, F. M., 1962, *Volcanoes: In History, In Theory, In Eruption*, University of Texas Press, Austin, 441 p.

Coombs, H. A., and Howard, A. D., 1960, United States of America: In *Catalogue of the Active Volcanoes of the World, Part 9*, International Volcanological Association, Naples, Italy.

Cotton, C. A., 1952, *Volcanoes As Landscape Forms*, 2nd ed., John Wiley and Sons, Inc., New York, 416 p.

Dole, H. M., ed., 1968, *Andesite Conference Guidebook: Oregon Dept. of Geology and Mineral Industries Bulletin 62*, 107 p.

Eaton, J. P., and Murata, K. J., 1960, How Volcanoes Grow: *Science*, vol. 132, no. 3432, pp. 925–938.

Green, Jack, and Short, Nicholas M., 1971, Volcanic Landforms and Surface Features, Springer-Verlag, New York.

Kruger, Christoph, ed., 1971, *Volcanoes*, G. P. Putnam's Sons, New York, 168 p.

Macdonald, Gordon A., 1972, *Volcanoes*, Prentice-Hall, Englewood Cliffs, N. J., 510 p.

Macdonald, Gordon A., and Abbott, A. T., 1970, *Volcanoes in the Sea—The Geology of Hawaii*, University of Hawaii Press, Honolulu, 441 p.

McBirney, Alexander R., 1968, Petrochemistry of the Cascade Andesite Volcanoes. In Doles, H. M., ed., *Andesite Conference Guidebook: Oregon Dept. of Geology and Mineral Industries, Bulletin 62*, pp. 101–107.

Rittmann, A., 1962, *Volcanoes and Their Activity*, Wiley-interscience Publishers, New York, 305 p.

Smith, A. L., and Carmichael, I.S.E., 1968, Quaternary Lavas from the Southern Cascades, Western U.S.A.: *Contributions to Minerology and Petrology*, vol. 19, pp. 212–238.

Williams, Howel, 1962, *Ancient Volcanoes of Oregon*, 3rd ed., Condon Lectures, University of Oregon Press, Eugene, Oregon, 68 p.

Wise, W. S., 1964, A Guide to the Volcanic Rocks of the Cascade Range: *Mazama*, vol. 46, no. 13, pp. 23–25.

3: How a Glacier Works

Crandell, D. R., 1965, Glacial History of Western Washington and Oregon: In Wright, H. E., and Frey, D. G., eds., *Quaternary of the United States*, Princeton University Press, Princeton, N. J., pp. 341–354.

Crandell, D. R., 1969, *The Geologic Story of Mount Rainier, A Look at the Geologic Past of One of America's Most Scenic Volcanoes: U.S. Geological Survey Bulletin 1292*, pp. 23–35.

Easterbrook, D. J., 1969, Pleistocene Chronology of the Puget Lowland and San Juan Islands, Washington: *Geological Society of America Bulletin*, vol. 80, pp. 2273–2286.

McKee, Bates, 1972, *Cascadia: The Geologic Evolution of the Pacific Northwest*, McGraw-Hill Book Co., New York, 394 p.

Porter, S. C., 1971, Fluctuations of Late Pleistocene Alpine Glaciers in Western North America: In Turkeian, K. K., ed., *The Late Cenozoic Glacial Ages*, Yale University Press, pp. 307–329.

Russell, I. C., 1897, Glaciers of Mount Rainier: *U.S. Geological Survey Annual Report 18, Part 2*, pp. 349–415.

Shelton, John H., 1966, *Geology Illustrated*, W. H. Freeman and Co., San Francsico.

Stagner, Howard R., 1966, *Behind the Scenery of Mount Rainier National Park*, The Mount Rainier Natural History Association, Longmire, Wash., 64 p.

Veatch, Fred M., 1969, *Analysis of a 24-Year Photographic Record of Nisqually Glacier, Mount Rainier National Park, Washington: U.S. Geological Survey Professional Paper 631*, 52 p.

4: Lassen Peak

Anonymous, 1850, Volcanic Eruptions, *Daily Pacific News*, San Francisco, August 21, 1850, p. 1, col. 2.

Anonymous, 1859, An Active Volcano in Calif, *Sacramento Daily Union*, March 18, 1859, p. 3.

Anderson, C. A., 1933, *Tuscan Formation of Northern California, University of California Publications: Bulletin of the Dept. of Geological Science*, vol. 23, no. 7, pp. 215–276.

Anderson, C. A., 1935, Alteration of the Lavas Surrounding the Hot Springs in Lassen Volcanic National Park: *American Mineralogist*, vol. 20, no. 4, pp. 240–52.

Anderson, C. A., 1940, The Hat Creek Lava Flow: *American Journal of Science*, vol. 238, pp. 477–492.

Chesterman, Charles W., 1971, Volcanism in California: *California Geology*, California Division of Mines and Geology, vol. 24, no. 8, pp. 139–147.

Coombs, H. A., and Howard, A. D., 1960, United States of America: *In Catalog of Active Volcanoes of the World, Part 9*. International Volcanological Association, Naples, Italy.

Crandell, D. R., 1972, Glaciation Near Lassen Peak, Northern California: *U.S. Geological Survey Professional Paper 800-c*, pp. C179–C188.

Crandell, D. R., Mullineaux, D. R., Sigafoos, R. S., and Rubin, Meyer, 1974; Chaos Crags Eruptions and Rockfall-Avalanches, Lassen Volcanic National Park, California:*Journal of Research U.S. Geological Survey*, vol. 2, no. 1, pp. 49–59.

Crandell, D. R., Mullineaux, D. R., and Bath, G. D., 1970, Late Glacial and Postglacial Dacitic Volcanism Near Lassen Peak, California: *Geological Society of America Abstracts with Programs 1970*, vol. 2, no. 2, Cordilleran Section, pp. 83–84.

Day, A. L. and Allen, E. T., 1925, *The Volcanic Activity and Hot Springs of Lassen Peak: Carnegie Inst. Washington Pub. no. 360,*. 190 p.

Decker, R. W., and Harlow, David, 1970, Microearthquakes at Cascade Volcanoes: *American Geophysical Union Transaction*, vol. 51, p. 351.

Diller, J. S., 1887, The Latest Volcanic Eruption in Northern California: *American Journal of Science*, 3rd. Ser., vol. 33, pp. 45–50.

Diller, J. S., 1889, *Geology of the Lassen Peak District*: U.S. Geological Survey, 1886–87, 8th Annual Report, pp. 395–432.

Diller, J. S., 1914, The Eruptions of Lassen Peak, California: *Mazama*, vol. 4, no. 3, pp. 54–59.

Diller, J. S., and Hillebrand, W. F., 1896, The Lassen Peak Region: *U.S. Geological Survey Bulletin 148*, pp. 191–193.

Finch, R. H., and Anderson, C. A., 1930, The Quartz-Basalt Eruptions of Cinder Cone, Lassen Volcanic National Park, California: *University of California Publications Bulletin of the Dept. of Geological Science*, vol. 19, pp. 245–273.

Finch, R. H., 1937, A Tree Ring Calendar for Dating Volcanic Events, Cinder Cone, Lassen National Park, California: *American Journal of Science*, vol. 33, pp. 140–146.

Harkness, H. W., 1875, A Recent Volcano in Plumas County: *California Academy of Sciences, Proceedings*, vol. 5, 1873–74, pp. 408–412.

Heath, J. P., 1960, Repeated Avalanches at Chaos Jumbles, Lassen Volcanic National Park: *American Journal of Science*, vol. 258, pp. 744–751.

Heath, J. P., 1967, Primary Conifer Succession, Lassen Volcanic National Park: *Ecology*, vol. 48, pp. 270–275.

Hill, Mary, 1970, ''Mount Lassen Is In Eruption and There Is No Mistake About That'': *Mineral Information Service*, California Division of Mines and Geology, vol. 23, no. 11, pp. 211–224.

Hinds, N. E. A., 1952, Cascade Range: *In Evolution of the California Landscape. California Division of Mines and Geology, Bulletin 158*, pp. 119–142.

James, David E., 1966, Geology and Rock Magnetism of Cinder Cone Lava Flows, Lassen Volcanic National Park, California: *Geological Society of America Bulletin*, vol. 77, pp. 303–312.

Loomis, Benjamin Franklin, 1926, *Pictorial History of the Lassen Volcano* (rev. ed., by Schulz, 1948), Loomis Museum Association, Mineral, Calif., 100 p.

Macdonald, G. A., 1963, Geology of the Manzanita Lake Quadrangle, California: *U.S. Geological Survey Quadrangle Map GQ-248*.

MacDonald, G. A., and Katsura, Takashi, 1965, Eruption of Lassen Peak, California, in 1915: Example of Mixed Magmas: *Geological Society of America Bulletin*, vol. 76, pp. 475-482.

Macdonald, G. A., 1966, Geology of the Cascade Range and Modoc Plateau: In *Geology of Northern California, California Division of Mines and Geology Bulletin 190*, pp. 65–96.

Moxham, R. M., 1970, Thermal Features at Volcanoes in the Cascade Range, as Observed by Aerial Infrared Surveys: *Bulletin Volcanologique*, vol. 34, pp. 77–106.

Oakshott, Gordon B., 1971, *California's Changing Landscapes: A Guide to Geology of the State*, McGraw-Hill Book Company.

Russell, Israel C., 1910, *Volcanoes of North America*, pp. 28-33.

Schulz, P. E., 1952, *Geology of Lassen's Landscape*, Ann Arbor, Mich., Edwards Brothers, Inc., p. 98.

Unger, J. D., and Coakley, J. M., 1971, Microearthquakes Near Lassen Peak, California: *U.S. Geological Survey Professional Paper 750—C*, pp. C156—C157.

Whitney, J. D., 1865, Geological Survey of California; Geology, volume 1, Report of progress and synopsis of the field work from 1860 to 1864. California Geol. Survey (Pubs.), 498 p.

Williams, Howel, 1928, A Recent Volcanic Eruption Near Lassen Peak, California: *California University Dept. of Geol. Sci. Bulletin*, vol. 17, no. 7, pp. 241-263.

Williams, Howel, 1929, The Volcanic Domes of Lassen Peak and Vicinity, California: *American Journal of Science*, vol. 18, pp. 313-330.

Williams, Howel, 1931, The Dacites of Lassen Peak and Vicinity, California: *American Journal of Science*, vol. 22, pp. 385-403.

Williams, Howel, 1932a, *Geology of the Lassen Volcanic National Park, California. University of California Publications in Geological Science*, vol. 21, no. 8, pp. 195-385.

Williams, Howel, 1932b, The History and Character of Volcanic Domes: *University of California Dept. of Geological Science Bulletin*, vol. 21, pp. 51-146.

5: Mt. Shasta

Chesterman, Charles W., 1971, Volcanism in California: *California Geology*, California Division of Mines and Geology, vol. 24, no. 8, pp. 139-147.

Christiansen, Robert L., and Miller, C. Dan, in press, Volcanic Evolution of Mt. Shasta, California, *Abstracts with Programs, Geological Society of America, Cordilleran Section Meeting*, Spring, 1976.

Condie, K. C., and Swenson, D. H., 1973, Compositional Variation in Three Cascade Stratovolcanoes: Jefferson, Rainier, and Shasta: *Bulletin Volcanologique*, vol. 37, no. 2, pp. 205-230.

Coombs, H. A., and Howard, A. D., 1960, United States of America: In *Catalogue of the Active Volcanoes of the World, Part 9*, International Volcanological Association, Naples, Italy.

Crandell, D. R., 1973, Hot Pyroclastic-Flow Deposits of Probable Holocene Age West of Mount Shasta Volcano, California: *Geological Society of America, Abstracts with Programs*, 69th Annual Meeting, Cordilleran Section, vol. 5, no. 1, p. 28.

Crandell, D. R., and Waldron, H. H., 1969, Volcanic Hazards in the Cascade Range: In Olson, R. A., and Wallace, M. M., eds., *Geologic Hazards and*

Public Problems, Office of Emergency Preparedness, pp. 5-18.

Diller, J. S., 1895, Mount Shasta: A Typical Volcano: *National Geographic Society Monograph*, vol. 1, no. 8, pp. 237-268.

Diller, J. S., 1915, Mount Shasta—Some of Its Geologic Aspects: *Mazama*, vol. 4, no. 4, pp. 11-16.

Eichorn, Arthur F., 1957, *The Mount Shasta Story,* rev. ed., the Mount Shasta Herald, Mount Shasta, Calif.

Finch, R. H., 1930, Activity of a California Volcano in 1786: *The Volcano Letter,* no. 308, p. 3.

Hardesty, William P., 1915, Physical Geography of Mount Shasta Region: *Mazama*, vol. 4, no. 4, pp. 17-18.

Hinds, Norman E. A., 1952, *Evolution of the California Landscape: California Division of Mines Bulletin 158,* pp. 119-130.

LaFehr, T. R., Gravity, Isostasy, and Crustal Structure in the Southern Cascade Range: *Journal of Geophysical Research*, vol. 70, no. 22, pp. 5581-5597.

Macdonald, Gordon A., 1966, Geology of the Cascade Range and Modoc Plateau: In Bailey, Edgar H., ed., *Geology of Northern California, California Division of Mines and Geology Bulletin 190*, pp. 65-95.

Miller, C. Dan, and Crandell, Dwight R., 1975, Postglacial Pyroclastic-Flow Deposits and Lahars from Black Butte and Shastina, West of Mt. Shasta, California, *Abstracts with Programs, Geological Society of America, Cordilleran Section,* pp. 347-348.

Moxham, R. M., 1970, Thermal Features at Volcanoes in the Cascade Range, as Observed by Aerial Infrared Surveys: *Bulletin Volcanologique*, vol. 34, no. 1, pp. 79-106.

Muir, John, 1918, *Steep Trails*, Houghton Mifflin, Boston and New York.

Oakshott, Gordon B., 1971, *California's Changing Landscape: A Guide to the Geology of the State*, McGraw-Hill Book Co.

Russell, Israel C., 1897, *Volcanoes of North America*, Macmillan, New York, pp. 225-228.

Shelton, John, 1966, *Geology Illustrated*, W. H. Freeman and Co., San Francisco, pp. 64-65.

Williams, Howel, 1932, Mount Shasta, A Cascade Volcano: *Journal of Geology*, vol. 40, no. 5, pp. 417-429.

Williams, Howel, 1934, Mount Shasta, California: *Zeitschrift Vulkanologie*, vol. 15, no. 4, pp. 225-253.

Williams, Howel, 1949, Geology of the Macdoel Quadrangle: *California Division of Mines Bulletin 151,* pp. 7-60.

6: Mt. McLoughlin

Crandell, D. R., 1965, Glacial History of Western Washington and Oregon: In, Wright, H. E., and Frey, D. G., eds., *Quaternary of the United States*, Princeton University Press, Princeton, N.J., pp. 341-354.

Emmons, Arthur B., 1886, Notes on Mount Pitt [McLoughlin]: *California Academy of Science Bulletin*, vol. 1, pp. 229-234.

Lynch, Bill, 1973, Monitoring Our Snoring Mountains: *Eugene* (Oregon) *Register-Guard Emerald Empire*, March 18, 1973, pp. 3-4.

Macdonald, Gordon A., 1972, *Volcanoes*, Prentice-Hall, Englewood Cliffs, N.J., 510 p.

Maynard, Leroy G., 1974, *Geology of Mt. McLoughlin*, unpublished Master of Science thesis, University of Oregon, Eugene, Oregon.

Montague, Malcolm J., 1973, The Little Glacier That Couldn't: *Mazama*, vol. 40, no. 13, pp. 73-75.

Phillips, Kenneth, 1939, Farewell to Sholes Glacier: *Mazama*, vol. 21, no. 12, pp. 37-40.

Russell, Israel C., 1897, *Volcanoes of North America*, Macmillan, New York, p. 236.

Williams, Howel, 1942, *The Geology of Crater Lake National Park, Oregon, with a Reconnaissance of the Cascade Range Southward to Mount Shasta: Carnegie Institution Publication 540,* pp. 18-20.

7: Crater Lake

Allen, J. E., 1936, Structures in the Dacite Flows at Crater Lake, Oregon: *Journal of Geology,* vol. 44, pp. 737-744.

Allison, I. S., 1966, *Fossil Lake Oregon: Its Geology and Fossil Fauna*, Oregon State University, Corvallis, 48 p.

Atwood, W. W., Jr., 1935, The Glacial History of an Extinct Volcano, Crater Lake National Park: *Journal of Geology,* vol. 43, pp. 142-168.

Blank, H. Richard, 1968, Aeromagnetic and Gravity Surveys of Crater Lake Region, Oregon: In Dole, H. M., ed., *Andesite Conference Guidebook: Oregon Dept. of Geology and Mineral Industries Bulletin 62,* pp. 42-52.

Borchardt, Glenn A., Norgren, Joel A., and Harward, Moyle E., 1973, Correlation of Ash Layers in Peat Bogs of Eastern Oregon: *Geological Society of America Bulletin*, vol. 84, no. 9, pp. 3101-3108.

Clark, Ella, E., 1966, *Indian Legends of the Pacific Northwest,* University of California Press, Berkeley.

Crandell, D. R., and Mullineaux, D. R., 1967, *Volcanic Hazards at Mount Rainier, Washington: U.S. Geological Survey Bulletin 1238.*

Crandell, D. R., Mullineaux, D. R., Miller, R. D., and Rubin, M., 1962, Pyroclastic Deposits of Recent Age at Mount Rainier, Washington: *U.S. Geological Survey Professional Paper 450-D,* pp. 64-68.

Crandell, D. R., and Waldron, H. H., 1969, Volcanic Hazards in the Cascade Range: In Olson, R. A., and Wallace, M. M., eds., *Geologic Hazards and Public Problems*, Office of Emergency Preparedness, pp. 5-18.

David, P. P., 1970, Discovery of Mazama Ash in Saskatchewan, Canada: *Canadian Journal of Earth Science*, vol. 7, pp. 1579-1583.

Diller, J. S., 1897, Crater Lake, Oregon: *National Geographic Magazine,* vol. 8, pp. 33-48.

Diller, J. S., and Patton, H. B., 1902, *The Geology and Petrography of Crater Lake National Park: U.S. Geological Survey Professional Paper 3, Part I: Geology.*

Dutton, Major C. E., 1886, Crater Lake, A Proposed National Park: *Science*, vol. 7, pp. 179-182.

Dutton, Major C. E., 1889, In *Eighth Annual Report, U.S. Geological Survey, Part I*, pp. 156-159.

Gorman, M. ·W., 1897, The Discovery and Early History of Crater Lake: *Mazama*, vol. 1, no. 2, pp. 150-161.

Fryxell, R., 1965, Mazama and Glacier Peak Volcanic Ash Layers: Relative Ages: *Science*, vol. 147, pp. 1288-1290.

Hansen, H. P., 1942, Post-Mount Mazama Forest Succession on the East Slope of the Central Cascades of Oregon: *American Midland Naturalist*, vol. 27, pp. 523-534.

Hansen, H. P., 1947, Postglacial Forest Succession, Climate, and Chronology in the Pacific Northwest: *American Philos. Soc. Trans.*, vol. 37, no. 1, pp. 1-130.

Harward, M.E., and Youngberg, C. T., 1969, Soils from Mazama Ash in Oregon: Identification, Distribution and Properties: In Pawluk, S., ed., *Pedology and Quaternary Research*, University of Alberta, Edmonton, Alberta, pp. 163-178.

Horberg, Leland, and Robie, R. A., 1955, Postglacial Volcanic Ash in the Rocky Mountain Piedmont, Montana and Alberta: *Geological Society of America Bulletin*, vol. 66, pp. 949-955.

Kirk, Ruth, 1975, *Exploring Crater Lake Country*, University of Washington Press, Seattle, 74 p.

Lidstrom, J. W., 1971, *A New Model for the Formation of Crater Lake Caldera, Oregon* (Ph.D. Thesis), Oregon State University, Corvallis.

Macdonald, Gordon A., 1972, *Volcanoes*, Prentice-Hall, Englewood Cliffs, N.J., 510 p.

Mason, Ralph S., 1961, Did Mt. Mazama Collapse in June or January? *Mazama*, vol. 43, no. 13, p. 31.

McBirney, Alexander R., 1968a, Compositional Variations of the Climactic Eruption of Mount Mazama: In Dole, H. M., ed., *Andesite Conference Guidebook: Oregon Dept. of Geology and Mineral Industries Bulletin 62*, pp. 53-56.

McBirney, Alexander R., 1968b, Petrochemistry of Cascade Andesite Volcanoes: In Doles, H. M., ed., *Andesite Conference Guidebook: Oregon Dept. of Geology and Mineral Industries Bulletin 62*, pp. 101-107.

Merriam, J. C., 1933, Crater Lake: A Study in Appreciation of Nature: *American Magazine of Art*, vol. 26, pp. 357-361.

Moore, B. N., 1934, Deposits of Possible *Nuée Ardente* Origin in the Crater Lake Region, Oregon: *Journal of Geology*, vol. 42, pp. 358-385.

Nasmith, H., Mathews, W. H., and Rouse, G. E., 1967, Bridge River Ash and Some Recent Ash Beds in British Columbia: *Canadian Journal of Earth Science*, vol. 4, pp. 163-170.

Powers, H. A., and Wilcox, R. E., 1964, Volcanic Ash from Mount Mazama (Crater Lake) and from Glacier Peak: *Science*, vol. 144, no. 3624, pp. 1334-1336.

Purdom, W. B., 1963, *The Geologic History of the Diamond Lake Area, Umpqua National Forest, Douglas County, Oregon:* U.S. Dept. of Agriculture, Forest Service, and Douglas County Park Dept.

Rai, D., 1971, *Stratigraphy and Genesis of Soils from Volcanic Ash in the Blue Mountains of Eastern Oregon* (Ph.D. Thesis), Oregon State University, Corvallis, 136 p.

Royce, C. F., Jr., 1967, Mazama Ash from the Continental Slope off Washington: *Northwest Science*, vol. 41, no. 3, pp. 103-109.

Rubin, M., and Alexander, C., 1960, U.S. Geological Survey Radiocarbon Dates: *A.J.S. Radiocarbon Supplement, 2*, pp. 129-185.

Shelton, John S., 1966, *Geology Illustrated*, W. H. Freeman, San Francisco.

Smith, W. D., and Swartzlow, C. R., 1936, Mount Mazama: Explosion Versus Collapse: *Bulletin of the Geological Society of America*, vol. 47, pp. 1809-1830.

Taylor, E. M., 1967, Accidental Plutonic Ejecta at Crater Lake, Oregon: *Geological Society of America 1967 Annual Meetings, Program, New Orleans*, p. 221.

Westgate, J. A., and Dreimanis, A., 1967, Volcanic Ash Layer of Recent Age at Banff National Park, Alberta, Canada: *Canadian Journal of Earth Science*, vol. 4, pp. 155-161.

Wilcox, R. E., 1965, Volcanic-ash Chronology: In *Quaternary of the United States,* Princeton University Press, Princeton, N.J., pp. 807-816.

Williams, Howel, 1941a, Calderas and Their Origin: *University of California Publications, Bulletin of the Department of Geological Science*, vol. 25, pp. 239-346.

Williams, Howel, 1941b, *Crater Lake: The Story of Its Origin,* University of California Press, 97 p.

Williams, Howel, 1942, *The Geology of Crater Lake National Park, Oregon: Carnegie Institution Publication 540,* 162 p.

Williams, Howel, 1957, *A Geologic Map of the Bend Quadrangle, Oregon, and a Reconnaissance Geologic Map of the Central Portion of the High Cascade Mountains,* Oregon Dept. of Geology and Mineral Industries in coop. with U.S. Geological Survey.

Williams, Howel, 1961, The Floor of Crater Lake, Oregon: *American Journal of Science*, vol. 259, pp. 81-83.

Williams, Howel, 1962, *Ancient Volcanoes of Oregon,* 3rd ed., Condon Lectures, University of Oregon Press, 68 p.

Williams, Howel, and Goles, Gordon, 1968, Volume of the Mazama Ash Fall and the Origin of Crater Lake Caldera: In Dole, H. M., ed., *Andesite Conference Guidebook: Oregon Dept. of Geology and Mineral Industries Bulletin 62*, pp. 37-41.

8: Mt. Thielsen

Cummins, William S., 1964, New Routes on Three Fingered Jack: *Mazama*, vol. 46, no. 13, pp. 52-53.

Diller, J. S., 1884, Fulgurite from Mt. Thielsen, Oregon: *American Journal of Science*, vol. 128, pp. 252-258.

Diller, J. S., and Patton, H. B., 1902, The Geology and Petrography of Crater Lake National Park: *U.S. Geol. Survey, Prof. Paper No. 3*.

Lathrop, T. G., 1968, Return of the Ice Age? *Mazama*, vol. 50, no. 13, pp. 34-36.

Nafziger, R. H., 1971, Oregon's Southernmost Glacier: a Three Year Report: *Mazama*, vol. 53, no. 13, pp. 30-33.

Purdom, W. B., 1963, *The Geologic History of the Diamond Lake Area, Umpqua National Forest, Douglas Co., Oregon*, published by U.S. Dept. of Agriculture, Forest Service, and Douglas Co. Park Department.

Taylor, Edward M., 1968, Roadside Geology, Santiam and McKenzie Pass Highways, Oregon: In Dole, H. M., ed., *Andesite Conference Guidebook*, Oregon Dept. Geology and Mineral Industries Bulletin 62, pp. 3-33.

Williams, Howel, 1933, Mount Thielsen, a Dissected Cascade Volcano: *University of California Publication, Dept. Geological Science Bulletin*, vol. 23, pp. 195-213.

Williams, Howel, 1957, *A Geologic Map of the Bend Quadrangle, Oregon and a Reconnaissance Geologic Map of the Central Portion of the High Cascade Mountains*, Oregon Dept. Geology and Mineral Industries, in coop. with U.S. Geol. Survey.

Williams, Howel, 1962, *Ancient Volcanoes of Oregon*, 3rd edition. Condon Lectures, University of Oregon Press, p. 68.

Williams, Ira A., 1921, Mount Thielsen: *Mazama*, vol. 6, pp. 19-25.

9: Newberry Volcano

Brogan, Philip F., n.d., *The Lava Butte Geological Area*, U.S. Dept. of Agriculture Forest Service, Pacific Northwest Region, 12 p.

Friedman, Irving, 1971, Obsidian Hydration Dates in the Newberry Volcano Area, Oregon: *Geological Survey Research for 1971: In U.S. Geological Survey Professional Paper 750-A*, p. A117.

Higgins, M. W., 1969, Air-fall Ash and Pumice Lapilli Deposits from Central Pumice Cone, Newberry Caldera, Oregon: *U.S. Geological Survey Professional Paper 650-D*, pp. D26-D32.

Higgins, M. W., 1973, Petrology of Newberry Volcano, Central Oregon: *Geological Society of America Bulletin*, vol. 84, no. 2, pp. 455-488.

Higgins, M. W., and Waters, A. C., 1967, Newberry Caldera, Oregon—A Preliminary Report: *The Ore Bin*, vol. 29, no. 3, pp. 37-60.

Higgins, M. W., and Waters, A. C., 1968, Newberry Caldera Field Trip: In Dole, H. M., ed., *Andesite Conference Guidebook. Oregon State Dept. of Geology and Mineral Industries, Bulletin 62*, pp. 59-77.

Higgins, M. W., and Waters, A. C., 1970, A Re-evaluation of Basalt-Obsidian Relations at East Lake Fissure, Newberry Caldera, Oregon: *Geological Society of America Bulletin*, vol. 81, no. 9, pp. 2835-2842.

Oregon Dept. of Geology and Mineral Industries, 1965, Articles on Recent

Volcanism in Oregon, reprinted from the *Ore Bin, Oregon Dept. of Geology and Mineral Industries — Misc. Paper 10.*

Peterson, N. V., and Groh, E. A., eds., 1965, *State of Oregon Lunar Geological Field Conference Guide Book: Oregon Dept. of Geology and Mineral Industries Bulletin 57,* 51 p.

Peterson, N. V., and Groh, E. A., 1969, The Ages of Some Holocene Volcanic Eruptions in the Newberry Volcano Area, Oregon, *Ore Bin*, vol. 31, no. 4, pp. 73-87.

Williams, Howel, 1935, Newberry Volcano, Central Oregon: *Geological Society of America Bulletin,* vol. 46, no. 2, pp. 253-304.

Williams, Howel, 1941, Calderas and Their Origin: *University of California Publications, Bulletin of the Department of Geological Sciences,* vol. 25, pp. 239-346.

Williams, Howel, 1962, *Ancient Volcanoes of Oregon,* 3rd ed. Condon Lectures, University of Oregon Press. 68 p.

10: The Three Sisters

Baldwin, Ewart M., 1964, *Geology of Oregon,* 2nd ed., J. W. Edwards, Publisher, Ann Arbor, Michigan, pp. 69-76.

Brogan, P. F., 1964, *East of the Cascades,* Binfords and Mort, Portland, Oregon, 304 p.

Ekman, Leonard C., 1962, *Scenic Geology of the Pacific Northwest,* Binfords and Mort, Publishers, Portland, Oregon, pp. 158-160.

Fairbanks, Harold Wellman, 1901, Notes on the Geology of the Three Sisters, Oregon: *Journal of Geology,* vol. 9, p. 73.

Hodge, Edwin T., 1925, Mount Multnomah, Ancient Ancestor of the Three Sisters: *University of Oregon Publications*, vol. 3, no. 2, 160 p.

Hopson, Ruth E., 1961, The Arctic Alpine Zone in the Three Sisters Region: *Mazama*, vol. 43, no. 13, pp. 14-27.

Hopson, Ruth E., 1960, Collier Glacier — A Photographic Record: *Mazama*, vol. 42, no. 13.

Hyslop, Robert S., 1971, South Sister's "Nordwand": *Mazama*, vol. 53, no. 13, pp. 21-23.

Newberry, John Strong, 1858, On the Parts of California and Oregon Explored: *American Journal of Science*, 2nd. series, vol. 26, no. 76, pp. 123-127.

Peterson, N. V., and Groh, E. A., 1965, *Lunar Geological Field Conference Guidebook; Oregon Dept. of Geology and Mineral Industries Bulletin 57,* 51 p.

Smith, Warren D., 1916, A Geologist's Thoughts on Returning from the Mazama Outing of 1916: *Mazama*, vol. 5, no. 1, pp. 24-28.

Stearns, Jane, 1912, Physiography of the Three Sisters: *Mazama*, vol. 4, no. 1, pp. 15-20.

Taylor, Edward M., 1965, Recent Volcanism between Three Fingered Jack and North Sister, Oregon Cascade Range: Oregon Dept. of Geology and Mineral Industries, *The Ore Bin*, vol. 27, no. 7, pp. 121-147.

Taylor, Edward M., 1968, Roadside Geology, Santiam and McKenzie Pass

Highways, Oregon, in Dole, H. M., ed., *Andesite Conference Guidebook: Oregon Dept. of Geology and Mineral Industries Bulletin 62,* pp. 3-33.

Williams, Howel, 1944, Volcanoes of the Three Sisters Region, Oregon, Cascades: *University of California Dept. of Geological Sciences Bulletin,* vol. 27, no. 3, pp. 37-84.

Williams, Howel, 1957, *A Geologic Map of the Bend Quadrangle, Oregon and a Reconnaissance Geologic Map of the Central Portion of the High Cascade Mountains,* Oregon Dept. of Geology and Mineral Industries, in coop. with U.S. Geological Survey.

Williams, Howel, 1962, *Ancient Volcanoes of Oregon,* 3rd edition, Condon Lectures, University of Oregon Press.

11: Mt. Jefferson

Condie, K. C., and Swenson, D. H., 1973, Compositional Variation in Three Cascade Stratovolcanoes: Jefferson, Rainier, and Shasta: *Bulletin Volcanologique,* vol. 37, no. 2, pp. 205-230.

Greene, Robert C., 1968, *Petrography and Petrology of Volcanic Rocks in the Mount Jefferson Area High Cascade Range, Oregon: U.S. Geological Survey Bulletin 1251-G.*

Hodge, Edwin T., 1925, Geology of Mount Jefferson: *Mazama,* vol. 7, no. 2, pp. 25-58.

Holden, Edward S., 1898, *A Catalogue of Earthquakes on the Pacific Coast 1769 to 1897: Smithsonian Miscellaneous Collection 1087,* p. 226.

McBirney, A. R., Sutter, J. F., Naslund, H. R., Sutton, K. G., and White, C. M., 1974, Episodic Volcanism in the Central Oregon Cascade Range: *Geology,* vol. 2, no. 12, pp. 585-589.

Sutton, Kenneth, 1974, *Geology of Mt. Jefferson,* unpublished Master of Science thesis, University of Oregon, Eugene, Oregon.

Sutton, Kenneth, 1975, written communication, unpublished field reports, maps, drawings, etc., on Mt. Jefferson.

Thayer, T. P., 1937, Petrology of Later Tertiary and Quaternary Rocks of the NorthCentral Cascade Mountains in Oregon: *Geological Society of America Bulletin,* vol. 48, no. 11, pp. 1611-1651.

Thayer, T. P., 1939, *Geology of the Salem Hills and the North Santiam River Basin, Oregon: Oregon Dept. of Geology and Mineral Industries Bulletin 15,* 40 p.

Walker, G. W., Greene, R. C., and Pattee, E. C., 1966, *Mineral Resources of the Mount Jefferson Primitive Area, Oregon: U.S. Geological Survey Bulletin 1230-D,* 32 p.

Williams, Ira A., 1916, Some Little-Known Scenic Pleasure Places in the Cascade Range in Oregon: *Oregon Bureau of Mines and Mineral Resources of Oregon,* vol. 2, no. 1, 114 p.

12: Mt. Hood

Ayeres, F. D. and Creswell, A. E., 1951, The Mount Hood Fumaroles, *Mazama:* vol. 33, no. 13, pp. 33-39.

Clark, Ella E., 1966, *Indian Legends of the Pacific Northwest*. Univ. of California Press, Berkeley and Los Angeles.

Courtney, W. F., 1902, Eruption of Mount Hood, *Everett Record*, May 17, 1902.

Crandell and Wise, written comm., 1973.

Deefeldorfer, George A., 1967, Onward and Upward: *Geological News Letter*, vol. 33, no. 9, pp. 69-73.

Folsom, M. M., 1970, Volcanic Eruptions: The Pioneers' Attitude on the Pacific Coast from 1800 to 1875: Oregon Dept. of Geology and Mineral Industries: *The Ore Bin*, vol. 32, pp. 61-71.

Hague, Arnold, 1871, Mt. Hood, *American Journal of Science*, series 3, vol. 1, pp. 165-167.

Hammond, Paul E., 1973, If Mount Hood Erupts: Oregon Dept. of Geology and Mineral Industries: *The Ore Bin*, vol. 35, no. 6, pp. 93-102.

Hazard, J. T., 1932, *Snow Sentinels of the Pacific Northwest*, Lowman and Hanford, Seattle.

Hodge, E. T., 1931, Stadter Buried Forest: *Mazama*, vol. 13, pp. 82-86.

Hodge, E. T., 1934, Volcanic and Seismic History of Oregon: *Proceedings of the fifth Pacific congress:* vol. 3, *Division of physical sciences*, A7, *Seismology and Volcanology*, pp. 2451-2460.

Hodge, E. T., 1935, Mt. Hood, Geological Society of the Oregon Country: *Geologic News Letter*, vol. 1, no. 13, pp. 3-4.

Holden, Edward S., 1898, *A Catalogue of Earthquakes on the Pacific Coast 1769 to 1897: Smithsonian Miscellaneous Publication 1087.*

Jillson, Willard Rouse, 1917, The Volcanic Activity of Mount St. Helens and Mount Hood in Historical Time: *Geographical Review*, vol. 3, pp. 482-483.

Lawrence, D. B., 1948, Mount Hood's Latest Eruption and Glacier Advances: *Mazama*, vol. 30, no. 13, p. 22-29.

Lawrence, D. G., and Lawrence, E. G., 1959, Radiocarbon Dating of events on Mount Hood and Mount St. Helens: *Mazama*, vol. 41, pp. 10-18.

McKee, Bates, 1972, *Cascadia: The Geologic Evolution of the Pacific Northwest*, McGraw-Hill Book Company, pp. 212-213.

Parker, Samuel, 1846, *Journal of an Exploring Party Beyond the Rocky Mounttains*, Ithaca, New York.

Peterson, N. V., and Groh, E. A., 1963, Recent Volcanic Landforms in Central Oregon: Oregon Dept. of Geology and Mineral Industries: *The Ore Bin*, vol. 25, no. 3, pp. 33-45.

Phillips, K. N., 1935, A Chemical Study of Fumaroles on Mount Hood: *Mazama*, vol. 18, pp. 44-46.

Reid, Harry Fielding, 1902, Notes on Mts. Hood and Adams and Their Glaciers: *Science*, n.s., vol. 15, p. 966.

Steel, William Gladstone, ed., 1899, Mountain Lore: *Oregon Native Son*, vol. 1, p. 276.

Steel, William Gladstone, ed., 1906, Mount Hood in Eruption: *Steel Points*, vol. 1, no. 1, p. 23.

Steel, William Gladstone, 1907a, Mount Hood: *Steel Points*, vol. 1, no. 3, pp. 89-99.

Steel, William Gladstone, ed., 1907b, Eruption of Mount Hood: *Steel Points*, vol. 1, no. 3, pp. 135-136.

Sylvester, A. H., 1908, Evidences of Recent Volcanic Activity and the Glaciers of Mt. Hood, Oregon: *Science*, vol. 27, p. 585.

Sylvester, A. H., 1908, Is our Noblest Volcano Awakening to New Life? *National Geographic Magazine,* vol. 19, pp. 515-525.

Symons, Thomas W., 1882, The Upper Columbia of the Great Plain of the Columbia, In *U.S. Senate, 47th Congress, Executive Document no. 186,* Ch. 9, pp. 98-104.

Williams, John H., 1912, *The Guardians of the Columbia,* J. H. Williams, Tacoma.

Wise, W. S., 1964a, The Geologic History of Mount Hood, Oregon: *Mazama,* vol. 46, pp. 13-22.

Wise, W. S., 1964b, A Guide to the Volcanic Rocks of the Cascade Range: *Mazama,* vol. 46, pp. 23-25.

Wise, William S., 1966, The Last Eruptive Phase of the Mt. Hood Volcano: *Mazama:* vol. 58, no. 13, pp. 14-19.

Wise, William S., 1968, Geology of the Mt. Hood Volcano: In Dole, H. M., ed., *Andesite Conference Guidebook, Oregon Dept. of Geology and Mineral Industries, Bulletin 62,* pp. 81-98.

Wise, William S., 1969, Geology and Petrology of the Mt. Hood Area: A Study of High Cascade Volcanism: *Geological Society of American Bulletin,* vol. 80, pp. 969-1006.

Writers Program of the Work Projects Administration in the State of Oregon, 1940, *Mount Hood: A Guide,* Oregon State Board of Control, 132 p.

13: Mt. Adams

Beckey, Fred, 1973, *Cascade Alpine Guide: Climbing and High Routes, Columbia River to Stevens Pass,* The Mountaineers, Seattle.

Ekman, Leonard C., 1962, *Scenic Geology of the Pacific Northwest,* Binfords and Mort, Portland, Oregon, pp. 138-142.

Ellingson, Jack A., 1969, Geology of the Goat Rocks Volcano, Southern Cascade Mountains, Washington: *Geological Society of America Abstracts with Programs, 1969, part 3, Cordilleran Section,* p. 15.

Fowler, Claude S., 1936, The Geology of the Mount Adams Country: *Geological Newsletter,* vol. 2, no. 1, pp. 2-5.

Gibbs, George, 1855, Report on the Geology of the Central Portion of Washington Territory: *U.S. Pacific Railroad Exploration: U.S. 33rd Congress, 1st Session, House Executive Document 129,* vol. 18, part 1, 1:494-512.

Hopkins, Kenneth D., 1969, Late Quaternary Glaciation and Volcanism on the South Slope of Mount Adams, Washington: *Geological Society of America Abstracts with Programs, 1969, part 3, Cordilleran Sec.,* p. 27.

Moxham, R. M., 1970, Thermal Features at Volcanoes in the Cascade Range, as Observed by Aerial Infrared Surveys: *Bulletin Volcanologique,* vol. 34, no. 1, pp. 77-106.

Phillips, K. N., 1941, Fumaroles of Mount Saint Helens and Mount Adams: *Mazama*, vol. 23, no. 12, pp. 37-42.

Rusk, C. E., 1919, *Mount Adams*, the Yakima Commercial Club, Yakima, Wash., 26 p.

Rusk, C. E., 1924, *Tales of a Western Mountaineer,* Houghton-Mifflin, New York.

Sheppard, Richard A., 1967, Petrology of a Late Quaternary Potassium-Rich Andesite Flow from Mount Adams, Washington: In *U.S. Geological Survey Professional Paper 575-C*, pp. C55-C59.

Smutek, Ray, 1972, Mount Adams—A History: *Off Belay,* no. 3, pp. 11-20.

Throssell, W. I., 1940, The Massif: Mt. Adams in Southwestern Washington: *Rocks and Minerals,* vol. 15, no. 1, pp. 14-19.

Williams, John H., 1912, *The Guardians of the Columbia*, John H. Williams, Tacoma, Wash., 144 p.

14: Mt. St. Helens

Allen, A. J., ed., 1848, *Ten Years in Oregon: Travels and Adventures of Doctor E. White and Lady,* Ithaca, N. Y., p. 200.

Anonymous, 1854, *Sketches of Mission Life among the Indians of Oregon:* New York, Carlton & Phillips, Sunday-School Union, 200 Mulberry Street.

Anonymous, 1859, *Weekly Oregonian*, Portland, Oregon, August 20, 1859.

Anonymous, 1894, Ascent of Mt. St. Helens: *American Naturalist*, vol. 28, pp. 46-48.

Anonymous, 1954, G.S.O.C. Field Trip to Mount St. Helens: *Geological News Letter,* vol. 20, no. 9, pp. 78-81.

Beckey, Fred, 1973, *Cascade Alpine Guide: Climbing and High Routes Columbia River to Stevens Pass,* The Mountaineers, Seattle.

Borchardt, Glenn A., Norgren, Joel A., and Harward, Moyle E., 1973, Correlation of Ash Layers in Peat Bogs of Eastern Oregon: *Geological Society of America Bulletin*, vol. 84, pp. 3101-3108.

Brewer, Henry Bridgman, 1842, Daybook from Sept. 3, 1839 to Feb. 13, 1843: In Holmes, Kenneth L., 1955, Mount Saint Helens' Recent Eruptions: *Oregon Historical Quarterly* vol. 56, pp. 197-210.

Burnett, Peter H., 1902, The Letters of Peter H. Burnett: *Oregon Historical Quarterly,* vol. 3, pp. 423-424.

Carithers, Ward, 1946, *Pumice and Pumicite Occurrences of Washington:* Washington Division of Mines and Geology, Report Investigation 15, 78 p.

Clark, Ella E., 1966 *Indian Legends of the Pacific Northwest*. Univ. of California Press, Berkeley and Los Angeles.

Coombs, H. A., and Howard, A. D., 1960, United States of America: In *Catalog of Active Volcanoes of the World, Part 9*, International Volcanological Association, Naples, Italy.

Crandell, Dwight R., 1969, Surficial Geology of Mount Rainier National Park, Washington: *U.S. Geological Survey Bulletin 1288*, 41 p.

Crandell, Dwight R., 1971, Postglacial Lahars from Mount Rainier Volcano, Washington: *U.S. Geological Survey Prof. Paper 677*, 75 p.

Crandell, Dwight R. Mullineaux, D. R., Miller, R. D., and Rubin, Meyer, 1962, Pyroclastic Deposits of Recent Age at Mount Rainier, Washington: In Short Papers in Geology, Hydrology, and Topography. *U.S. Geological Survey Prof. Paper* 450-D, pp. D64-D68.

Crandell, Dwight R., and Mullineaux, D. R., 1967, *Volcanic* Hazards at Mount Rainier, Washington: *U.S. Geological Survey Bulletin 1238*, 26 p.

Crandell, Dwight R., and Mullineaux, D. R., 1973, Pine Creek Volcanic Assemblage at Mount St. Helens, Washington: *U.S. Geological Survey Bulletin 1383-A*, 23 p.

Crandell, Dwight R., Mullineaux, Donal R., Rubin, Meyer, 1975, Mount St. Helens Volcano: Recent and Future Behavior. *Science*, vol. 187, no. 4175, pp. 438-441.

Crandell, D. R., and Waldron, H. H., 1969, Volcanic Hazards in the Cascade Range. In Olson, R. A., and Wallace, M. M., Geologic Hazards and Public Problems, Office of Emergency Preparedness, pp. 5-18.

Dana, James D., 1849, United States Exploring Expedition During the years 1838, 1839, 1840, 1841, 1842, under the commands of Charles Wilkes, *U.S.N. vol. 10, Geology*. Philadelphia, p. 640.

Decker, R. W., and Harlow, David, 1970, Microearthquakes at Cascade Volcanoes (abstract), *American Geophysical Union Transactions*, vol. 51, no. 4, p. 351.

De Mofras, Eugene Duflot, 1925, Extract from Exploration of the Oregon Territory, the Californias, and the Gulf of California, Undertaken during the Years 1840, 1841 and 1842, trans. and ed. by N. B. Pipes: *Oregon Historical Quarterly*, vol. 26, pp. 151-190.

Diller, J. S., 1899, Latest Volcanic Eruptions of the Pacific Coast: *Science*, new series, vol. 9, pp. 639-640.

Diller, J. S., 1915, The Relief of Our Pacific Coast: *Science*, vol. 41, pp. 48-57.

Dryer, Thomas J., 1853, Ascent of Mount Saint Helens: *Weekly Oregonian*, Portland, Oregon, Sept. 3, 1853, p. 2.

Dryer, Thomas J., 1854, Eruption of Mount Saint Helens: *Weekly Oregonian*, Portland, Oregon, February 25, 1854, p. 2.

Dutton, C. E., 1885, Letter: *Science*, vol. 6, pp. 46-47.

Elliott, C. P., 1897, Mount Saint Helens: *National Geographic Magazine*, vol. 8, pp. 226-230.

Emmons, S. F., 1877, The Volcanoes of the Pacific Coast of the United States: *Journal of the American Geographical Society*, vol. 9, pp. 45-65.

Erdmann, C. E., and Warren, W., 1938, Report on the Geology of Three Dam Sites on the Toutle River, Cowlitz and Skamania Counties, Washington: *U.S. Geological Survey Open-File Report*, 119 p.

Folsom, M. M., 1970, Volcanic Eruptions: The Pioneers' Attitude on the Pacific Coast from 1800 to 1875: Oregon Dept. of Geology and Mineral Industries, *The Ore Bin*, vol. 32, pp. 61-71.

Forsyth, C. E., 1910, Mount St. Helens, *The Mountaineer*, vol. 3, pp. 56-62.

Frémont, John C., 1845, *Report of the Exploring expedition to the Rocky*

Mountains in the year 1842, and to Oregon and North California in the years 1843-44, Washington D.C., p. 193-94.

Frost, Joseph H., 1934, The Journal of John H. Frost, ed. N. B. Pipes: *Oregon Historical Quarterly,* vol. 35, pp. 373-74.

Gairdner, Meredith, 1836, Letter. *The Edinburgh New Philosophical Journal,* vol. 20, no. 39, p. 206.

Gary, George, 1923, Diary of Rev. George Gary, ed. F. G. Young: *Oregon Historical Quarterly,* vol. 24, pp. 76-77.

Gibbs, George, 1855, Report on the Geology of the Central Part of Washington Territory. U.S. 33rd Congress, 1st session, *House Document 129*, vol. 18, part 1, pp. 494-512.

Gibbs, George, 1872, Physical Geography of the Northwestern Boundary of the United States: *Journal of the American Geographical Society.*

Greeley, Ronald, and Hyde, J. H., 1972, Lava Tubes of the Cave Basalt, Mount St. Helens, Washington: *Geological Society of America Bulletin*, vol. 83, pp. 2397-2418.

Halliday, W. R., 1963, Features and Significance of the Mount St. Helens Cave Area: *National Parks Magazine*, vol. 37, no. 195, pp. 11-14.

Hawkins, L. L., 1903, Lava Caves of St. Helens: *Mazama*, vol. 2, no. 3, pp. 134-35.

Holden, Edward S., 1898, *A Catalogue of Earthquakes on the Pacific Coast 1769 to 1897: Smithsonian Miscellaneous Publication 1087.*

Holmes, Kenneth L., 1955, Mount Saint Helens' Recent Eruptions: *Oregon Historical Quarterly,* vol. 56, pp. 197-210.

Hopson, C. A., 1971, Eruptive Sequence at Mt. St. Helens, Washington: *Geological Society of America Abstracts with Programs*, vol. 3, no. 2, p. 138.

Hopson, C. A., Waters, A. C., Bender, V. R., and Rubin, M., 1962, The Latest Eruptions from Mount Rainier Volcano: *Journal of Geology,* vol. 70, pp. 635-646.

Hyde, J. H., 1970, *Geologic Setting of Merrill Lake and Evaluation of Volcanic Hazards in the Kalama River Valley near Mount St. Helens, Washington:* U.S. Geological Survey Open-File Report, 17 p.

Hyde, J. H., 1973, *Late Quaternary Volcanic Stratigraphy, South Flank of Mount St. Helens, Washington* (Ph.D. Thesis). University of Washington, Seattle, 114 p.

Hyde, J. H., and Crandell, D. R., 1972, Potential Volcanic Hazards near Mount St. Helens, southwestern Washington (abstract): *Northwest Science Programs and Abstracts.*

Jillson, W. R., 1917a, New Evidence of a Recent Volcanic Eruption on Mt. St. Helens, Washington: *American Journal of Science*, vol. 44, no. 259, pp. 59-62.

Jillson, Willard Rouse, 1917b, The Volcanic Activity of Mount St. Helens and Mount Hood in Historical Time: *Geographical Review,* vol. 3, p. 482-483.

Jillson, W. R., 1921, Physiographic Effects of the Volcanism of Mt. St. Helens: *Geographical Review,* vol. 11, pp. 398-405.

Kane, Paul, 1925, *Wanderings of an Artist,* Radisson Society, Toronto (reprint of the 1859 edition).

Landerholm, Carl, ed., 1956, *Notices and Voyages of the Famed Quebec Mission to the Pacific Northwest*, Oregon Historical Society.

Landes, Henry, 1901, The Volcanoes of Washington, *Northwest Journal of Education*, vol. 12.

Lawrence, D. B., 1938, Trees on the March: *Mazama*, vol. 20, no. 12, pp. 49-54.

Lawrence, D. B., 1939, Continuing Research on the Flora of Mt. St. Helens: *Mazama*, vol. 21, no. 12, pp. 49-59.

Lawrence, D. B., 1941, The "Floating Island" Lava Flow of Mt. St. Helens: *Mazama*, vol. 23, no. 12, pp. 56-60.

Lawrence, D. B., 1954, Diagrammatic History of the Northeast Slope of Mt. St. Helens, Washington: *Mazama*, vol. 36, no. 13, p. 41-44.

Lawrence, D. B., and Elizabeth G., 1958, Bridge of the Gods Legend, Its Origin, History and Dating, *Mazama*, vol. 40, no. 13, p. 33-41.

Lawrence, Donald B. and E. G., 1959, Radiocarbon Dating of some Events on Mount Hood and Mount St. Helens: *Mazama*, vol. 41, no. 13, p. 10-18.

Lee, Daniel, and Frost, J. H., 1844, *Ten Years in Oregon*, New York, no. 257.

Moxham, R. M., 1970, Thermal Features at Volcanoes in the Cascade Range, as Observed by Aerial Infrared Surveys: *Bulletin Volcanologique*, vol. 34, pp. 77-106.

Mullineaux, D. R., 1964, Extensive Recent Pumice Lapilli and Ash Layers from Mount St. Helens Volcano, Southern Washington (abstract): *Geological Society of America Special Paper 76*, p. 285.

Mullineaux, D. R., and Crandell, D. R., 1960, Late Recent Age of Mount St. Helens Volcano, Washington: *In U.S. Geological Survey Research 1960: Short Papers in the Geological Sciences*, pp. B307-B308.

Mullineaux, D. R., and Crandell, D. R., 1962, Recent Lahars from Mount St. Helens, Washington: *Geological Society of America Bulletin*, vol. 73, pp. 855-870.

Mullineaux, D. R., Hyde, J. H., and Rubin, Meyer, 1972, Preliminary Assessment of Upper Pleistocene and Holocene Pumiceous Tephra from Mount St. Helens, Southern Washington (abstract): *Geological Society of America Abstracts with Programs*, vol. 4, no. 3, pp. 204-205.

Nasmith, H., Mathews, W. H., and Rouse, G. E., 1967, Bridge River Ash and Some Recent Ash Beds in British Columbia: *Canadian Journal of Earth Science*, vol. 4, pp. 163-170.

Norgren, J. A., Borchardt, G. A., and Harward, M. E., 1970, Mt. St. Helens Y Ash in Northeastern Oregon and South Central Washington (abstract): *Northwest Science*, vol. 44, p. 66.

North Pacific History Company of Portland, Oregon, 1889, *History of the Pacific Northwest: Oregon and Washington*, vol. 2, pp. 96-97.

Okazaki, Rose, Smith, H. W., Gilkeson, R. A., and Franklin, Jerry, 1972, Correlation of West Blacktail Ash with Pyroclastic Layer T from the 1800 A.D. Eruption of Mount St. Helens: *Northwest Science*, vol. 46, pp. 77-89.

Parker, Samuel, 1846, *Journal of an Exploring Tour Beyond the Rocky Mountains* (4th edition). Ithaca, pp. 223-229; 293-312; 329-351.

Peterson, N. V., and Groh, E. A., 1963, Recent Volcanic Landforms in Central Oregon: Oregon Dept. of Geology and Mineral Industries: *The Ore Bin*, vol. 25, no. 3, pp. 33-45.

Parrish, Josiah L., 1906, Letter dated January 13, 1892 to W. G. Steel: *Steel Points*, vol. 1, no. 1, pp. 25-26.

Phillips, K. N., 1941, Fumaroles of Mount St. Helens and Mount Adams: *Mazama*, vol. 23, no. 12, p. 37-42.

Plummer, F. G., 1893, Western Volcanoes: Chances That Western Washington May See Disastrous Eruptions: *Tacoma Daily Ledger,* Feb. 28, 1893, p. 3, col. 1-4.

Plummer, Frederick G., 1898, Reported Volcanic Eruptions in Alaska, Puget Sound, etc., 1690 to 1896. In Holden, Edward S., *A Catalogue of Earthquakes on the Pacific Coast 1769 to 1897. Smithsonian Miscellaneous Publication 1087,* Washington, D.C,

Pryde, P. R., 1968, Mount Saint Helens: A Possible National Monument: *National Parks Magazine,* vol. 42, no. 248, pp. 7-10.

Powers, Alfred, 1944, *Legends of the Four High Mountains*, Portland, Oregon Junior Historical Journal.

Schminky, Bruce, 1954, Records of eruptions of Mount St. Helens: Geol. Soc. Oregon Country, *Geol. News Letter,* vol. 20, no. 9, p. 81-82.

Smith, Henry W., Okazaki, Rose, and Aarsted, John, 1968, Recent Volcanic Ash in Soils of Northeastern Washington and Northern Idaho: *Northwest Science*, vol. 42, pp. 150-160.

Steel, William Gladstone ed., 1899, Mountain Lore: *Oregon Native Son*, vol. 1, p. 276.

Steel, William Gladstone, ed., 1906, Eruption of Mount Saint Helens: *Steel Points*, vol. 1, no. 1, pp. 25-26.

Sterling, E. M., 1968, *Trips and Trails, 2: Family Camps, Short Hikes, and View Roads in the South Cascades and Mt. Rainier.* The Mountaineers, Seattle.

Stevens, Charles, 1936, Letters of Charles Stevens, ed. Nellie Pipes: *Oregon Historical Quarterly,* vol. 37, pp. 250-251.

Stevens, Charles, 1937, Letters of Charles Stevens: *Oregon Historical Quarterly*, vol. 38, p. 73.

Strong, Emory, 1969, Early Accounts of the Eruption of Mt. St. Helens: *Geological News Letters*, vol. 35, no. 1, pp. 3-5.

Swan, James G., 1857, *The Northwest Coast; or, Three Years Residence in Washington Territory,* Harper & Brothers, New York, p. 395.

Thornton, J. Quinn, 1855, *Oregon and California in 1848,* Harper & Brothers, New York, vol. 1, pp. 256-257.

Unger, John D., and Mills, Kay F., 1973, Earthquakes near Mount St. Helens, Washington, *Geological Society of America Bulletin*, vol. 84, no. 3, pp. 1065-1068.

Verhoogen, Jean, 1937, *Mount St. Helens, A Recent Cascade volcano: California University Publication Geological Science*, vol. 24, p. 263-302.

Westgate, J. A., and Dreimanis, A., 1967, Volcanic Ash Layers of Recent Age at Banff National Park, Alberta, Canada: *Canadian Journal of Earth Science*, vol. 4, pp. 155-161.

Wilcox, R. E., 1965, Volcanic-Ash Chronology: In Wright, H. E., Jr., and Frey, D. G., *The Quaternary of the United States*, Princeton University Press, N. J., pp. 807-816.

Wilkes, Charles, 1845, *Narrative of the United States Exploration During the Years 1838, 1839, 1840, 1841, and 1842*, Philadelphia, vol. 4, pp. 439-40.

Williams, John H., 1912, *The Guardians of the Columbia*, J. H. Williams, Tacoma, Wash., 144 p.

Williams, I. A., 1922, Tree Casts in Recent Lava: *Natural History*, vol. 22, no. 6, pp. 543-548.

15: Mt. Rainier

Beckey, Fred, 1973, *Cascade Alpine Guide: Climbing and High Routes Columbia River to Stevens Pass*, The Mountaineers, Seattle.

California Division of Mines and Geology, 1970, Mount Rainier Restless: California Division of Mines and Geology, *Mineral Information Services*, vol. 23, no. 4, pp. 86-87.

Condie, K. C., and Swenson, D. H., 1973, Compositional Variation in Three Cascade Stratovolcanoes: Jefferson, Rainier, and Shasta: *Bulletin Volcanologique*, vol. 37, no. 2, pp. 205-230.

Coombs, Howard A., 1936, The *Geology of Mount Rainier National Park, Washington*. Washington University. (Seattle) Pub. Geol., vol. 3, pp. 131-212.

Coombs, Howard A., 1960, United States of America: in Part 9 of *Catalogue of the Active Volcanoes of the World*, International Volcanological Association, Naples, Italy, pp. vii-xii, 1-58.

Crandell, Dwight R., 1963a, Paradise Debris Flow at Mount Rainier, Washington: In *Short Papers in Geology and Hydrology: U.S. Geological Survey Professional Paper 475-B*, pp. B135-B139.

Crandell, Dwight R., 1963b, Surficial Geology and Geomorphology of the Lake Tapps Quadrangle, Washington: *U.S. Geological Survey Professional Paper 388-A*, pp. A1-A84.

Crandell, Dwight R., 1965, The Glacial History of Western Washington and Oregon: In Wright, H. E., Jr., and Frey, D. G., *The Quaternary of the United States*, Princeton University Press, N. J., pp. 341-354.

Crandell, Dwight R., 1969a, *The Geologic Story of Mount Rainier: U.S. Geological Survey Bulletin 1292*, 43 p.

Crandell, Dwight R., 1969b, *Surficial Geology of Mount Rainier National Park, Washington. U.S. Geological Survey Bulletin 1288*, 41 p.

Crandell, Dwight R., 1971, *Postglacial Lahars from Mount Rainier Volcano, Washington: U.S. Geological Survey Professional Paper 677*, 75 p.

Crandell, Dwight R., 1973, *Potential Hazards from Future Eruptions of Mount Rainier, Washington: U.S. Geological Survey Miscellaneous Geologic Investigations*, Map I-836.

Crandell, D. R. and Fahnestock, R. K., 1965, *Rockfalls and Avalanches from Little Tahoma Peak on Mount Rainier, Washington: U.S. Geological Survey Bulletin* 1221-A, 30 p.

Crandell, D. R., and Miller, R. D. 1964, Post-Hypsithermal Glacier Advances at Mount Rainier, Washington: In *Geological Survey Research 1964: U.S. Geological Survey Professional Paper 501-D*, pp. D110-D114.

Crandell, D. R., Mullineaux, D. R., Miller, R. D. and Rubin, Meyer, 1962, Pyroclastic deposits of Recent Age at Mount Rainier, Washington: In *Short Papers in the Geologic and Hydrologic Sciences: U.S. Geological Survey Professional Paper 450-D*, pp. D64-D68.

Crandell, D. R., and Mullineaux, D. R., 1967, *Volcanic Hazards at Mount Rainier, Washington: U.S. Geological Survey Bulletin* 1238, 26 p.

Crandell, D. R., and Waldron, H. H., 1956, A Recent Volcanic Mudflow of Exceptional Dimensions from Mount Rainier, Washington, *American Journal of Science*, vol. 254, p. 349-362.

Crandell, Dwight R., and Waldron, H. H., 1969, Volcanic Hazards in the Cascade Range: In Olson, R. A., and Wallace, M. M., *Geologic Hazards and Public Problems, Conference Proceedings,* Office of Emergency Preparedness, pp. 5-18.

Diller, J. S., 1915, The relief of our Pacific coast: *Science* vol. 41, p. 48-57.

Emmons, Samuel Franklin, 1877, Volcanoes of the Pacific Coast of the U.S.: *Journal of the American Geographical Society,* vol. 9, pp. 45-65.

Fiske, R. S., Hopson, C. A. and Waters, A. C., 1963, *Geology of Mount Rainier National Park, Washington: U.S. Geological Survey Professional Paper 444,* 93 p.

Folsom, M. M., 1970, Volcanic Eruptions: The Pioneers' Attitude on the Pacific Coast from 1800 to 1875: Oregon Department of Geology and Mineral Industries: *The Ore Bin*, vol. 32, pp. 61-71.

Frémont, J.C., 1845, *Report of the Exploring Expedition to the Rocky Mountains in the Year 1842, and to Oregon and North California in the Years 1843-1844,* Blair and Rives, Washington, D. C., 693 p.

Friedman, Jules D., 1972, Aerial Thermal Surveillance of Volcanoes of the Cascade Range, Washington, Oregon, and Northern California: *EOS (Amer. Geophys. Union, Trans.)* vol. 53, no. 4, p. 533, 1972.

Grater, R. J., 1948, The Flood that Swallowed a Glacier: *Natural History*, vol. 57, pp. 276-278.

Hague, Arnold and Iddings, Joseph P., 1883, Notes on the Volcanoes of Northern California, Oregon and Washington Territory: *American Journal of Science*, 3rd series, vol. 26, no. 153, pp. 222-235.

Haines, Aubrey L., 1962, Mountain Fever! Historic Conquests of Rainier, *Oregon Historical Society,* Portland, Oregon.

Hazard, Joseph T., 1933, *Snow Sentinels of the Northwest,* Lowman and Hanford, publisher, Seattle.

Holden, Edward S., 1898, *A catalogue of Earthquakes on the Pacific Coast, 1769 to 1897: Smithsonian Miscellaneous Collections No. 1087,* Smithsonian Institution, Washington D.C.

Hopson, C. A., Waters, A. C., Bender, V. R., Rubin, Meyer, 1962, The Latest Eruptions from Mount Rainier Volcano: *Journal of Geology*, vol. 70, pp. 635-646.

Kirk, Ruth, 1968, *Exploring Mount Rainier*, University of Washington Press, Seattle & London.

Kiver, Eugene P., and Mumma, Marten P., 1971, Summit Firn Caves, Mount Rainier, Washington: *Science*, vol. 173, pp. 320-322.

Kiver, Eugene P., and Steel, William K., 1975, Firn Caves in the Volcanic Craters of Mount Rainier, Washington: *National Speleological Society Bulletin*, vol. 37, no. 1.

Lange, Ian M., and Avent, Jon C., 1973, Ground-Based Thermal Infrared Surveys as an Aid in Predicting Volcanic Eruptions in the Cascade Range: *Science*, vol. 182, no. 4109, pp. 279-281.

Macdonald, Gordon A., 1972, *Volcanoes*, Prentice-Hall, Englewood Cliffs, N.J., 510 p.

Matthes, F. E., 1914, *Mount Rainier and Its Glaciers*, National Park Service, pp. 1-48.

Miller, M. M., 1961, Wind, Sky and Ice report from Project Crater, 1959-1960, *Harvard Mountaineering*, n. 15.

Molenaar, Dee, 1971, *The Challenge of Rainier*, The Mountaineers, Seattle.

Moxham, R. M. 1970, Thermal Features at Volcanoes in the Cascade Range, as Observed by Aerial Infrared Surveys: *Bulletin Volcanologique*, vol. 34, no. 1, pp. 77-106.

Moxham, R. M., Boynton, G. R., and Cote, C. E., 1972, Satellite Telemetry of Fumarole Temperatures: *International Union of Geology and Geophysics*, vol. 36, no. 1, pp. 191-199.

Moxham, R. M., Crandell, D. R. and Mariatt, W. E., 1965, Thermal features at Mount Rainier, Washington, as revealed by infrared surveys: *U.S. Geological Survey Professional Paper 525-D*, pp. 93-100.

Mullineaux, D. R. Sigafoos, R. S., and Hendricks, E. L., 1969, A Historic Eruption of Mount Rainier, Washington: *U.S. Geological Survey Professional Paper 650-B*, pp. 315-318.

Plummer, Frederick G., 1893, Western Volcanoes: Chances That Western Washington May See Disastrous Eruptions: In *Tacoma Daily Ledger*, February 28, 1893, p. 3, col. 1-4.

Plummer, Frederick G., 1898, Reported Volcanic Eruptions in Alaska, Puget Sound, etc., 1690 to 1896: in Holden, E. S., *A Catalgue of Earthquakes on the Pacific Coast, 1769 to 1897:* Smithsonian miscellaneous collection No. 1087, Smithsonian Institution, Washington, D.C.

Russell, Israel C., 1898, Glaciers of Mount Rainier, with a Paper on the Rocks of Mount Rainier, by G. O. Smith: *U.S. Geological Survey 18th Annual Report, Part 2*, pp. 349-423.

Schear, R., 1965, Mount Rainier: Inside Look at a Smoldering Volcano: *Seattle Magazine*, vol. 2, no. 16, pp. 30-33; 46-47.

Sigafoos, R. S. and Hendricks, E. L., 1961, *Botanical Evidence of the modern*

History of Nisqually Glacier, Washington: U.S. Geological Survey Professional Paper 387-A, 20 p.

Stagner, Howard R., 1966, *Behind the Scenery of Mount Rainier National Park*, rev. ed., Mt. Rainier National Historic Assoc., 64 p.

Stevens, Hazard, 1876, The Ascent of Takhoma: *Atlantic Monthly*, vol. 38, pp. 513-530.

Unger, John D., and Decker, Robert W., 1970, The Microearthquake Activity of Mount Rainier, Washington: *Bulletin of the Seismological Society of America*, vol. 60, no. 6, pp. 2023-2035.

Veatch, Fred M., 1969, *Analysis of a 24-year Photographic Record of Nisqually Glacier, Mount Rainier National Park, Washington: U.S. Geological Survey Professional Paper 631*, 52 p.

Wickhersham, James, 1892, Address before the Tacoma Academy of Science, Feb. 6, 1892 (cited in Plummer, F. G., *Guide Book to Mount Tacoma*, Tacoma, Washington, News Publishing Co., 1893, 12 p.).

Williams, John H., 1911, *The Mountain That Was "God"*, G. P. Putnam & Sons, N.Y.; John H. Williams, Tacoma.

16: Glacier Peak

Borchardt, Glenn A., Norgren, Joel A., and Harward, Moyle E., 1973, Correlation of Ash Layers in Peat Bogs of Eastern Oregon: *Geological Society of America Bulletin*, vol. 84, no. 9, pp. 3101-3108.

Ford, A. B., 1959, *Geology and Petrology of the Glacier Peak Quadrangle, Northern Cascades, Washington* (Ph.D. Thesis), University of Washington, Seattle, 374 p.

Ford, A. B., 1960, Metamorphism and Granitic Intrusion in the Glacier Peak Quadrangle, Northern Cascade Mountains of Washington (abstract): *Geological Society of America Bulletin* vol. 71, no. 12, part 2, p. 2059.

Fryxell, Ronald, 1965, Mazama and Glacier Peak Volcanic Ash Layers— Relative Ages: *Science*, vol. 147, no. 3663, pp. 1288-1290.

Powers, H. A., and Wilcox, R. E., 1964, Volcanic Ash from Mount Mazama (Crater Lake) and from Glacier Peak: *Science*, vol. 144, no. 3624, pp. 1334-1336.

Rigg, G. B., and Gould, H. R., 1957, Age of Glacier Peak Eruption and Chronology of Post Glacial Peat Deposits in Washington and Surrounding Areas: *American Journal of Scienie*, vol. 255, pp. 341-363.

Tabor, R. W., and Crowder, D. F., 1969, *On Batholiths and Volcanoes— Intrusion and Eruption of Late Cenozoic Magmas in the Glacier Peak Area, North Cascades, Washington: U.S. Geological Survey Professional Paper 604.*

Vance, J. A., 1957, *The Geology of the Sauk River Area in the Northern Cascades of Washington:* Seattle, Washington University, Ph.D. thesis, 312 p.

Wilcox, R. E., 1965, Volcanic Ash Chronology: In Wright, H. E., Jr., and Frey, D. G., eds., *The Quaternary of the United States*, Princeton University Press, Princeton, N.J., pp. 807-816.

Williams, Hill, ed., 1975, Glacier Peak's Last Debris Spree: Seattle *Times*, Sept. 25, B3.

17: Mt. Baker

Anonymous, 1859, *Pioneer Democrat:* Olympia, Washington Territory, vol. 8, no. 1, Nov. 25.

Anonymous, 1860, *Pioneer Democrat:* Olympia, Washington Territory, Dec. 28.

Anonymous, 1863, *Washington Sentinel*, August 18.

Anonymous, 1865, Volcanic Eruptions in North California and Oregon: *American Journal of Science*, 2nd series, vol. 40, no. 119, p. 264.

Borah, Leo A., 1933, Washington, The Evergreen State: *National Geographic*, vol. 63, no. 2, p. 144.

Burke, Raymond, 1972, *Neoglaciation of Boulder Valley, Mount Baker, Washington* (Master's Thesis), Western Washington State College, Bellingham.

Coleman, Edmund T., 1869, Mountaineering on the Pacific: *Harper's New Monthly Magazine*, Nov.

Coleman, Edmund T., 1877, Mountains and Mountaineering Far West: *Alpine Journal*, vol. 8, no. 57, pp. 233-242.

Coombs, H. A., 1939, Mount Baker, a Cascade Volcano: *Geological Society of America Bulletin*, vol. 50, no. 10, pp. 1493-1510.

Coombs, H. A., 1960, United States of America: *Catalogue of the Active Volcanoes of the World*, Part 9, International Volcanological Association, Naples, p. vii-xii, 1-58.

Crandell, Dwight R., and Waldron, H. H., 1969, Volcanic Hazards in the Cascade Range: In Olson, R. A., and Wallace, M. M., eds., *Geologic Hazards and Public Problems*, Office of Emergency Preparedness, pp. 5-18.

Davidson, George, 1885, Recent volcanic activity in the U.S.: Eruptions of Mount Baker: *Science*, vol. 6, no. 138, p. 262.

Diller, Joseph Silas, 1915, The relief of our Pacific Coast: *Science,* vol. 41, pp. 48-57.

Easterbrook, Don J., and David A. Rahm, 1970. *Landforms of Washington*, Department of Geology, Western Washington State College, Bellingham, Washington, pp. 20-23.

Easton, C. F., unpublished, Mt. Baker, Its Trails and Legends: compilation of photographs, newspaper articles and manuscript commissioned in 1911 by the Mount Baker Club and archived at the Whatcom County Museum of Natural History, Bellingham, Washington, 262 p.

Edson, Lelah Jackson, 1968, *The Fourth Corner, Highlights from the early Northwest*, Whatcom Museum of History and Art, Bellingham, pp. 151-156.

Frank, David, Post, Austin, and Friedman, Jules D., 1975, Recurrent Geothermally Induced Debris Avalanches on Boulder Glacier, Mount Baker,

Washington: *U.S. Geological Survey Journal of Research*, vol. 3, no. 1, pp. 77-87.

Friedman, J. D., Frank, D. G., Preble, Duane, and Painter, J. E., 1973, Thermal Surveillance of Cascade Range Volcanoes Using ERTS-1 Multispectral Scanner, Aircraft Imaging Systems and Ground-Based Data Communication Platforms, in Symposium on Significant Results Obtained from the Earth Resources Technology Satellite-1, New Carrollton, Md., Mar. 5-9, 1973: NASA SP-327, p. 1549-1560.

Gibbs, George, 1855, Report on the Geology of the Central Portions of Washington Territory: *U.S. Pacific Railroad Explorations, U.S. 33d. Congress 1st session, H. Ex Document 129*, vol. 18, part 1, 1:494-512.

Gibbs, George, 1870, Physical Geography of the Northwestern Boundary of the United States: *American Geographic Society Journal*, vol. 3, pp. 134-157.

Gibbs, George, 1874, Physical Geography of the Northwestern Boundary of the United States: *American Geographic Society Journal,* Vol. 4, pp. 298-392.

Holden, Edward S., 1898, *A Catalogue of Earthquakes on the Pacific Coast 1769 to 1897, Smithsonian Misc. Coll. No. 1087.*

Hyde, J. H., and Crandell, D. R., 1975, Origin and Age of Postglacial Deposits and Assessment of Potential Hazards from Future Eruptions of Mount Baker, Washington: U.S. Geological Survey Open-File Report, 75-286, 22 p.

Malone, Stephen D., and Frank, David, 1975, Increased Heat Emission from Mount Baker, Washington, in press.

Misch, Peter, 1952, Geology of the Northern Cascades of Washington: *The Mountaineer,* vol. 45, no. 13, pp. 4-22.

Perrey, A., 1832-1856, *Bulletins de L'Academie Royale des Sciences,* First Series, Brussels, Belgium.

Perrey, A., 1832-1856, Notes sur les Tremblements de Terre: in *Bulletins de L'Academie Royale des Sciences*, First Series, Brussels, Belgium.

Phillips, James W., 1971, *Washington State Place Names,* University of Washington Press.

Plummer, F. G., 1893, Western volcanoes: Chances that Western Washington May See Disastrous Eruptions: *Tacoma Daily Ledger,* Feb. 28, p. 3, col. 1-4.

Plummer, F. G., 1898, Reported Volcanic Eruptions in Alaska, Puget Sound, etc., 1690-1896: In Holden, Edward S., 1898, *A Catalogue of Earthquakes on the Pacific Coast 1769 to 1897, Smithsonian Institution Misc. Col. 1087,* pp. 24-27.

Rusk, C. W., 1924, *Tales of a Western Mountaineer,* Houghton-Mifflin, New York.

Smith, G. O. and Calkins, F. C., 1904, A geological Reconnaissance across the Cascade Range near the 49th parallel: *U.S. Geological Survey Bulletin, no. 235,* pp. 1-99.

Steel, William Gladstone, 1906, Ascent of Mount Baker: *Steel Points*, vol. 1, no. 1, pp. 27-28.

18: Mt. Garibaldi

Barton, Robert H., Christiansen, E. A., Kupsch, W., Mathews, W. H., Gravenor, C. P., Bayrock, L. A., 1966, Quaternary, Chapter 14: In *Geological History of Western Canada,* Alberta Society of Petroleum Geologists, Calgary, Alberta, pp. 195-200.

Brock, R. W., 1928, Volcanoes of the Canadian Cordillera: *Proc. 3rd Pan-Pacific Sci. Cong.,* Tokyo, pp. 688-710.

Burwash, E. M. J., 1914a, Pleistocene Volcanism of the Coast Range of British Columbia: *Journal of Geology*, vol. 22, pp. 260-267.

Burwash, E. M. J., 1914b, The Pleistocene Volcanoes of the Coast Range of British Columbia: *B. C. Academy of Science Papers 1910-1914*, pp. 67-75.

Crickmay, Colin Hayter, 1930, The Structural Connection between the Coast Range of British Columbia and the Cascade Range of Washington: *Geology Magazine*, vol. 67, pp. 482-491.

Hanson, George, 1934, The Recent Volcanoes of Canada: *5th Pacific Sci. Cong. Canada, 1933, Proceedings,* vol. 3, pp. 2291-2294.

Mathews, W. H., 1938, Geology of the Garibaldi Lake Area: *Canadian Alpine Journal*, vol. 25, 1937, pp. 107-112.

Mathews, W. H., 1951a, Historic and Prehistoric Fluctuations of Alpine Glaciers in the Mount Garibaldi Map-Area, Southwestern British Columbia: *Journal of Geology,* vol. 59, pp. 357-380.

Mathews, W. H., 1951b, The Table, A Flat-Topped Volcano in Southern British Columbia: *American Journal of Science*, vol. 249, pp. 830-841.

Mathews, W. H., 1952, Mount Garibaldi, A Supraglacial Pleistocene Volcano in Southwestern British Columbia: *American Journal of Science*, vol. 250, pp. 81-103.

Mathews, W. H., 1957, Petrology of Quaternary Volcanics in the Mount Garibaldi Map Area, Southwestern British Columbia: *American Journal of Science*, vol. 255, pp. 400-415.

Mathews, W. H., 1958, Geology of the Mount Garibaldi Map-Area, Southwestern British Columbia, Canada: *Bulletin of the Geological Society of America*, vol. 69, pp. 161-198.

McBirney, Alexander R., 1968, Petrochemistry of the Cascade Volcanoes: In Doles, H. M., ed., *Andesite Conference Guidebook; Oregon Dept. of Geology and Mineral Industries Bulletin* 62, pp. 101-107.

McTaggart, K. C., 1970, Tectonic History of the Northern Cascade Mountains: In *Structure of the Southern Canadian Cordillera*, Geological Association of Canada Special Paper no. 6, pp. 137-148.

Nasmith, H., Mathews, W. H., Rouse, G. E., 1967, Bridge River Ash and Some Other Recent Ash Beds in British Columbia: *Canadian Journal of Earth Science*, vol. 4, no. 1, pp. 163-170.

Souther, J. G., 1970a, Recent Volcanism and Its Influence on Early Native Cultures of Northwestern British Columbia: In Early Man and Environments: In Smith, R. A., and Smith, J. W., eds., *Northwest North America*, Calgary University Archaeological Association Annual, Paleoenvironmental Workshop, 2nd. Proc., University of Calgary Students Press, Calgary, Alberta, pp. 53-64.

Souther, J. G. 1970b, Volcanism and Its Relation to Recent Crustal Movements in the Canadian Cordillera: *Canadian Journal of Earth Science*, vol. 7, pp. 553-568.

Souther, J. G., and Lambert, M. B., 1972, Volcanic Rocks of the North Canadian Cordillera: *International Geolog. Cong. Guidebook,* no. 24, Part A12, 54 p.

Sutherland-Brown, A., 1969, Aiyansh Lava Flow, British Columbia: *Canadian Journal of Earth Science*, vol. 6, pp. 1460-1468.

Taylor, W., 1936-38, Glacier Retreat in Garibaldi Park: *Canadian Alpine Journal*, vol. 24, 1936, pp. 103-108, June, 1937; vol. 25, 1937, pp. 117-127, 1938.

Westgate, J. A., and Dreimanis, A., 1967, Volcanic Ash Layers of Recent Age at Banff National Park, Alberta, Canada: *Canadian Journal of Earth Science*, vol. 4, pp. 155-161.

19: Cascade Ice and Fire: Now and in the Future

Anonymous, 1975, Volcanoes and Ice Ages: A Link?: *Science News*, vol. 107, p. 100.

Beckey, Fred, 1973, *Cascade Alpine Guide: Climbing and High Routes, Columbia River to Stevens Pass,* The Mountaineers, Seattle.

Chesterman, Charles W., 1971, Volcanism in California: *California Geology,* vol. 24, no. 8, pp. 139-147.

Crandell, Dwight R., 1965, The Glacial History of Western Washington and Oregon: in Wright, H. E., Jr., and Frey, David G., eds., *The Quaternary of the United States*, Princeton University Press, Princeton, N.J., pp. 341-353.

Crandell, Dwight R., 1969, *The Geologic Story of Mount Rainier*, U.S. Geological Survey Bulletin 1292.

Crandell, Dwight R., *Postglacial Lahars from Mount Rainier Volcano, Washington:* U.S. Geological Survey Professional Paper 677, 75 p.

Crandell, Dwight R., 1972, Glaciation near Lassen Peak, Northern California: U.S. Geological Survey Professional Paper 800-C, pp. C179-C188.

Crandell, Dwight R., 1973, *Potential Hazards from Future Eruptions of Mount Rainier, Washington:* U.S. Geological Survey Misc. Geol. Inv. Map I-836.

Crandell, Dwight R., and Mullineaux, Donal R., 1967, *Volcanic Hazards at Mount Rainier:* U.S. Geological Survey Bulletin 1238, 26 p.

Crandell, Dwight R., and Mullineaux, Donal R., 1973, *Pine Creek Volcanic Assemblage at Mt. St. Helens, Washington:* U.S. Geological Survey Bulletin 1383-A, 23 p.

Crandell, Dwight R., and Mullineaux, Donal R., 1975, Technique and Rationale of Volcanic-Hazards Appraisals in the Cascade Range, Northwestern United States: *Environmental Geology.*

Crandell, Dwight R., Mullineaux, Donal R., and Rubin, Meyer, 1975, Mt. St.

Helens Volcano: Recent and Future Behavior: *Science*, vol. 187, no. 4175, pp. 438-441.

Crandell, Dwight R., and Waldron, H. H., 1969, Volcanic Hazards in the Cascade Range: in Olson, R. A., and Wallace, R. M., eds., *Geologic Hazards and Public Problems:* Office of Emergency Preparedness, Region 7 Conf. Proc., Santa Rosa, Calif., May 27-28, pp. 5-18.

Decker, R. W., 1973, State-of-the-Art in Volcano Forecasting: *Bulletin Volcanologique*, vol. 37, no. 3, pp. 372-393.

Dodge, Nicholas A., 1964, Recent Measurements on the Eliot Glacier: *Mazama*, vol. 46, no. 13, pp. 47-49.

Dodge, Nicholas A., 1971, The Eliot Glacier: New Methods and Some Interpretations: *Mazama*, vol. 53, no. 13, pp. 25-29.

Gorshkov, G. S., 1971, Prediction of Volcanic Eruptions and Seismic Methods of Location of Magma Chambers—A Review: *Bulletin Volcanologique*, vol. 35, pp. 198-211.

Hammond, Paul E., 1973, If Mt. Hood Erupts: *The Ore Bin*, vol. 35, no. 6, pp. 93-102.

Hammond, Paul E., 1974, The Pulse of the Cascade Volcanoes: *Pacific Search*, vol. 8, no. 8, pp. 5-9.

Lange, Ian M., and Avent, Jon C., 1973, Ground-Based Thermal Infrared Surveys as an Aid in Predicting Volcanic Eruptions in the Cascade Range: *Science*, vol. 182, no. 4109, pp. 279-281.

Lathrop, T. G., 1968, Return of the Ice Age?: *Mazama*, vol. 50, no. 13, pp. 34-36.

McKee, Bates, 1972, *Cascadia: The Geologic Evolution of the Pacific Northwest*, McGraw-Hill, New York.

Molenaar, Dee, 1971, *The Challenge of Rainier*, The Mountaineers, Seattle.

Montague, Malcolm J., 1973, The Little Glacier That Couldn't: *Mazama*, vol. 55, no. 13, pp. 73-75.

Nafziger, Ralph H., 1971, Oregon's Southernmost Glacier: A Three Year Report: *Mazama*, vol. 53, no. 13, pp. 30-33.

Phillips, Kenneth N., 1938, Our Vanishing Glaciers: *Mazama*, vol. 20, no. 12, pp. 24-41.

Phillips, Kenneth N., 1939, Farewell to Sholes Glacier: *Mazama*, vol. 21, no. 12, pp. 37-40.

Post, Austin, 1970, Recent Changes in Glaciers of the North Cascades, Washington, U. S. Geological Survey unpublished preliminary report.

Post, Austin, 1974, Mount Rainier's Glaciers Currently Advancing—And Retreating, U.S. Geological Survey, Tacoma, Washington, Press Release, March 26, 1974.

Richards, Carl Price, 1937, Photographic Survey of the Glaciers of Mt. Jefferson and the Three Sisters: *Mazama*, vol. 19, no. 12, pp. 66-75.

Russell, Israel C., 1901, *Glaciers of North America*, Ginn and Co., Boston.

Veatch, Fred M., 1969, *Analysis of a 24-Year Photographic Record of Nisqually Glacier, Mt. Rainier National Park, Washington*, U.S. Geological Survey Professional Paper 631.

Glossary of Geologic Terms

Aa—Hawaiian word used to describe a lava flow which is characterized by a surface broken into rough, angular, "clinkery" fragments. Good examples of these jagged, slaggy flows occur along the McKenzie Pass Highway between the North Sister and Mt. Washington.

Ash—fine particles of pulverized rock blown from an explosion vent. Measuring less than about 1/10th inch in diameter (under 4 mm), ash may be either solid or molten when first erupted. By far the commonest variety is vitric ash, glassy particles formed by gas bubbles bursting through liquid magma. *Lithic* ash is formed of older rock pulverized during an eruption, while in *crystal* ash each grain is composed of a single crystal or groups of crystals with only traces of glass adhering to them. Many ash deposits are mixtures of all three kinds in various proportions.

Ash flow—a turbulent mixture of gas and rock fragments, most of which are ash-sized particles, ejected violently from a crater or fissure. This mass of pyroclastics is normally of very high temperature and moves rapidly down the slopes of a volcano or even along a level surface. Extensive ash flows have been erupted from Mt. Mazama, Broken Top, and Mt. St. Helens. When solidified, ash flow deposits are often called *ignimbrites*. See *Pyroclastic flow* and *block-and-ash flow.*

Basalt—a lava relatively poor in silica and rich in magnesium and ferrictic. When poured out in sufficient volume with a high temperature and gas content, it typically flows long distances from its source and is the characteristic lava of most shield volcanoes. The outpouring of highly fluid basalts created the vast inland plateaus of Washington and Oregon during Miocene time.

Bergschrund—a crevasse at the back of a glacier between the glacier and the rock headwall, formed by melting and the movement of the glacier.

Block—angular chunk of solid rock ejected during an eruption. Accumulations of blocks may form *breccia.*

Block-and-ash flow—variety of a pyroclastic flow, a turbulent mass of hot fragments, varying in size from under 1/10th inch to many feet in diameter, which sweeps downslope as the result of an eruption. Block-and-ash flows are commonly caused by the collapse of the side of a dome while still hot, as at Mt. St. Helens.

Blocky lava—lava which, when congealed, exhibits a surface broken into large angular fragments. Whereas aa lava has a spiny, scoriaceous crust, blocky flows have one littered with sharp boulders.

Blowhole—a miniature crater, usually secondary in nature to the main vent of a volcano, through which gas is discharged. Blowholes often form on the surface of a thick lava flow, the result of rapidly escaping gas.

Bomb—fragment of molten or semi-molten rock 2½ inches to many feet in diameter which is blown out during an eruption. Because of their plastic condition when first ejected, bombs are often modified in shape during their flight through the air and/or by their impact on the ground. As the outer crust cools and solidifies, continued expansion of the interior by gas pressure sometimes causes cracking, which may form a bomb surface resembling the crust of freshly baked bread (*breadcrust* bombs).

Breccia—a rock composed of many distinct fragments, often sharp and/or angular, embedded in a matrix of fine material. Breccias are sometimes formed when shattered blocks of volcanic rock are transported by avalanches or volcanic mudflows.

Caldera—the Spanish word for cauldron, a large basin-shaped volcanic depression—by definition at least a mile in diameter. Such large depressions are typically formed by the subsidence of volcanoes. Crater Lake occupies the best-known caldera in the Cascades. Calderas are to be distinguished from craters, which they always exceed in size.

Cinder cone—a volcanic cone built entirely of loose framental material (pyroclastics). Most cinder cones are symmetrical, with a circular ground plan and steep, regular slopes terminating in a single summit crater. Although the eruptions which build these pyroclastic cones are always explosive, lava commonly flows quietly from the foot of the cone.

Clinker—rough fragment of lava on the surface of aa flows, so named because of its resemblance to clinkers formed in the grate of a furnace.

Cirque—an ampitheater-like depression in mountain regions, formed by the plucking action of glacial ice.

Composite cone—another term for a *stratovolcano*, a large volcanic cone constructed of both lava flows and fragmental material. All of the largest Cascade volcanoes are of this type.

Conduit—the feeding pipe of a volcano, the ''throat'' through which material passes on its way to the earth's surface. When filled with congealed lava (a plug), a central conduit is often relatively resistant to erosion. As a result, the solidified conduit fillings can remain standing as high pinnacles after the surrounding cone has been eroded away. Mt. Thielsen and Union Peak are good examples of such eroded volcanic necks.

Crater—the bowl-shaped hollow, usually at or near the top of a volcano, through which lava and pyroclastics are ejected. In cross-section, most craters are cylindrical or funnel-shaped.

Dacite—lava with a high silica content. Dacites are usually slow moving and viscous when erupted and can form flows of exceptional thickness. When unusually stiff and pasty, they may form steepsided domes, such as Lassen Peak. The only major stratovolcanoes in the Cascades formed principally of dacite lava are Glacier Peak and Mt. Garibaldi.

Detonation—an explosion made by the combustion of gases or by the abrupt release of gases from a volcanic vent.

Dike—relatively thin walls of solidified lava which cut through, vertically or obliquely, the interior of a volcanic cone. Dikes are formed when liquid lava rises to fill cracks or crevices within the volcano. Some dikes are the congealed feeding pipes of parasitic cones or lava flows. They are visible only when exposed by erosion.

Dome—a rounded protrusion of lava which, when erupted, was too viscous to flow laterally and instead piled up above the erupting vent. When the lava mass is an upheaved, consolidated conduit filling, the resultant mound is called a *plug dome*.

Dormant—literally, "sleeping." The term used to describe a volcano which is presently inactive but which may erupt again. Most of the major Cascade volcanoes are now believed to be dormant rather than extinct.

Ejecta—the material thrown out of a volcano.

Engulfment—the inward collapse of a volcano, perhaps as the result of an evacuation of the magma chamber. The collapse basin thus formed is called a *caldera*.

Eruption—the process by which solid, liquid, and gaseous materials are ejected onto the earth's surface by volcanic activity. Eruptions range from the quiet overflow of liquid rock to the tremendously violent expulsion of pyroclastics.

Eruption cloud—the column of gases, ash and larger rock fragments rising from a crater or other vent. If it is of sufficient volume and velocity, this gaseous column may reach many miles into the stratosphere, where high winds may carry it long distances from its place of origin. The eruption cloud from Mt. Mazama, for example, was probably carried by the winds entirely around the world.

Eruptive vent—the opening through which volcanic material is emitted.

Fault—a crack or fracture in the earth's surface along which there has been differential movement. It may represent the juncture between two adjoining blocks or plates into which the earth's crust is broken. Movement along a fault can cause earthquakes, or, in the process of mountain building, can release underlying magma and permit it to rise to the surface.

Fissure—elongated fractures or cracks on the slopes of a volcano, or any ground surface. Fissure eruptions typically produce liquid flows, but pyroclastics may also be ejected.

Fumarole—a vent or opening through which issue steam, hydrogen sulphide, or other gases. The craters of many dormant volcanoes, such as Rainier, Shasta, Lassen, and Hood, now contain active fumaroles. Some give off chemically active fluids or gases which radically alter or corrode the surrounding rock, changing it eventually into such substances as opal or clay. This process can hasten the erosion and eventual destruction of volcanic peaks.

Glowing avalanche—a superheated mass of incandescent ash, blocks, dust, and other gas-rich material which bursts from an erupting vent and rushes down a mountainside at great speed. Although most of the material hurtles across the ground surface, great clouds of turbulent ash often rise thousands of feet above it. There have been large glowing avalanches from Shastina, Mazama, St. Helens, and Glacier Peak during post-glacial time.

Glowing cloud—the turbulent mass of gas and dust which rises above the glowing avalanche. It is also known as a *nuée ardente*.

Holocene Epoch—the 10,000-12,000-year-long period of time which has elapsed since the end of the Pleistocene Epoch (Ice Age). It is the geologic period in which we now live.

Hot avalanche—a glowing avalanche (q.v.).

Horizontal blast—an explosive eruption in which the resultant cloud of hot ash and other material moves laterally rather than upward. Lassen Peak's famous "Hot Blast" of 1915 was such an eruption.

Hydrothermally altered rock—rock that has been decomposed or otherwise chemically changed by prolonged action of hot steam and/or acidic solutions. Such rock is often decayed into soft opal or clay, making it extremely susceptible to erosion or sliding. It is thought that the former summit of Mt. Rainier was thus decomposed before it slid off to form the Osceola Mudflow.

Hypersthene—a mineral found in basic rocks, or in intermediate rocks such as andesite.

Ignimbrite—rock consisting of vitric (glassy) ash, usually produced by hot ash flows.

Incandescent ash flow—an intensely hot, gas-charged flow of pyroclastic material.

Intrusive rock—volcanic rock which, when molten, was intruded into pre-existing rocks without ever reaching the surface as lava. Dikes and volcanic plugs are good examples.

Lapilli—literally, "little stones," round to angular rock fragments measuring 1/10 inch to 2½ inches in diameter, which may be ejected in either a solid or molten state.

Lahar—the Indonesian term for a mudflow originating on the slopes of a volcano.

Lava—magma which has reached the surface through a volcanic eruption. The term is most commonly applied to streams of liquid rock which flow from a crater or fissure. It also refers to cooled and solidified masses of rock.

Lava tree mold—the hollow impression left when a tree has been engulfed by a lava flow. As the tree is carbonized by the heat from the surrounding molten rock, water escaping from the trunk cools a thin crust of lava which hardens around the tree trunk. As the tree decays or crumbles into ash, the solidifying lava forms a mold in the exact shape of the tree. See *tree wells*.

Lava tubes—caves or tubes formed inside a lava flow. Although there are several means by which lava caves can be created, the most common explanation is that the liquid interior of a lava stream continues to flow after the top and sides have cooled and hardened. The center of the flow then drains away, leaving behind a hollow tube. The solidified crust of the flow forms the sides and roof of the tunnel.

Magma—molten rock confined beneath the surface of the earth. When erupted onto the surface it is called *lava*.

Magma chamber—the underground supply house of volcanoes. These are envisioned as subterranean cavities containing the gas-rich liquid magma which feeds volcanoes.

Microearthquakes—extremely small tremors which are perceptible only to sensitive scientific instruments. Seismographs especially designed to detect these mini-quakes are placed near active or dormant volcanoes to determine the frequency of shocks in and adjacent to the volcano's subterranean magma chamber. An increase in seismic activity can be the first indication of an impending eruption.

Nuée ardente—the French term for a turbulent cloud of hot ash or dust which rises above the front and sides of a *glowing avalanche* (q. v.).

Obsidian—a dense, black, glassy volcanic rock almost devoid of bubbles or mineral crystals. It is a highly silicic form of rhyolite. Large obsidian flows have emerged in the recent past from Newberry Caldera and the flanks of the South Sister.

Pahoehoe—Hawaiian word for congealed lava which is characterized by a smooth, ropy, or billowy surface. It is contrasted to aa, which has a rough, slaggy crust. Pahoehoe flows often contain lava tubes or caves, such as those near Mt. St. Helens.

Parasitic cone—a (typically small) secondary cone built on the flanks of a larger volcano. It is parasitic because it taps the magma chamber of the older volcano, thus using material that would otherwise be erupted by the main cone. Shastina, on the west side of Mt. Shasta, is the largest parasitic cone in the Cascades.

Paroxysm—a violently explosive eruption of unusual magnitude.

Pelean eruption—eruption which follows the pattern of the 1902 outburst of Mt. Pelée, Martinique. The volcano produced glowing avalanches and glowing clouds which utterly destroyed the city of St. Pierre and killed at least 28,000 people.

Phreatic eruption—violent steam explosion that produces little or no new lava. It characteristically blows out solid fragments of the pre-existing rock of the volcanic cone.

Pliocene Epoch—period of geologic time immediately preceding the Pleistocene and lasting from about 7,000,000 to 2 or 3,000,000 years before the present. During this epoch numerous shield volcanoes and basaltic cones were built in the Cascades.

Pleistocene Epoch—period of geologic time immediately preceding the Holocene Epoch and lasting from 2 or 3,000,000 to 10,000 years before the present. It was characterized by repeated development of ice caps and valley glaciers in the Cascade Range, and hence is popularly known as the Ice Age. Most of the large stratovolcanoes in the Cascades were erected during this period.

Plug—solidified lava that fills the conduit or "throat" of a volcano. It is usually more resistant to erosion than the material making up the surrounding cone and may remain standing as a solitary pinnacle when the rest of the original structure has been eroded away. The pointed spires of Mts. Thielsen and Washington are examples of volcanic plugs exposed by erosion.

Plug dome—the steep-sided, rounded mound formed when viscous lava wells up into a crater and is too stiff to flow away. It piles up as a dome-shaped mass, often completely filling and burying the vent from which it emerged. Lassen Peak is the largest and best known plug dome in the Cascades.

Pumice—solidified form of rock-glass which was highly charged with gas when blown from a crater. Usually light-colored, it is full of tiny bubbles or vesicles, which makes it buoyant.

Pyroclastics—the Greek word for "fire-broken," referring to fragmented volcanic rock thrown out during an eruption. Another Greek word for this kind of fragmental ejecta is *tephra* (q.v.), which applies to all material blown out through the air.

Pyroclastic flow—a volcanic flow of hot gas and fragmental material (pyroclastics); it may be composed of either pumice or lithic (non-vesicular) debris, or a mixture of both. See *ash flow* and *block-and-ash flow*.

Quaternary—the geologic period that includes both the Pleistocene and Holocene Epoch. It began a maximum of 3,000,000 years ago.

Rhyolite—lava rock extremely rich in silica and with a high glass content. Because they are stiff and pasty when erupted, rhyolite lavas do not normally flow far from their source.

Scoria—glassy fragments of dark-colored rock, often the product of sprays of semiliquid lava shot into the air from explosions accompanying a lava flow. Scoria range in size from 1/10th to 2½ inches.

Seismograph—instrument which detects and records earthquakes, including those too weak to be perceptible to most persons.

Shield volcano—a broad, very gently sloping volcano built almost exclusively of lava flows. Named for their supposed resemblance to a warrior's shield laid flat with the curved side upward, these volcanoes are characterized by quiet effusive eruptions with little or no explosive action.

Silicic lava—lava rich in silica (over 65%) and having a relatively low melting point (850 degrees Centigrade). It usually emerges as a stiff, viscous mass and does not flow long distances. Silicic lavas may congeal near the erupting vent to form steep-sided domes, such as Lassen Peak and Chaos Crags. Rhyolite, dacite, and obsidian are typical silicic lavas.

Solfatara—term derived from the Solfatara volcano in Italy which is characterized by the quiet emission of sulphurous gases. A form of fumarolic activity, the solfatara can hydrothermally alter the chemical composition of the rocks surrounding vents.

Stratovolcano—a volcano composed of both lava flows and fragmental (pyroclastic) material. A cross-section through a stratovolcano reveals alternating layers (strata) of lava, ash, breccias, etc. It is also called a *composite volcano* (q.v.).

Tephra—term used by Aristotle to describe air-borne pyroclastic ("fire-broken") material which has been erupted by a volcano.

Tree-mold—a hole in a lava flow, created by lava forming the hollow impression of a tree trunk. See *Lava tree mold*.

Tree-well—the cylindrical hole in a lava flow caused by the carbonization or decay of a tree trunk which had been engulfed in the flow.

Tuff—rock formed of pyroclastic material; it usually refers to ash-sized and perhaps other material; if coarser, it may be called a lapilli tuff. See *Welded tuff*.

Vent—opening in the earth's surface through which volcanic material is ejected.

Vulcan—Roman god of fire and the forge, after whom volcanoes are named.

Vulcanian eruption—a type of eruption characterized by violent explosions which send dark cauliflower clouds of ash into the air. Vulcanian explosions are thought to be caused by previously trapped gas suddenly breaking through congealed rock in a vent.

Vitric—term describing volcanic material consisting chiefly of glassy matter, such as vitric ash which is at least 75% glass.

Welded tuff—rock composed of fine-grained material which was hot enough when emplaced to weld or fuse together.

————————